HORIZONS IN RADIONICS

HORIZONS IN RADIONICS

Energy medicine for the 21st century

Edited by Tony Scofield MSc, PhD

*A symposium volume to celebrate the
Diamond Jubilee of the
Radionic Association*

ʊ

Trencavel Press

First published in Great Britain in 2003
by the Trencavel Press, 3 Broadfield Court,
Broadfield Road, Folkestone, Kent CT20 2JT,
United Kingdom
www.trencavel.co.uk

ISBN 0 9545786 0 0

Produced in association with the Radionic
Association Ltd., Baerlein House, Goose Green,
Deddington, Banbury, Oxon OX15 0SZ,
United Kingdom

Typeset by Trencavel Press
Printed by Hythe Printers Ltd.,
Pennypot Industrial Estate, Hythe, Kent

Contents

Cover design by Alan Gwilt.
We are extremely grateful to Anna Gwilt of Primavera for financial support for
the cover design.

Authors

EDEN, Enid A.

Enid came into radionics from an agricultural background, having originally only intended to treat her own animals. Having had great success with this, she decided to change from farming to radionics.

She joined the Radionic Association in 1961 and became a Qualified Member in 1962, having completed the training with Elizabeth Baerlein.

She was a member of Council from 1965 until 1980, during which time she served for periods on the Membership and Research committees. She was a director of the Radionic Trust from 1967 until it was disbanded in 1979. Having been set up for education and research, the Radionic Trust formed the teaching committee which eventually became the School of Radionics. Very soon after becoming a Director, she joined this committee, although she had been teaching since 1965. She was Head of Training from 1968 to 1978.

Armyn Wodehouse and Enid A. Eden formulated the radionic training in horticulture and agriculture and compiled the rate book which is still in use.

Enid A. Eden was a founder Director/Trustee of The Keys College of Radionics and is currently Chairman of the College. She is still practising and teaching in all aspects of radionics – human, animal, agriculture and horticulture.

FELLOWS, Linda

Linda has a PhD in Biochemistry from the University of London, where she was latterly a Visiting Professor, and has worked in both academic research and in industry. After discovering radionics as a patient, she qualified with the RA and now combines radionic practice with other activities.

FRANKISH, Doris

Doris worked as a newspaper journalist in the north east for 43 years and was latterly a sub-editor with Thompson newspapers. A radionic practitioner for 20 years, she is interested in innovative distant work, including transmuting of disturbed energy lines and the treatment of those suffering from possession. She claims to be 'ghost-buster to the gentry'!

FRANKS, Nick

Nicholas Franks was born in 1951 in Manchester, UK. He graduated from Manchester University in 1973 with a degree in Economics. Soon afterwards he co-founded a pro-audio electronics manufacturing company with one of his school friends. The company developed into a world wide exporter and was granted the Queen's Award for Export three times in the 1980s. He left the company in 1997.

He started teaching himself classical homeopathy in 1994 and radionics in 1995 but has a long history of interest in esoteric matters, including mediumship. He became a Member of the Radionic Association in 2000 and apart from treating people, concentrates on developing radionic theory, instruments and therapeutic methods.

GWILT, Alan

Alan has a degree in Fine Art and was latterly Senior Lecturer in Art and Design at the London Institute. The Radionic Association is pleased to have ready access to his talent; the cover of this book for example.

Alan serves on the council of the RA and he also teaches at the School of Radionics of the RA. He has a large practice and is drawn particularly to its spiritual aspect which he believes is central to an understanding of radionics.

HIGHAM, Sally

Sally joined the Radionic Association in 1962 and qualified as a member in 1963. She was elected a Fellow in 1968 and from that time on until 1996 she served on many of the Association's committees, including some 16 years on the Council. She was also active in the School for many years and was an examiner for 18 years. Sally has not only been an active radionic practitioner longer than most but has also lent her time to the Association for most of her professional life, and her views on radionic practice are the more valuable because of it.

LOWE, Gillian

Gill is a graduate of Edinburgh University and worked in a Medical Research Council unit for cancer research before having a family. She has been involved in radionics for 11 years, both as a practitioner and a tutor for the School of Radionics, and as Head of Assessors for the School.

MANZOOR, Ina

Ina became a Qualified Member of the Radionic Association in 1978 and had very early on decided that the study of radionic rates and their making was a most worthwhile and enlightening pursuit. Ina came originally from Austria and was brought up on naturopathic principles, which facilitated her next step into energy medicine. For the past ten years, she has been travelling to and from India as an ardent follower of Sri Sathya Sai Baba to whom she ascribes her intuitive guidance.

MARSHALL, Cathy

Cathy Marshall has been involved in radionics since the 1980s. Originally trained as a teacher, Cathy taught for many years at the Radionic Association School study weekends and has taught many of the younger members of the Association who are practising today. She continues to teach Licentiates from her home as well as running occasional flower remedy courses and talks for the general public in her area.

Cathy's particular interest is the subtle anatomy and she gained her Fellowship of the Radionic Association from a study on the alta major. Cathy has two grown up daughters and lives with her husband in Suffolk

PARSONS, Galea
Galea has an extensive practice, which encompasses humans, horses and dogs. She has been a Qualified Member of the Radionic Association for 30 years and has spent much of this time researching and working with rates, and the subtle anatomy of man, animals and in particular the horse.

She currently serves on the Radionic Association Council and teaches in the School of Radionics. Galea is an established Flower and Vibrational Essence practitioner, a White Eagle healer, and in more recent years has qualified as a Reiki healer and a Bowen practitioner.

She grew up in Sussex, roaming the Downs with various dogs and horses, qualified as a B.H.S.A.I. and taught in this field for several years. During this period she spent several years working for an equine veterinary practice. Her interests include horses, reading, yoga, astrology, walking mainly in Hampshire where she lives with a very supportive husband. She has two grown up children.

SCOFIELD, Tony
Tony has a PhD in Animal Physiology from the University of Nottingham and worked for many years as a lecturer in the University of London. He has conducted research and published in a number of areas including physiology, homeopathy and healing. He developed an interest in dowsing for, and re-balancing of, land energies for which he designed 'The Harmonizer', now commercially available. Tony is currently chairman of the Council of the Radionic Association and editor of its journal.

Introduction

Sixty years ago, in 1943, the Radionic Association was formed. This book is produced to mark the Association's Diamond Jubilee and celebrate its achievements during its first 60 years. It is not claimed to be a comprehensive textbook of radionics, but rather a resource for those who wish to learn more about the subject, and for practitioners and students who want to expand their knowledge of specific areas. Each chapter is written by a member of the Association and reflects to some extent his/her particular area of interest. Subjects covered include the evolution of radionic techniques, the relationship of radionics to other therapies such as homeopathy, and a range of subjects and conditions that have benefited from radionic intervention.

Radionics is a dynamic and evolving field and many of the chapters are testament to these changes. Only through evolution and change will any therapy survive in the face of our rapidly changing world. In the past, the absence of any credible scientific explanation of how radionics works has hampered attempts to bring its benefits to a wide audience. Recent advances in physics demonstrate that there are links between us beyond the familiar space-time framework of everyday reality and, although we cannot yet say that radionics has been explained, the idea of analysis and treatment at a distance is at least now no more challenging than other areas of contemporary science.

What is radionics?

For those new to this healing art there is probably no more succinct introduction than that printed on the back of the *Radionic Journal*, the Association's quarterly house journal.

> *Radionics is a healing technique in which our natural ESP faculties are used both to discover the energetic disturbances underlying illness and to encourage the return of a normal energetic field that supports health. It is*

independent of the distance between practitioner and patient.

A trained and competent practitioner can discover factors contribut-ing to disease within any living system, be it a human being, an animal, a plant or the soil itself. Suitable therapeutic energies can then be made available to help restore optimum health. The origins of radionics are attributed to a distinguished American physician, Doctor Albert Abrams (1863-1924) of San Francisco, and it has since been developed by numer-ous other research workers and exponents including Ruth Drown, George de la Warr, T. Galen Hieronymus, Malcolm Rae and David Tansley. But radionics should not be thought of as a recent invention – it harnesses ancient human skills that have been neglected.

The nature of the energetic processes entrained in radionics are not yet fully understood, but there is now ample evidence that we are all linked in some way at a higher level of mind, and it is believed that this is the level engaged during radionic practice. Radionic healing is not so much directed at the physical reality of the body, but rather at the invisible energy matrices which are believed to lie behind it.

For the purpose of assessment and treatment, radionics sees organs, diseases and remedies as having their own particular frequency or vibra-tion. These factors are expressed in numerical values, which are known as 'rates', and radionic instruments are provided with calibrated dials on which such 'rates' are set for analysis and treatment purposes. These figures have a significance more symbolic than mathematical.

Basic to radionic practice is a disciplined dowsing or radiesthetic skill. In trained hands radionics can be used to help to restore the health of peo-ple, animals, plants and the soil wherever in the world that need exists, and with no depletion of material resources.

The Radionic Association

The forerunner of the Radionic Association was a study group formed in 1942 by Dr Hugh Wyllie, Mr and Mrs de la Warr, Mrs Dundas, Mrs Ruby Hodgson and two chiropractors, Mary Walker and Darle Davis.[2] After several meetings, on November 13th 1943[5a] they formed the Radi-onic Association of Great Britain, with Hugh Wyllie as president, to fur-ther research and interest in the subject. Initially, meetings were held in London and slowly interest was aroused and the Association started to grow.

The first residential conference was held in 1958 and conferences have proved to be extremely popular since.[2] Also in 1958 a lending library was established and a course for potential operators was set up. This was a one-day course organised by the de la Warrs at the Delawarr Laboratories in Oxford. The Delawarr Laboratories had been formed to further research in radionics and they produced the lavishly illustrated research journal, *Mind and Matter*, from June 1957 to September 1960. A two-day course was also run by Lavender Dower and Elizabeth Baerlein at their house at Swinbrook, Burford, Oxfordshire.

In July 1954 the Association launched its journal, *Radionic Therapy* (which became the *Radionic Quarterly* in 1957 and the *Radionic Journal* in winter 1994/5), and this forms an important part of the Association's activities to this day.

The Association became incorporated as a company limited by guarantee on March 30th 1960. At this time the Association had grown to 180 members. Membership has fluctuated above and below this number reaching nearly 600 around 1980.[2] At the time of writing membership is around 307 with 67 full members.

In 1962 the Radionic Trust, also a company limited by guarantee, was formed by the Association to provide teaching of radionic therapy, anatomy and physiology and later to distribute literature and encourage and support research in radionics.[1] It had been hoped to register the Trust as a charity but this was not possible under the rules of the Charity Commission. The Trust held the governership of the School of Radionics until 1980 when this was passed back to the Radionic Association.

In 1962 the Radionic Trust purchased a house, Keys in Burford, Oxfordshire, to act as its headquarters. This was sold in 1972 and administration of the Trust moved to the home of Elizabeth Baerlein and Lavender Dower at Swinbrook.

Proceeds of the sale provided a large part of the income of the Association for a number of years, as did donations from various trusts and individuals.[6]

Like all such organisations there have been disagreements and splits amongst the membership. In 1964, for example, the Delawarr Laboratories and the Association drifted apart and the Delawarr Society provided similar training functions to that of the Association.

In 1967 the Keys Trust was formed, as a charity, on the initiative of the Radionic Association, with the object of raising funds for the promotion of healing, some of which was earmarked for radionics.[7] At the time this appeared to be the only feasible route to forming a charity associated with the Radionic Association. In 1974 a second parallel trust, the Healing Research Trust (HRT), was formed with trustees in common and the terms of the trust deed were broadened to include other areas of healing. The Keys Trust was retained to keep the goodwill attached to it. The trustees took the HRT on to found the Institute of Complementary Medicine in 1981 with a capital of £4000.[4]

Conflict occurred in 1983 between the School Management Committee and others who wished to form their own schools.[6] A small group of the School Management Committee stated their intention to take the School of Radionics away from the Association and set up a register outside the Association, and as a result Council dissolved the School Management Committee and eventually reformed the School. However, in 1985 a number of the members left to form Keys College, another training organisation, which joined the Institute of Complementary Medicine.

In 1984 the Association decided not to join the ICM but to join another umbrella organisation representing complementary health practitioners, the British Complementary Medicine Association.[6] When the Confederation of Healing Organisations was formed as a charity in 1984, the Association also became a member of this umbrella organisation. Fortunately, many members of Keys College also remained members of the Radionic Association and relations between the organisations are good. In 2003 the Delawarr Society ceased to operate and was effectively incorporated back into the Radionic Association.

Training new practitioners has always been a key role of the Association. The School of Radionics is very active in training and is owned and governed by the Radionic Association but run as a separate body. The qualifications of Licentiate and Member of the Radionic Association (LicRadA and MRadA) are, however, awarded by the Council of the Association on the recommendation of the School Committee. Fellowship of the Radionic Association may be awarded on presentation of a satisfactory thesis in some area of radionics. Honorary memberships and fellowships are occasionally awarded to those who have made significant contributions to radionics.

Radionics has not remained static. Members have introduced new concepts and instruments over the years and driven the evolution of radionics forward. Some of the chapters in this book illustrate these sometimes dramatic changes. Nothing will last if it doesn't help the patient and it is testament to the effectiveness of the ideas of people like Malcolm Rae, who introduced new concepts, as well as the base 44 instrument, in 1965, and David Tansley, who later incorporated elements from Eastern traditions, that their concepts still form an important part of the basis of radionics as it is practised today.

With the ever increasing interest in radionics it was felt important that the Association have a permanent base and in 1987, after appeal to members, the old fire station at Deddington was purchased and named Baerlein House after Elizabeth Baerlein, a loyal, hardworking and influential member of the Association for many years. It is from here that the Association operates today with two paid part-time administrators. The growth in enquiries for treatment and training, and from the press, ensures that the office is kept busy. Our web-site www.radionic.co.uk attracts increasing numbers of hits and also means ever increasing work for the office and Council members!

As a professional organisation the Radionic Association cannot become a charity but in 1989 the Healing Education Trust was set up and registered with the Charity Commission by the Association to advance education in the branches of healing already established by the Radionic Association. It provides money for use as bursaries and to provide educational literature and to support seminars, lectures and training courses.

This is necessarily only the briefest summary of the Association's history, but it is important to acknowledge the debt of current members to the pioneers. Past splits and disagreements have paradoxically ensured the survival of a wide base of ideas and methods which are fuelling the creativity and dedication of today's practitioners. Working in a less hostile scientific landscape, they are set to make a significant contribution to our understanding of the power of human consciousness.

In 1985, on the occasion of the silver jubilee of the formation of the limited company, Vicki Roberts wrote an inspiring editorial in which she described her sensing of the Spirit that lay behind the letter of company law:[5]

> 'A Company then, such as ours, if seen in that way becomes not just a convenience, a status symbol, but a living entity. It may be seen not only to manifest the united spirit of Goodwill of those living individuals who are its members at any given time, but also to contain the love and creative spirit of all those who have served and shared in its work before us, our

fellows and well-wishers over the years, and the potentials called forth by the needs of the future. It is like a cross, its vertical reaching heavenward, bringing inspiration through to the needs of the earthed base. The arms at its sides stretch forth to the minds and hearts of those in the world. At its centre is the place where the heart of our Association beats and exchanges the energies which flow in and out – the spiritual and practical, learning and teaching, giving and accepting. Since this is our twenty-fifth Anniversary, I visualise it as a silver cross.'

One can visualise the diamond, hard and indestructible, radiating the light that enters it, in our case from our body of members. Its characteristics, 'light, life, the sun, durability, incorruptibility, invincible constancy, sincerity, innocence'[3] provide an admirable symbolism on which to base the next years of the Association. But as Vicki said '... the future of our Association – the springing, blossoming and fruition of its coming work – is literally in our hands, yours and mine.'[5]

References

1. Baerlein E. (1980) The Radionic Trust – its history and achievements. *Radionic Quarterly*. 26 (2), 17-18.
2. Baerlein E. and Dower A. L. G. (1980) *Healing with Radionics*. Thorsons, Wellingborough.
3. Cooper J.C. (1982) *An Illustrated Encyclopaedia of Traditional Symbols*. Thames and Hudson, London.
4. Dower L. (1983) The Institute of Complementary Medicine. *Radionic Quarterly*. 29 (2), 20.
5. Roberts, V. (1985) Editorial. *Radionic Quarterly* 31 (2), 3-4.
5a. Roberts, V. (2003) Personal communication.
6. Smith G. (1984) Where are we going? *Radionic Quarterly*. 31 (1), 24-26.
7. Wilcox J. (1975) The Healing Research Trust. *Radionic Quarterly*. 21 (2), 10-13.

I should like to thank Vicki Roberts for her help in compiling this brief history of the Association.

THE RADIONIC ASSOCIATION
ITS OBJECTIVES AND ACTIVITIES

Objectives

The Association, which was founded in 1943, exists to train, and serve as the professional body for, qualified radionic practitioners, and also to provide a forum for others who wish to learn more about this fascinating science. The Association aims to promote the practice of radionics as an honourable and skilled profession, to foster research into the science of radionics and to provide a centre for the collection and dissemination of information.

Activities

The Association publishes quarterly the Radionic Journal, supplied free of charge to all members, holds regular meetings in London and elsewhere, offers training courses through the School of Radionics, maintains a lending library of over 1000 titles, supplies lists of qualified practitioners, handles queries and requests for information about radionics, and maintains the Radionic Association web site.

The activities of the Association are directed by a Council which meets four times a year. The Association Office is staffed by a Secretary and an Assistant Secretary who deal with day to day correspondence and implement directives from Council.

Membership

Associate Membership is open to all* over the age of 18.

All Associates receive the Journal, a Newsletter, and notification of meetings. Associate Members who are not already members of a radionic organisation can vote at the Annual General Meeting (hence the description 'Voting Associates'.) (Applicants who are members of another radionic organisation receive identical privileges except for the right to vote at the AGM – please ask the Office for an application form for Non-Voting Associates.)

Students of the School of Radionics first join as Associate Members. As their training progresses they first reach the grade of Licentiate Member, and finally that of a fully Qualified Member of the Radionic Association, at which point they are allowed to use the designation MRadA. Holders of each of these grades are allowed to practise professionally. Qualified Members who give exceptional service to the Association and/or who do distinguished research work may later, at the Council's discretion, be awarded a Fellowship (FRadA).

Council reserves the right to decline applications without explanation

Subscriptions

Please apply to the Secretary or visit the web site for details of subscription rates.

Training

Training for the examinations of the Association is provided by training courses approved by the Association. Details of these courses are available from the Secretary.

Enquiries

Enquiries and requests for membership application forms and publications are welcomed by the Secretary at: **Baerlein House, Goose Green, Deddington, Banbury, Oxon. OX15 0SZ.** Tel/Fax: (01869) 338852;

e-mail: **radionics@association.freeserve.co.uk**   web site: **www.radionic.co.uk**

Linda Fellows

<table>
<tr><td>

Mind over Matter – the Challenge of Radionics

</td><td>

1

</td></tr>
</table>

Wisdom is knowing how little we know.

Socrates

Radionics and the prevailing world-view

To most people with a 'common-sense' view of the world radionics seems absurd. A patient sends a lock of hair and a request for help to the practitioner. With the help of a dowsing pendulum and charts of putative subtle energy systems of the body, the practitioner is able to determine what is impeding the flow of vitality in the client and contributing to dis-ease. To remove the blockages, the practitioner uses an instrument upon which are placed numbers called 'rates', which represent organs, states of organs and/or intended treatments, to send corrective 'energies' to the client. The distance between the patient and practitioner is of no consequence – they can be at opposite sides of the world, and there is no diminution of the healing effect with distance.

The 'instruments' used by practitioners may be complex computer-driven devices, but most of them are not powered by electricity and some are apparently little more than patterns of various kinds. Perhaps the best known are the 'black boxes' which carry dials on which 'rates' are set, the more modern equivalent using digital displays. Take a 'black box' apart and you will find little that is meaningful to physicists. This has led to accusations of fraud.[18]

Despite this, radionics has over the years attracted a following of convinced practitioners and grateful patients who have struggled to find a scientifically-acceptable explanation of their experiences. Many eminent medically and scientifically-trained figures became involved but the ever-present 'psychic' element in radionics could not be tolerated. In 1981 David Tansley, a leading practitioner of the time, concluded that radionics was 'magic' and that a scientific explanation would never be found. He did propose that radionics was a 'right-brain' phenomenon, akin to artistic creativity and intuition, in line with the prevailing theories of brain function of his time, but his use of the word 'magic' alarmed the radionic establishment, so keen was it to be accepted by mainstream science. [21]

The drive to find an explanation for radionics in the world of physics meant that the growing body of evidence from psychologists for distant perception and transmission of thoughts was ignored. Vasiliev in Russia, Jung, Freud, all had evidence that minds could connect over great distances and were in no way confined to the heads of individuals. 'The ego-personality is the personality so far as one is conscious of it, but distant healing and remote viewing experiments have shown that the individual consciousness is surrounded by an indefinitely extended unconscious psyche.' [8, 9, 19]

What Tansley did not foresee in the '80s was that a revolution in physics was imminent which would change the map of 'reality' within 20 years. Consciousness, far from being a side product of brain, we now see as fundamental, and 'solid' matter as an ephemeral precipitate on a sea of barely-understood formative energies lying behind both consciousness and matter. This revolution in our world view is profound and has been compared in significance to that which followed the proof by Copernicus and Galileo that the earth moved round the sun, when for all previous ages commonsense had suggested the opposite.

Radionics can be accommodated within this new world view. We cannot yet claim to understand it fully, but there is no longer any need to apologise for being interested in it. 'Science' is just as inexplicable.

Does radionics really work?

Before probing the implications of this new scientific revolution, let us consider what evidence there is that radionics actually works! Anecdotal evidence we have in abundance, but large scale studies are few. The nature of radionics is incompatible with clinical trials of the double blind kind, which are the only measure acceptable to mainstream science. All we have to support claims are surveys of patient satisfaction carried out at various times. For instance, in 1977 Alan Mayne conducted a survey of patients of Radionic Association practitioners. Of over 2500 cases, he found that approximately 60% claimed treatment to be completely successful, 30% partially successful and 10% unsuccessful. A later survey by Tom Lafferty in 1998 also showed a high level of patient satisfaction. Some small studies with clinically assessed patients have been useful, for instance medical and educational confirmation of the improved status of 36 children diagnosed as dyslexics and treated radionically over a period of 6 years (still ongoing) is on record (Forder, pers. comm.). [10,13,16] Despite the paucity of formal evidence for radionics, there is supportive data from other studies. Distant healing encompasses not only radionics but a variety of mentally directed techniques including prayer, and the results of many such trials have been published. Astin *et al.* in 2000 analysed 23 trials (which met strict inclusion criteria) involving 2774 patients: 5 using prayer, 11 using non-contact therapeutic touch, and 7 other forms of distant healing. Of these 13 (57%) showed a positive treatment effect, 9 showed no effect over control and 1 showed a negative effect. The authors conclude that the evidence 'merits further study' and quote Larry Dossey: *'If ... mental intentions can be shown to facilitate healing at a distance , this would clearly imply that human beings are more connected to each other and more responsible to each other than previously believed. That connection could be actuated through ... God, consciousness, love, electrons, or a combination. The answers to such questions await further research.'* [2]

Let us assume on the basis of the above that radionic healing is a genuine effect, at least some of the time, and ask how it might be explained.

The revolution in physics unfolds

In the early part of the 20th century it was discovered that both light and sub-atomic particles had strange properties: they could behave both like waves and also as particles, it depended on how they were observed. The mathematics which was devised to explain these phenomena was known as quantum mechanics, and it made some unexpected predictions. Firstly, it seemed that when particles were observed as waves, the influence of the wave extended out to infinity. As this was true for all particles, it implied that all particles were potentially in touch with all other particles in the universe. Another prediction was that two particles, once together or 'entangled', would remain connected no matter how far apart they were subsequently placed in the universe, and that an operation performed on one would cause a simultaneous change in the other *irrespective of distance*. (Interactions independent of distance became known as *non-local interactions*, meaning independent of location.) For a signal to pass from one particle to the other instantaneously over any distance implied that it could travel faster than the speed of light. This violated Einstein's theory that nothing could move faster than the speed of light, and he was very unhappy about it. He refused to accept that quantum mechanics was complete, predicting that new factors, so-called hidden variables, remained to be discovered which would prove that non-local interactions could not happen. [11]

The issue was not resolved at the time of Einstein's death in the '50s. In the '60s British mathematician John Bell took another look at non-locality and devised some mathematical statements which would be true if Einstein *were* correct, and that quantum theory was still incomplete. When he tested these statements against what was known of the sub-atomic world, he found that the statements were *not* true, implying that Einstein was mistaken and that non-locality might be real. [5]

Physicists of the day were still reluctant to embrace non-locality, but were finally forced to confront it when Aspect *et al.* in Paris in 1972 obtained the first experimental proof of it under laboratory conditions. This was later confirmed by others, and the principle is now so well-established that the possibility of transporting vast amounts of data via linked systems is being discussed. [1,4,6]

Physicist David Bohm explained non-locality in another way. He believed that it was misleading to think of the sub-atomic world existing in the same spacial matrix as the everyday world. He proposed that underneath a manifest everyday reality was a different reality from which it sprang. He called these the Explicate and Implicate Orders respectively, and suggested that time and space were properties only of the explicate manifest world of physical experience. The interpretation of non-locality from Bell's and Aspect's results was misleading: sub-atomic particles do not communicate instantly over vast distances – there is no vast distance to cross because *they are all at the same location*. [14]

Corresponding to Bohm's suggested Implicate Order is the Creative Vacuum of Davidson and others. When matter is cooled to absolute zero, all molecular motion should cease, but mysterious residual activity is perceptible which is described as the energy of the Vacuum – called a vacuum because according to the old world view it should contain nothing at all. This residual energy is believed to be a marker for a vast reservoir of energy which is inaccessible to most of our present equipment but which our mathematics suggests could make up over 90% of the energy of the Universe. Davidson suggests that what we see in our day to day world is the dance, the puppet show, but not the strings which are being pulled in the Vacuum. [7]

What controls physical form?

The recent sequencing of the DNA of the human genome was rightly hailed as a triumph, but will it really, as claimed, take us any closer to the secrets of life? Every atom in our bodies is replaced within 5-7 years, even DNA itself, but the form remains the same. As Mansfield says: *'DNA clearly defines the content, if not the structural arrangement, of cells individually. It probably enables each cell to receive and interpret information about the forms and functions in which it is involved. It cannot, however, originate the form or functions of the whole organism: for that we must look* outside the cell.' [7, 15]

Davidson suggested, like Bohm, that consciousness is the life force and is rooted in the Vacuum, the only power that can control the complex functions of living bodies, which it patterns, organises and administers. The process is normally unconscious (to us), but can sometimes be brought under conscious control. (e.g. by biofeedback). He also suggested that the Vacuum state, upon which all atomic particles appear as energy patterns, is linked to our subtle and mental energetic structures and acts as an instrument which links mind to observed phenomena. He was in no doubt that radionics was a phenomenon of the Vacuum state. *'Psychic phenomena are manifestations of activity within the Vacuum and more subtle states of matter, and it is within the Vacuum that homoeopathy and radionics work.'*

To describe – as we do – radionics as distant healing is probably misleading: at the level of the Vacuum *all is at one point*.

What is the role of instruments and rates in the radionic process?

Rates and instruments are characteristic of the healing art we know as radionics. If Davidson is correct that we access Vacuum energies in the radionic process, what might be their role?

Rates are controversial. They are revered by some practitioners as conveying hidden truths or mystic significance, (see Manzoor, chapter 7), but others invent their own or work with patterns etc. where rates are not required. Many believe that the use of the same rates by large groups of practitioners reinforces their effectiveness – it certainly makes teaching easier – but Tansley's opinion was: *'No matter how well aligned the rates may be to esoteric principles, the over-riding factor that makes them effective is the practitioner: they are 'dead' till he employs them through the force of his belief ... If I took a naturally gifted healer and taught him a system of radionics based on a series of rates derived from random numbers, then that practitioner would get results just the same.'*

He dismissed the beliefs of earlier practitioners that rates represented some kind of vibrational frequency of organs or treatment methods: *'Rates – merely act as a focal point between physical and subtle levels of matter .. (they are) a device and not a realistic set of numbers that actually represent the frequencies of the factor in question ...'* [21]

Rates are probably best thought of as symbols which can be manipulated psychically, i.e at the level of the Vacuum. Jung believed that psychic existence can only be represented by symbols. In the old esoteric traditions symbols were described as telesomatic images and defined thus: 'A telesomatic image is imaginary, yet a genuine Inner construction of force and form designed for a particular purpose and having as much reality in its own dimensions as we have in Outer terms ... It objectifies on levels of existence which to us are subjective. It functions as an operative focus between our Inner and Outer states of being.' [12] Rates seem to be symbols which allow practitioners to manipulate the vacuum state. Those practitioners who deduce and work with integrated sets of rates which reveal practical and esoteric connections are also extracting information from the Vacuum.

What of instruments? Although instruments are necessary to induce the required discipline and structure in the early years of training, some practitioners later abandon complex devices in favour of very simple systems. As Tansley noted: *'Some practitioners do not use instruments at all ... they write down rates.. against the name of the patient. Results arrived at in this manner are "equal to anything arrived at through instrumented treatment."*

'Radionics is a form of mental healing and instruments are not always needed to detect or measure those energies which provide a picture of the patient. They are simply the link or key-factor in a process of energy exchanges which takes place at a level far beyond the physical. Instruments may have their part to play but only in so far as they function as a link and a focus for the healing power of the practitioner.'

Tansley refers to Phoebe Payne & Laurence Bendit's *The Mystery of Healing*, in which a research team made up of psychics and medical doctors well versed in esoteric teachings concluded 'radionic instruments are nothing more than a link or key factor which serves to relate the practitioner to the patient via some form of mental and emotional activity.'

Tansley also commented *'Instruments which run on mains power or batteries ... work whether they are switched on or not ... of the various designs ... each works as well as the next.'*

Despite Tansley's dismissive attitude to instruments, paradoxically many practitioners find that they are indispensable in a busy practice. Yes, it *is* possible to work without instruments and hold the entire process in the mind, but to do so routinely is to risk profound exhaustion and ultimately the breakdown of the health of the practitioner. Why this happens is not yet understood, but 'burnout' is well known in many healing disciplines – and Tansley himself died at 53. [21]

How is information obtained about a patient and how is healing transmitted?

The honest answer to both of these questions is we don't know, but we can speculate.

For an analysis to proceed with any accuracy the client must first have given permission, and experience suggests that the client controls the interaction, possibly at an unconscious level. The control takes the form of limiting the information accessible to the practitioner through dowsing, and in rejecting healing if it is not wanted. For effective radionic treatment, both practitioner and client must be committed to the process.

Information is obtained by mentally bringing the patient to mind, usually with the help of a hair sample or some other object unique to that person, then mentally posing a series of questions which require yes/no answers using a dowsing pendulum. The swing of the pendulum indicates yes or no. By proceeding through a set programme of questions the practitioner can build up a picture of what is going wrong with the client's subtle and physical structures. The 'subtle' structures are putative energy fields not detectable by the ordinary senses or by any conventional instruments. Their existence has been part of traditional Eastern, particularly Hindu, teaching for several thousand years, and the knowledge was originally obtained intuitively.

During the early years of the 20th C the model of reality used by radionic practitioners was conventional anatomy and physiology, plus some concepts of disease (miasms, nosodes) which form part of the homeopathic approach, but in the '50s Tansley introduced the traditional Eastern (mainly Hindu) models of subtle energy structures which, it is believed, underpin the manifest physical state.[20]

The Eastern model posits an invisible structure of several layers which govern the physical vitality, emotional and mental states and intuitive and spiritual aspects of the multi-faceted human being. For optimum *physical* health each of these layers needs to be free of obstruction and working in harmony with each other layer. The only way in which information about the condition of these subtle structures can be obtained is through the super-sensible skill of dowsing.[22]

Using a model of reality which includes these subtle structures has apparently greatly increased the power of radionics to deal with the diseased state, since many physical problems begin with defects at the subtle level (see Chapter 8 for some cases). If dealt with radionically at that level they can seemingly often be reversed, sometimes before physical symptoms develop.

All information obtained by means of a radionic analysis is intuitive, or one might say psychic, in origin. It is proposed that its origin is at some higher level of the client's personal consciousness to which he/she consciously has no access, but which nevertheless is 'aware' of the client's energetic deficits and can transmit this information to an unconscious level of the practitioner who then 'transforms' it down into conscious awareness by means of a pendulum.

What is the mechanism of radionic healing?

Once the analysis is complete corrective energies, symbolised by rates, patterns or other symbols, are directed at the appropriate level of the client, usually by means of a radionic instrument. We can only speculate that the procedure takes place, as Davidson suggests, at the level of the Vacuum where everyday spacial reality no longer applies. That mental intention arising in the conscious mind of the practitioner can by this means bring about an improvement in the physical condition of another human being, no matter what their location on this planet, is a major challenge to conventional thought. We can only ever explain things in terms of what we already know, and trying to explain the currently inexplicable may be, at least for the moment, futile.

What makes a radionic practitioner?

Radionics as an identifiable way of healing may only be a century old, but the human skills which it exploits doubtless go back to the dawn of human origins. Anthropologist Oubré suggests that it was the faculty of numinous – or intuitive – perception which drove the evolution of the hominid brain.[17] It is similar to, possibly identical with, the creative essence which underlies human creativity in art, music and indeed in conventional science where so often crucial advances also arise from intuitive insight. As in all areas of human endeavour only a few reach genius status, but many people of lesser talents can make a valuable contribution. It is certain that the skills required for radionic healing can be entrained in far more people than it has been in the past, when the movement was almost a secret society so weary and wary was it of external criticism. What is needed is a reasonable aptitude, plus commitment and an open mind.

A glorious future?

To assume that radionics will now be accepted and embraced by society at large is probably premature. The implications of the revolution in physics are not easily digested by physicists let alone the general public. In these early years of the 21st century we are also witnessing the response of mainstream medicine to the grass-roots driven alternative medicine movement of the 20th. The UK House of Lords Report on Alternative Medicine of 2000 dismissed radionics as lacking both evidence and credibility, along with Traditional Chinese Medicine and Ayurveda. Evidence of the double-blind trial type *is* lacking, but may never be achievable with this particular healing modality.[12a]

In the long term truth and the human creative spirit will prevail. Radionics is not a substitute for conventional medicine, itself a product of human creativity finding expression on the physical plane[3], but it enables therapeutic interventions to be made on planes of existence outside the reach of physical medicine. But is this anything new? If Oubré is correct, ritual (radionic procedures are unquestionably ritualistic) and psychospiritual practices may have served as important mechanisms for facilitating cultural advances among our remote ancestors for 1.6 million years.[17] Remnants of these ancient traditions are to be found in all traditional societies which have escaped the ravages of sanitisation through contemporary 'logic'. Today we need a cultural advance like no other – one which will save the planet from the ravages of materialism.

Radionic techniques draw on innate, ancient human skills. They can help people, animals, plants and the land itself. They can empower and give hope. The challenge for us as practitioners is to avail ourselves of the shifts in the scientific landscape to bring the information to anyone who would care to make use of it.

Bibliography

1. Aspect A., Dalibard J., and Roger G. (1982) Experimental test of Bell's inequalities using time-varying analyzers. *Physical Review Letters.* 49, 1804.
2. Astin J., Harkness E., and Ernst E. (2000) The efficacy of distant healing: a systematic review of randomised trials. *Annals of Internal Medicine.* 132, 903-910.
3. Bailey A. A. (1934) *A Treatise on White Magic.* Lucis Press, London.
4. Bouwmeester D., Pan J.-W., Mattle K., Eibl M., Weinfurter H., and Zeilinger A. (1997) Experimental quantum teleportation. *Nature.* 390, 575-579.
5. Buchanan M. (1998) Why God plays dice. *New Scientist,* 27-30 (August 22nd).
6. Cookson C. (1998) That old black spooky magic. In: *Financial Times, Jan. 17-18th,* London.
7. Davidson J. (1989) *The Secret of the Creative Vacuum.* C.W. Daniel, Saffron Walden.
8. Dossey L. (1993) *Healing Words. The Power of Prayer and the Practice of Meditation.* Harper, San Francisco.
9. Dossey L. (1996) Distance, time and the non-local mind: dare we speak of the implications? *Journal of Scientific Exploration.* 10, 401-409.
10. Forder V. (2003) Radionic treatment of dyslexic children (pers.com).
11. Goswami A. (1993) *The Self-Aware Universe – How Consciousness Creates the Material World.* Simon and Schuster, London.
12. Gray W. (1970) *Inner Traditions of Magic.* Samuel Weiser, York Beach, Maine.
12a Hawkes N. (2000) Lords puncture myths of alternative medicine, pp. 4, *The Times.* November 29th, p. 4.
13. Lafferty T. (1998) A survey of Radionic care of human patients. *Radionic Journal.* 44 (2), 17-24.
14. Laszlo E. (1993) *The Creative Cosmos.* Floris Books, Edinburgh.
15. Mansfield P. (1998) From reductionism to holism in our understanding and treatment of cancer. *The Ecologist.* 28 (2), 113-116.
16. Mayne A. (1977) The radionic treatment statistics questionnaire – results of a statistical analyis. *Radionic Quarterly.* 23 (4), 21.
17. Oubré A. Y. (1997) *Instinct and Revelation – Reflections on the Origin of Numinous Perception.* Gordon & Breach, London.
18. Russell, Edward W. (1973) *Report on Radionics.* Neville Spearman, London.
19. Storr A. (1983) *The Essential Jung.* Fontana, London.
20. Tansley D. V. (1972) *Radionics and the Subtle Anatomy of Man.* Health Science Press, Saffron Walden.
21. Tansley D. V. (1982) *Radionics: Science or Magic?* C.W. Daniel, Saffron Walden.
22. Westlake A. T. (1985) *The Pattern of Health,* 3rd edn. Element Books, Shaftesbury.

Tony Scofield

Radionics – the Early Years | 2

The electronic reactions are either the greatest miracle of the age, or else the greatest fake.

I claim nothing except to have established a principle.

For God's sake, you fellows, never diagnose names, diagnose numbers.

They laugh and jeer at my work now, for they don't yet understand. But some day – some day – they will realise that I was right. (His last words[104])

Albert Abrams

Radionics, like homeopathy before it, began with a serendipitous observation that was followed up by an inquiring mind. Like homeopathy, radionics has had a rough ride with the medical establishment and, whereas homeopathy is now gaining a degree of respectability, radionics is still, by many, relegated to the quack fringe. It is, however, younger than homeopathy and may, in the fullness of time, also achieve some degree of acceptance by mainstream medicine.

Radionics reputedly began with a chance observation of Albert Abrams (1863-1924), a San Francisco physician, that the sound obtained while percussing, with the fingers, the stomach of a patient unexpectedly changed in the presence of cancer.

Abrams was, however, not the first to note anomalous changes in the percussive tone under the influence of external forces. George Starr White[105] had, by 1881, developed a system using his 'Sympathetic-Vagal Reflex' to investigate and treat disease. He had noted that the percussive tone of the abdomen changed depending on the direction the patient

Fig. 2.1 George Starr White

faced and concluded that energy from the 'Magnetic Meridian' changed the tonicity or tension of the viscera to elicit the reflex. These changes could only be induced in a darkened room with the body grounded to earth. He found that some people would not elicit the reflex and concluded that some underlying factor in the individual was blocking the response. By experimentation he found that shining coloured lights on individuals could overcome this block and that diseases could be differentiated by the colours that would elicit the percussive reflex response. From these observations White developed a system of diagnosis and treatment using colour and marketed a range of equipment for this purpose. Later Abrams was to claim that he could purify vaccines by exposing them to different coloured lights[7,61] and he was also to use coloured salves on the patient's abdomen to potentiate treatment from the oscilloclast.[50,92]

It is clear that Abrams was aware of White's work as he refers to it in his books. Abrams does not describe the discovery of his system of diagnosis but simply describes the procedures of 'electronic medicine' almost in a fully developed form. One has the impression that he was building on White's observations and that the basic concepts were already, at least to him, part of 'received wisdom'. Nevertheless, it was Abrams' work that developed White's basic observations into the diagnostic system using variable resistance to differentiate diseases that lead to radionics, as we know it today.

Albert Abrams had, by the early years of the twentieth century, been moving from mainstream medicine, in which he was greatly respected[50] (see Flaxman, 1953 for a good biography and bibliography of Abrams[50]), to developing his method of treatment ('spondylotherapy', originally known as 'spinal therapeutics') which involved percussing the spine in order to invoke spinal reflexes through motor nerves to specific viscera.[29,50] Spondylotherapy evolved from a merging of his ideas on nerve reflexes with those of osteopathy. Abrams had begun publishing his epon-

Fig. 2.2 Albert Abrams

ymous 'reflexes' in 1898, the first being the cardiac reflex which was a change in the size of the heart and aorta in response to irritation of the skin above the organs.[50] Other reflexes followed including, amongst others, the lung, liver and stomach. Spondylotherapy attracted a large band of followers. The *Journal of the American Medical Association*, never a supporter of these innovative practices, suggested that it might be considered an attempt to give the general medical man something akin to osteopathy and chiropractic.[49]

During his time as a post-graduate at the University of Heidelberg (where he gained his MD in 1882) he studied under Professor de Sauer who lectured on the radiational nature of disease, and on his return to the United States Abrams began a series of investigations to test the validity of de Sauer's theories.[84] In order to detect this 'human energy' Abrams found that the human subject was the most sensitive detector and he utilised the stomach reflex, which involved percussing the stomach while energy was brought to the area from different parts of the body via a wire. In the presence of diseases the sound changed. Moreover, the reaction could, in some diseases, be modified by a bar magnet, thus introducing the idea of polarity.[1]

The sources of energy i.e. the regions of the body from which it could be transferred to the stomach region by means of the wire, varied in different diseases and, along with the polarity effects, could be used as a diagnostic aid. In *'Human Energy'*[1] Abrams produces a table of the Electronic Reactions that are characteristic of a number of diseases (the *Electronic Reactions of Abrams* (ERA) was first announced in 1910[66]). It was obvious that a number of diseases shared common characteristics and the method was a rather blunt instrument for diagnostic purposes.

An estimate of the severity of the disease could be obtained by noting how far from the stomach the tip of the wire could be held before the dulling sound of the stomach reflex disappeared.[1] Like Starr White he found that colour could influence the percussion sounds.[1] He concluded that disease was electromagnetic in nature.[31] (This later became known as the *Electronic Theory of Medicine*). He thus reasoned that diseased tissue should show a characteristic effect of an electric current flowing through the body which could be detected with sensitive enough instruments. The most sensitive at the time was Einthoven's (of ECG fame) string galvanometer. In order to place the electrodes for measurement it was necessary to determine the position of the abdominal organs and this was done by percussing the abdomen with the fingers [30] and it has been suggested that while percussing in this way Abrams made his crucial discovery.

There are various versions of this discovery but the one most reported is that he first noticed that when he percussed a patient with an epithelioma of the lip, while demonstrating the position of the stomach to a class at Stanford University Medical School, in 1910 [91], the stomach area sounded dull instead of the normal hollow sound. [80] Another version states that the percussive sound changed as an X-ray machine, which was being installed along the corridor, was switched on and off. [77,82,106] Perkins, who knew Abrams, describes the discovery in some detail but writes some years after the events (1956) [82] and had admitted much earlier that he was unsure of the order of events. [80]

Whatever the initial stimulus, Abrams went on to investigate the change of note with various disease states. Holding a pathological specimen against the forehead of a subject could also induce the characteristic percussion change associated with the disease. [28] Abrams also noted that percussion sounds at other places on the body seemed characteristic of certain diseases [28], but it was percussion of the area around the umbilicus that became the standard method. A head band was often used with three electrodes placed over three diagnostic areas, the S.V. (Splanchno-Vascular), P.D. (Pulmo-Diagnostic) and E.D. (Entero-Diagnostic) and by use of one of these electrodes a reflex reaction was normally obtainable in the umbilical region where it was easiest to hear percussive changes. [28] Different areas in this region were used to differentiate the various diseases. [28] Finding the electronic reflex in disease specific areas, and there were various ways of doing this, was replaced by the use of site specific rates on the rheostat and the use of the general reflex area around the umbilicus. [28]

The percussion tests were made with the patient standing facing west (at right angles to the horizontal component of the earth's magnetic field). [3,23,82] This observation led Hudgings to suggest that the energy used in the diagnosis is conveyed through the machine by the magnetic currents of the earth. [61] Colours influenced the reaction and redheaded boys could

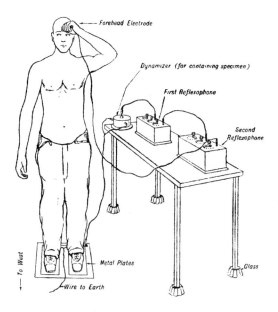

Fig. 2.3 Abrams' diagnostic system

not be used.[41] Experimentally the vascular reactions in a rabbit's ear could also be used as a subject.[41] In order to make examination easier for weakened patients wires were connected from the forehead of the patient to a healthy person (the 'subject' or 'reagent') and the tests were made on the healthy subject. This showed that disease radiations could be transmitted along wires. As several diseases were found to give similar reactions Abrams fitted a decade resistance box into the wire connecting the patient with the healthy subject.[28]

W. E. Boyd, the inventor of the emanometer (see chapter 13), considered that Abrams' important discovery was that the 'attachment of apparatus could modify the human reactions and make them selective in nature'.[22] The resistance box seems to have been called a *reflexophone* by most post-Abrams workers[20,80] but the original reflexophone was an instrument Abrams devised to replace the abdomen in percussion.[2] The original rheostat Abrams used was called a *biodynamometer.*[2,3] The percussive sound associated with diseases would change for specific conditions at precise settings of the resistors.[84] Because resistance was introduced it was long thought that it was the resistance in the circuit that tuned the emanations coming from the body but Colson later found that the resistances were not important but considered it was the capacity and inductance in the circuit induced by the resistance coils that was important, and later *radioscopes* were produced in which tuning relied on coils like a radio.[28,33]

In his earlier work with spondylotherapy Abrams had noted that he could determine the severity of disease by the distance the transmit-

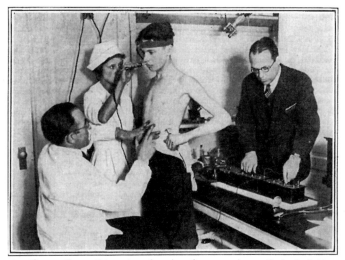

An Abrams diagnostician at work, using the percussive method of eliciting
the electronic reactions in the reagent. The patient is represented by a specimen of his blood, which is placed in the Abrams apparatus and wired up with
the reagent. The nurse is "localizing" an infected tooth

Fig. 2.4 Abrams' diagnostic technique(from *Scientific American*
investigation[67-72])

ting wire was held from the patient's body before the percussion sound
changed.[28] In the same manner, he now inserted a second rheostat into his
circuit to determine the strength of radiation from an organ which would
be indicative of its functional state.[3,28] In order to service individuals living far away from his office he found that he could use a blood sample as
a witness which he placed in a metal cup (the *dynamizer*) with connecting
wires to the head and foot plates attached to a healthy reagent on whom
the percussion was performed.[84] Using a bar magnet held close to the area
of dullness he observed the effect of each pole on the percussive response
and thus characterized the 'polarity' of the disease. If it persisted with the
N pole and disappeared with the S pole then the energy was positive and
vice versa.[3] Abrams describes experiments using a pith ball in which he
demonstrated the existence of different radiations from the right and left
sides of the body and between sexes.[4] However, W. E. Boyd failed to con-
firm the electrical differences as would be predicted by Abrams' observations, and cautioned against using the term 'polarity', with its electrical
connotations, to describe the phenomena Abrams observed with his mag-
nets.[24] A good description of his practical method can be found in Cave

(1922)[26,28] and Abrams (1917)[3].

Percussion was not an easy technique to learn and Abrams introduced another method that involved stroking the abdomen of a healthy subject with a glass rod which would 'stick' when the stomach reflex was induced.[84] Reputedly, Dr Earl Smith, one of Abrams' students, reasoned that if you could rub a glass rod over the skin then the skin could be rubbed over glass, and the development of the stick pad began.[84] Various materials were tried for the stick pad or rubbing plate, fine-grained hardwoods being particularly popular, and it eventually became the standard detection method. The last stick pad instruments tended to use a rubber sheet stretched over a plate. A Dr Wood of Chicago produced a Bakelite rubbing plate and it was Wood and another doctor, from Dakota, that Wilcox believes were the first to suggest that disease could be treated from a distance using blood spots as witnesses.[106] Although doctors still used a subject for many years after Abrams' death (e.g. Guyon Richards[89]) the stick pad soon began to replace this cumbersome method and the Calbro-Magnowave[84] and Drown's early instruments incorporated one.

Abrams tried to remove the subject completely and produced a tambour-based instrument, the *reflexophone*, to replace the stomach reflex.[2] He is also reputed to have invented the *oscillophone* that contained tuned wires connected to the diagnostic instrument. This also produced changes in tone when tapped in the presence of blood specimens.[61] He also experimented with other devices.[61] These included the *sphygmobiometer* that incorporated a variable condenser to store the energy that would then be released, at specific settings of the rheostat characteristic for various diseases, to invoke the reflexes. The first part (the *biometer*) containing the condenser, conductance coil and resistance coil was connected to a *sphygmophone*, a tambour based device. Using a finger plethysmograph, blood pressure changes induced by the 'vagal reflex' could be recorded with the sphygmophone.[2] He was also able to utilise the telephone to connect the patient to the diagnostic system (*telediagnosis*).[2]

Using ERA techniques it was believed that disease could be detected before clinical signs appeared.[100] Abrams also began to find syphilis in many of his patients and concluded that this provided a suitable environment for other diseases to develop.[76,95,100] This has echoes of Hahnemann's miasms where most chronic diseases were believed to be due to one of three miasms. However, in homeopathy the Syphilis miasm, the others being Psora and Sycosis, accounted for only about 13% of the cases, the psoric group being considered by far the most important contributor.[88] Using handwriting as a witness Abrams determined that many famous people from the past had syphilis, including the poet Longfellow, which proved a hard pill for some of his supporters to swallow![8,51,62] Abrams was in good company, however, for the eminent physician Sir William Osler had declared earlier 'Know syphilis in all its manifestations and all else clinically will be revealed unto you.'[100] Abrams believed that most people acquired the syphilis through contaminated vaccines. He believed that to eradicate disease the syphilis must be eradicated first. Indeed, he funded an 'International Association for Racial Purification' to achieve this end.[95] (This was *not* a racist organization!)

Using his diagnostic method Abrams found that by introducing a substance known to be a remedy effective against a disease e.g. quinine for malaria, the percussive dullness could be dispersed.[26] He believed the vibratory rates of the two were similar, as they gave similar reactions in his percussive tests, and the application of one on the other destroyed the disease, a situation similar to Hahnemann's 'Similia Similibus Curentur'.[26] Using the scientific concepts of his day Abrams reasoned that 'one man differs from another man only in the sense that his electrons show varying rates of vibration'[1] and that disease must represent a disarrangement of the electrons composing healthy tissue.[30] If such was the case why could not these electrons be rearranged? If the vibrations could be measured and something with a similar rate administered then this should induce a resonance in the tissue which should destroy the disease.[27]

Along with the engineer Hoffman, Abrams developed his own instrument, the *oscilloclast* (literally 'vibration breaker'), to provide these corrective vibratory rates.[81] The basis of the oscilloclast was a shock excitation circuit.[30] This is simply a tuned circuit that will vibrate for a short time at a definite rate when briefly energized by a shock. The circuit was tuned in Abrams' laboratories and the instruments sealed to prevent tampering.[30] The shock was provided by a special interrupter, originally motor driven, but later by a magnetic vibrator based on the 1923 Hoffman patent (US1445951).[102] In 1938 mechanical interruption was abandoned for electronic chopping using vacuum tubes and a condenser.[84] Variable damping is an essential feature of the circuit and is provided by a series of resistance coils. The output was thus a train of highly damped vibrations of very small magnitude, but definite frequency (11 in all[32]), whose damping could be adjusted between wide limits on a graduated scale. As well as the short wave energies developed by the instrument, a tiny amount of the alternating supply current passes from the instrument to the patient by induction between the primary and secondary coils.[32] An alternating magnetic field is also produced.[34] Details of the workings of the oscillo-clast are given in various publications of Thomas Colson who makes the point that Abrams was led to the design *by intuitive processes.*[30,32,33,35]

Many were bemused by the electrical basis of the oscilloclast.[62] The

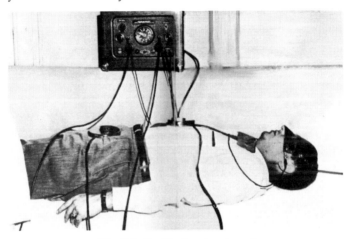

Fig. 2.5 Oscilloclast treatment

Scientific American investigation published a highly critical report that also challenged its therapeutic effectiveness. They claimed it was no more than an electrical buzzer[71] and it had been called in the US press 'A contraption which might have been thrown together by a ten year old boy who knows little about electricity, to mystify an eight year old boy who knows nothing about it.'[62] Nevertheless, it and its predecessors were extensively used for many years.

There were only 11 treatment positions on the oscilloclast and the correct one was determined using the diagnostic instrument and the abdominal reflex. Later workers were able to allot specific disease conditions to one or other of the buttons.[31,34] These rates were known as 'Destructive rates'[28] as treatment was essentially destructive rather than constructive.[61] A third rate known as the 'Constructive Rate' was introduced by Jean du Plessis to normalize functional activities of organs and tissues, particularly endocrine.[28] Later developments involved the use of the diagnostic vibratory rate as the 'destructive rate' and the use of 'personal rates' worked out for each patient which would be broadcast for any disease.[28] For treatment of herds of animals the oscilloclast has been used to treat the drinking water with appropriate rates.[56]

In discussing Abrams' methods Frederick Strong suggested that thoughts may be a great creative power, with humans merely acting as 'step-down transformers' for the 'great vibratory "broadcasting station".'[99] Abrams certainly found that thoughts could inhibit the manifestation of disease reflexes in the subject and he believed Strong's ideas were a plausible hypothesis. However, he himself was determined to 'de-occult the occult' and stick 'with almost morbid intensity to the canons of modern science and the methods of the laboratory'. He certainly believed that the energy from the oscilloclast was 'a physical vibration of a definite nature, and has *in itself* nothing to do with mental suggestion (although the latter may help or retard its action).'[99] Although Abrams recognised occult phenomena he believed they were merely manifestations of 'human energy'.[2]

Abrams' work was thrust into the public gaze by the fulsome words of support from the novelist Upton Sinclair in his *The Book of Life*[96] (the two parts originally published in 1921 and 1922) and then in a series of articles in *Pearson's Magazine* (1922).[95] He also defended Abrams in a letter to the *Journal of the American Medical Association*[94] although, in a letter to Abrams, Sir James Barr expressed his doubt that Sinclair's support would benefit him.[92] This growing public interest in Abrams' methods stimulated critical, and often hostile, interest, particularly by the *Journal of the American Medical Association*, and investigation by various other bodies.[6,7,9,19,28,79,107] The *Scientific American* concluded that the techniques were worthless[72] but when it was successful the mechanism was psychic in nature, rather like an Ouija board or automatic handwriting[67], but the International Hahnemannian Society produced three reports (1923, 1925, 1926) which were favourable.[28,63] In 1924 Abrams' methods, as developed by the Scottish homeopath W. E. Boyd, were investigated by a committee of the Royal Society of Medicine under the chairmanship of Sir Thomas Horder with generally good results.[60]

Abrams had founded the American Association for Medico-Physical Research and the journal *Physico-Clinical Medicine* to promote his ideas, and on his death the College of Electronic Medicine (founded 1922 and the name changed to Electronic Medical Foundation in 1954[107]) was endowed from his estate and carried on developing the oscilloclast and other instruments (notably the *Depolaray*).[55] They published the *Journal of Electronic Medicine* (formerly *Physico-Clinical Medicine*) which is an invaluable source of information on the oscilloclast and its development.[55]

In 1925 an instrument called Big Bertha was developed which, like the original 'tick-tock' oscilloclast, was a spark gap transmitter.[55] This proved successful in practice and some were used for many years. The College continued its development of the instrument and in 1926 produced an 'Improved Oscilloclast'. About 50 were made but they proved difficult to tune as there was only a single tuning dial and the settings were close together. By 1928 the two tubes of the original oscilloclast had been replaced by one and a few were made. However, by 1931 a new two-tube version with 'a basic carrier wave of two metres' was on the market but in practice it proved difficult to maintain the instrument on its proper frequency. By 1937 a two-tube Short-Wave Oscilloclast and Combined Depolarizer electrodes with a basic carrier wave of seven metres, which was substantially the same as the original Abrams instrument, was developed.[55] The makers, however, considered the instrument to be a major improvement on the original of Abrams.[55] By 1954 the FDA claimed that some 5000 oscilloclasts and other devices were in use.[51] (In 1923 there were about 3,500 practitioners.)[72] The electronic reflex of Abrams was also adapted to locate gas, oil, water, metals etc. in the ground[28], an observation reminiscent of the uses dowsing is put to. An excellent review of Abrams' discoveries is given by A. H. Bell.[21]

Developments after Abrams

The success of Abrams stimulated the development of a number of other instruments e.g. Oscillotron, Depolaray, Electropad, Neurolinometer, Radioclast.[63,84,107] *Scientific American* reported some 50 types of such equipment in 1924.[69]

Many users, as well as their critics, were critical of the theoretical foundations of Abrams' instruments, particularly the use of resistances in the circuit.[46] F.C. Ellis, an electrical engineer from Chicago, also claimed that the rates that were supposedly specific for the various disease conditions were far from specific and reactions would occur at other settings, thus reducing the diagnostic value of the instrument.[46] He developed an instrument using two parallel wires for 'tuning' and removed the 'resistance' element from the system.[46,100] At one end the wires were connected to two closely spaced plates between which a blood specimen was placed, whilst the other end was a movable short-circuiting bridge. Near the plates was another bridge, not in metallic contact with the wires, which was used to collect the energy from the subject who stood on a metallic plate connected to it by a wire (the 'Indicator'). From the other side of the bridge a wire lead to a variable air-gap mechanism and thence by wire to the subject's forehead (the 'Intensity gage').[47, 63] The air gap was used to measure the intensity of the energy. As with Abrams' and Boyd's methods a human subject was necessary to detect reactions although he no longer need to face west and external interferences were much reduced.[46] He developed a treatment instrument, designed 'to deal in electrons, not interference waves', with which diagnosis was no longer necessary.[46] The diagnostic instrument could also be used for selecting remedies.[5] Ellis' *Micro-Dynameter* was condemned by the US courts in 1962 as 'not safe for use even in the hands of a licensed practitioner'.[107]

The Jehovah's Witnesses were supporters of Abrams' methods until 1953 and promoted and even invented new devices to cure fellow members.[86] These included the *Radio Disease Killer* (RDK Corporation of Brooklyn) and the 'automatic electronic diagnosis' instrument of Dr R. A. Gamble, a prominent Bible Student.[65, 86, 103] The instrument, the *Electronic Radio Biola* was claimed to 'automatically diagnose and treat diseases by the use of electronic vibrations with a '100% correct diagnosis'![87] It was based on Abrams' concepts and claimed to catch and store 'disease vibrations' in a 'radio wave trap, where they are registered, measured and held, and can be returned to the patient at will and used to destroy the very disease that created them'.[87] Water was used as the wave trap.

The *Pathoclast* was first produced in 1919 by Dr J. W. Wigelsworth, with the aid of his brother A. E. Wigelsworth, and the Pathometric Corporation, Chicago was founded to train operators and produce the instruments.[66] It differed from other instruments in the use of variable condensers for tuning and vacuum tubes for amplification. High frequency oscillations, supposedly picked up from the patient or witness by means of a special flat coil (the 'patho-collector'), were highly amplified and fed back in inverted phase to damp out and neutralise the signal.[75] Treatment could be broadcast over distances with this device although such experiments were frowned upon by the Pathoclast laboratories who believed people in the path of the rays may be in danger.[75] The use of mains electricity was fundamental to the device.[66] This device also incorporated a stick pad or rubbing plate that incorporated a heater, presumably to keep the plate dry. Vials of water could be charged with the patient's vibrations and used to represent the patient[75] or even used for treatment.[66] Treatment was either automatic or by means of rates.[75] As the tuning method was fundamentally different from other designs rates were not transferable. The Universal Society of Pathometrists represented users and they called their system *Vibronics* to distinguish it from radionics.[66]

The *Calbro-Magnowave* (1924[66]), developed by *Cal*dwell and *Bro*nson (from whom it was named), incorporated a treatment tuning circuit for the first time, opening the door to a tremendous variety of treatment possibilities. It also permitted the use of 'personal' treatment rates, individually developed for each patient for 'thorough elimination of disease factors'. It also incorporated a 'clearing circuit' so that energy from a previous client could be purged from the instrument before use. A 'rubbing plate' was incorporated into the circuit which eliminated the need to percuss or stroke the abdomen of a subject and the procedure was speeded up.[84] Over a thousand instruments were made in the late 1920s and early 1930s and it was the first, and perhaps only, radionic instrument to attain wide sales. A convention of users adopted the term 'radionic' as descriptive of their equipment and the same convention formed the 'International Radionic Association' which continued in existence for nearly 30 years.[84] Although Russell[91] believes the term 'radionic' was adopted about 1935 the earliest reference that I have to its use is a 1931 paper by Mary Senseman on the selection of homeopathic remedies by radionic means.[93] The editor has a footnote 'This test, we imagine, is something allied to the electronic reactions'. The earliest textbook on radionics that I have located, which, from the preface, I believe refers to the Calbro-Magnowave, is H.J. Rogers' *The New Radionics* of 1936.[90]

T.G. Hieronymus, an electrical engineer, became involved in radionics after being asked to produce a treasure finding device based on Abrams' principles. This was unsuccessful but stimulated him to develop an instrument for treatment, as well as his patented instrument for detecting the emanations of substances which could be used for analyzing compounds (Patent GB663978; 1952).[57] He developed the Pathoclast (for which he acquired the rights and copyright[21a]) into the *Electro-Biometer* and made it the most advanced condenser-tuned instrument yet made. It also included the facility for charging vials of water with a radionic treatment rate selected for the patient.[84] These would be used as remedies by the patient. Despite its complex electronics, including amplification valves, quite a few operators found that they could use the equipment for diagnostic analysis just as effectively when the power supply was cut off! Hieronymus had already realised that the Abrams instrument was electrically unsound but nevertheless worked.[57] Experimenters e.g. John Campbell, editor of *Analog/Astounding Science Fiction* magazine and others,[25, 64] also found that the construction of many parts of the machine was not critical, indeed the amplifier could be drawn in Indian ink on paper, so it became clear that the machine was a symbolic representation of a process that is occurring in the mind of the operator.[53,91] *Scientific American* also reported a practitioner using the Abrams technique, to his own satisfaction, with connections in the resistance box interrupted.[68]

The Hieronymus instrument was considered to detect and utilize 'Eloptic' radiation which seemed to emanate from all materials.[53] It has since become evident that 'electricity plays no part in the operation of the true radionic detection equipment'.[84] However, the use of amplification was felt to improve the efficacy of the treatment device, as treatment time was considerably shortened with amplification. The early partner of Hieronymus, A. Stanley Rogers (died 1959), became involved with a number of radionic techniques before developing the *White Light Radionic Analyser*.[54] This particular analyser was based on the Calbro-Magnowave.

The same period saw the development of the *Radioclast*[84] (1930[66]). This contained amplifying valves like the Pathoclast but had relatively few tuning dials that limited its range of treatment technique. Laurence[66] also notes the *Hemovitameter* (1936) as being a development in the radionic line.

The successors to the Calbro-Magnowave were the instruments produced by the Art Tool & Die Co. of Detroit, Michigan from the mid-1930s to 1942 when shortage of electronic parts due to the war forced the company to discontinue production. A number of improvements to the Calbro-Magnowave were incorporated, mainly in response to the teachings of A. Stanley Rogers.[84] The tuning dials were increased from six to nine per row which increased the tuning combinations. They found that the greater the number of tuning dials in the row the greater the therapeutic effect.[84] They also incorporated toggle switches for switching tuning rates in and out of the circuit; this saved time for the practitioner who could use pre-set tuning rates. A number of rates could be incorporated at the same time, as well as a personal rate. Unfortunately, the availability of pre-set rates led to practitioners limiting their analysis to those rates provided.

Analyzing the patient was, of course, a time consuming process and attempts were made to produce automatic treatment devices that would eliminate the diagnostic stage. The *Autoclast* was developed by the ERA Electric Company in New York and was on sale in 1924. Diagnosis was automatic depending on the patient's own emanations which were made audible by a telephone incorporated into the device. [13] A development from the Autoclast was the *Patho-Oscillograph* which, by means of small vibrating mirrors, reflected a beam of light onto film and claimed to produce photographic curves of diseases which could be used in diagnosis. [12] The Art Tool & Die Co. later also produced an automatic radionic instrument, the *Electro-Metabograph*. [84] This was designed to register the readings automatically without the operator rubbing the plate. Apparently the adjustments on these instruments were very sensitive and only one man was capable of keeping them balanced. After his retirement a replacement could not be found and users of the instrument either discontinued their use or had a rubbing plate installed. This is reminiscent of a number of radionic instruments, particularly the cameras, where one, or a very limited number of people, were capable of operating them.

Further developments in America included the Hunter instruments with a large specimen well for testing the suitability of combinations of vitamins, minerals and food supplements for the patient. Mark L. Gallert (1915-1985), who studied with A. Stanley Rogers, added improvements to basic radionic instruments to make the equipment more sensitive and easier to operate. Three tuning controls were added to the metallic element under the rubbing plate; one to tune the detector plate to the characteristics of the operator, and two for tuning the instrument to the radiational characteristics of the environment in which it was used. [84] Gallert introduced a two layered rubbing plate and a multi-layered (7) detector assembly, each layer with a characteristic pattern. Various other technical modifications were made but only a limited number of instruments were produced as their production was never a commercial undertaking. [84] Gallert's system was based on a series of personal rates. [54]

Heil Eugene Crum invented the *Coetherator* (1936), a box containing the witness and a light bulb, wire and a glass tube filled with water. The practitioner spoke the names of popular diseases while rubbing a pedal. He broadcast treatments and claimed also to perform agricultural treatments. He was prosecuted by the Indiana Supreme Court in 1941. [18]

Ruth Drown

The most significant figure in radionic development in America immediately after Abrams was Ruth Drown (1892-1965). In 1923 Drown attended a lecture by Dr Frederick F. Strong on the application of radio energies to the treatment of disease. Drown already had experience with radios and possessed an intuitive ability with their construction.[37] She went to work with him as an office assistant. Strong used Abrams' methods and Drown became skilful in ministering to his patients.[37] Her skills were recognised by Dr Thomas McAllister, also an Abrams practitioner, who asked her to work for him full time during which he gave her personal instruction in the medical arts.[37] In 1927 she became licensed as a Doctor of Chiropractic in California.[37] She produced her first instrument in 1929.[17,36,43] It had 9 dials arranged in three rows, most dials having the standard 10 steps (hence the origin of the 'Base 10' instrument). Some instruments also had a dial to select one of 10 different coloured lights. The vibrational 'rates' for the various organs, tissues and diseases, which she worked out for her system, were put onto the dials. These would be used for diagnostic and broadcast purposes. These rates represented the unique molecular vibration characteristics of the tissues concerned.[43] Although she ran courses on the diagnostic instrument she was initially very secretive about how to obtain a treatment rate although, apparently, much later she did begin to teach students how to obtain it.[38] Like some devices today she would also use sealed vials with witnesses.

Fig. 2.6 Ruth Drown

Drown was one of the first people to incorporate a rubbing plate or stick pad in the instrument so localization of disease could be carried out within the instrument without the aid of a 'reagent' or 'subject'. A rubber diaphragm was used as the stick pad and may have been the first use of this method.[37] Her instrument was not powered by electricity as she believed that commercial electric power was in some way inimical to the energies she was seeking to tune and manipulate.[37] Instead, she believed that all vibratory rates were present in the atmosphere being received by humans,

Fig. 2.7 Drown H.R.V. model

and by tuning her equipment a particular rate set up a resonant circuit between the equipment and the patient, intensifying its effect.[84] Unlike the Abrams instruments, it was not subject to extraneous disturbances.[36] For analysis the patient placed his feet on two plates of German silver, which were connected to the instrument. For treatment a lead was taken from the instrument to a plate of block tin placed over the solar plexus which sent the energy back into the tissue from whence it came.[36, 44] By converting the block tin to a container for lactose pills and fastening it to the foot plate with the treatment cord a remedy could be made by potentization[44], a technique much developed by others in later years. The same set-up, using a blood sample in place of the lactose pills, could be used to broadcast the treatment.[44]

Analysis was always done directly on the patient using the instrument[41] but broadcasting treatment was a significant advance in radionics. Drown believed that life was energy acting through substance and each atom had the complete energy of every part of the body from which it came.[42] The blood crystal, therefore, retained the vibrational characteristics of the person from which it came and continued to provide a link with that patient which could be utilised for analysis and to broadcast radionic rates. It has to be said that all these arguments are philosophical rather than based on scientific fact. It has been suggested that not everyone benefited from Drown's treatment because there was no power behind the broadcast treatment which thus became attenuated.[84] This has been suggested as a factor in her legal persecution although, apparently, her selling of instruments at high prices to laymen may also have been significant.[84] She had a wide following and called her work 'Radio Therapy' and tried to separate it from radionics. One commentator believed that her ability and knowledge transcended the limited scope of her equipment. [84]

The Drown Radio Therapeutic Instruments were a means to catch and hold a certain amount of Life Force of a patient being treated. Indeed the patient's own energy was being used as the means of treatment [42] being focussed back into specific areas of the body for treatment. [48] The instrument acted as a selecting station, helping to harmonize this Life Force and bring about health in the physical body. [42] The Life Force was considered to be made up of electrons and she called protons 'strong force field electrons' which is pushing scientific rationalisation rather too far! In fact the physical explanations for the action of her instrument are very dated and inaccurate. She tried, as many do today, to try to explain the working of her instruments on a rather poor understanding of atomic theory as it was at the time (the 1930s). Her physiological explanations are also rather strange e.g. 'The blood plasma is destructive to form (as also is the energy flowing over the nervous system), if not supplied with electrons from the earth. These electrons are drawn through the pores of the skin and through the blood vessels ...' [42]

Drown also developed equipment to make photographs of cross-sections of internal organs from a blood spot. [37] These 'Radio-Vision' pictures were made from 1935 on. [36] The 'camera' could only be used after a complete analysis of the patient had been made and, in effect, was a diagnostic instrument with a photographic attachment added. [36,43] No satisfactory explanation has been made as to how this was done although a committee which tested her claims believed the images to be merely simple fog patterns produced by exposure of the film to white light before it had been fixed adequately, and they could see no resemblance between numerous of her photographs and the anatomical structures they were supposed to represent. [17,51,107] Her own thoughts on the matter include the belief that the photographs were 'what might be called a conglomerate mass of energy from the ethers.' [42] The patient needed to be alive as Life Force needed to be present to make the photographs. The blood witness was considered as crystallised light whose energy passes around the world at the speed of light and could be trapped by the instrument. [42] 'Life is conditioned in motion'. [42]

As Drown could not always get the camera to work, and it rarely worked for anyone else, it is likely to be a mediumistic talent akin to some form of psychic photography. [38,84] Apparently by 1960 she had lost the power to make photographs in this way and could not understand why. [38] Leonard Chapman, who had known Drown in the early days of radionics, tantalisingly commented that 'there are certain laws and regulations governing these spiritual things, and if you can't comply with those laws you lose the power!' [38]

Chapman certainly believed both Drown's and Abrams' work was divinely inspired and Drown told Riley Crabb that 'much of her pioneering work in radionics was inspired and guided by the Master Morya'. [38] This had come as a surprise to her! At the time he revealed his presence she had never heard of him and, according to Chapman, knew nothing of Theosophy and his influence in the founding and overshadowing of the Society. However, Frederick Strong was a student of Theosophy and it is possible that she may have come into contact with it early in her career. [37] Moreover, according to Constable, Drown had been a student of metaphysics since 1916 and 'meditated daily upon the instrument she was trying to make concrete on the physical plane'. [37] Master Morya is a master of masters on the First Ray of Will or Power. This was, of course, one of Drown's outstanding characteristics as a pioneer in radionics. [38] Oddly enough the use of ESP, or psychic powers, 'at this stage of evolution' was considered 'a cumbrous and unwelcome humbug' in radionics and the Drown system and the physicians trained in its use aimed to avoid this. [36]

Drown's work became influenced by the Kabbalah after she was given a copy of MacGregor Mather's' *Kabbalah Unveiled* in the 1930s. [36,40] A commentator in 1961 even suggested that the nine dials of her instruments were based on 'the Sephiroth of the Tree of Life of the Western Mystery tradition'. [44] As the development of radionics involved a great deal of work with numbers it is not surprising that ideas began to flow connecting the numbers with the Kabbalistic Tree of Life. Certain consistencies began to present themselves repeatedly and she felt that her findings confirmed the relationships between Man and the Cosmos embodied in the Kabbalah. [36] Relationships between her rates and the Tree of Life were discerned and Constable believes that such are the consistencies that it is impossible to discard the rates as being arbitrary and meaningless and of no application outside the Drown system. [36] However, as the rates are reduced to one of ten numbers in the numerological analysis, these relationships may be difficult to demonstrate statistically in a satisfactory way.

Like others after her (e.g. de la Warr) rates were made by holding the thought in the mind while rotating the dials until a stick was obtained. [106]

The rates she obtained were examined for kabbalistic relationship after their making rather than made to a specific system. In view of the way rates are made the views of Malcolm Rae are interesting. He viewed a rate as an 'exact immutable numerical representation of a thought. It is a crystallisation of a thought, and once a thought is converted into a rate it is unchangeable.'[85] The fact that there are in existence several rates for the same condition may reflect the imperfections of the humans producing them!

Charged in 1951 by the Food and Drug Administration for mislabelling her diagnostic instruments[36,37,107] she was found guilty and fined $1000 and stopped shipping across state lines.[97] As a result of an undercover operation by the California State Department of Public Health in 1963 Drown, with her daughter Cynthia Chatfield, also a chiropractor, and their assistant Mrs Margaret Lunness, were taken to court on charges of theft and grand theft.[107] Evidence presented indicated that advice countermanding the patients' physicians had been given which could lead to life threatening situations e.g. a reduction of insulin intake by a diabetic.[97] These stresses led directly to Ruth Drown's death in 1965 while awaiting trial. This took place in 1966 and the other defendants were convicted and, in 1967, were sentenced to prison (Chatfield) and probation (Lunness).[97] Young's book, *The Medical Messiahs*, gives details of Drown's prosecution.[107]

One aspect of Drown's work that attracted attention was haemorrhage control. This aspect was cited in the Certificate of Merit for 1946 awarded her by the New York Museum of Science and Industry 'for her efforts in stimulating interest in the human body and the correction of its ills.'[42] The award crowned 29 years of research and 17 years of practice.

Testing times

Tests were particularly common in the early years of radionics and have done nothing to help the therapy and, although workers realise that the test situation is not an appropriate model for the real clinical case, many cannot resist the attempt to demonstrate their skills. An academic committee that tested Ruth Drown with the blood of ten patients concluded that 'her technique is to find so much trouble in so many organs that usually she can say "I told you so" when she registers an occasional lucky positive guess. In these particular tests, even this luck deserted her.'[17]

In 1924 *Scientific American* had concluded that Abrams' techniques, when they worked, were psychic in nature.[67] Indeed, Abrams had recognised that the 'will to believe was a prerequisite in this work'.[68] Lindemann[73] went further and suggested radionics to be a form of ceremonial magic, the tuner being solidified thought form with the rates representing agreements with the subtle nature spirits. He observed that most practitioners agree that the more people using a particular system, the better it works for everyone. David Tansley certainly believed radionics to be magic.[101] History suggests that yesterday's magic often becomes tomorrow's scientific breakthrough.[74]

Tests, whether covert or overt, have almost invariably failed to show that radionic techniques have any value in 'diagnosing' conditions and where animal blood has been sent as human clearly impossible results have been obtained.[9,11,51] Abrams' methods were put through rigorous testing by the staff of *Scientific American* in the early 1920s with poor results (see *Scientific American* October, 1923-September, 1924). These tests involved the diagnostic ability of the practitioner as measured against conventional methods, or their ability to match samples of blood.[70] They did not test the healing ability of the practitioners, although this was suggested by one practitioner but was not undertaken before the conclusion of the investigation.[70] However, the Third Report of the International Hahnemannian Committee of July 1926 reported the clinical findings of physicians treating cancer with the Abrams technique. 541 cases were reported with a remarkable 482 apparent recoveries.[63] These were not clinical trials in the modern sense of course, having no controls, but do represent the faith many doctors had in the method in those early days.

Tests conducted by the Committee chaired by Sir Thomas Horder[58-60] also involved matching remedies or substances, and the results from these were often startlingly accurate. The claims of Abrams had aroused the interest of Dr C. B. Heald, the Medical Adviser to the Director of Civil Aviation in Britain, on the grounds that if they were found to be substantially true the technique might be developed to keep in touch with variations in the medical fitness of civil pilots. A preliminary investigation authorized by the Director of Civil Aviation was interesting and suggestive but not conclusive enough to interest the Air Ministry in proceeding any further. However, Heald persevered and enlisted the help of scientists at the Air Ministry and War Office (Leroy, Hart and Whately Smith). He also managed to interest Sir Thomas Horder, a 'medical man of established reputation' in chairing a committee of investigation. Hart and Whately

Fig. 7 (a).

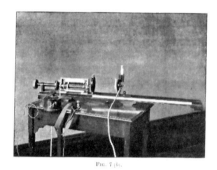

Fig. 7 (b).

Fig. 2.8 Boyd's emanometer technique [22a]

Smith were involved in devising the conditions of the tests and analysis of the data. The tests were made in conjunction with Dr W. E. Boyd who had modified Abrams' technique to produce his own instrument, the *Emanometer*, and the technique using this instrument, which involved extensive copper shielding of the subject, was used for the tests.

Preliminary tests made by Boyd in Glasgow to match sputa specimens were successful (1 in 30 chance of the result being obtained by accident). Further tests made in London by Dr W. R. McCrae to measure the 'intensity' of specimens on the sliding scale, or to determine if they were or were not 'screened' by a metallic shield during measurement, were unsuccessful. Boyd considered that the screening procedures available in McCrae's lab were not good enough and the tests moved to Boyd's own laboratory in Glasgow in June 1924. Test 1 involved discriminating between two apparently identical substances and all of 25 tests were successful (the odds against this happening by chance were 1 in 33,554,432). Sulphur 10M was the active substance used and the operator (who did the percussing) and subject (whose abdomen was percussed) were local Gallowgate boys who evidently worked at a phenomenal speed as Whately Smith, who conducted the experiments by placing the samples in a hatch, was at times barely able to keep up with them!

The second and third trials involved the selection and identification, in each case, of one specific substance from a number of others. Both tests were completely successful with a 1 in 180 and 1 in 7,776 chance of the results being obtained by accident alone. The fourth test was a repetition of the first with 18/20 correct results (odds against chance of 1 in 5,518) and the fifth test was a screening experiment and all 16 tests were successful (1 in 65,536 chance of the result being an accident).

In view of the success of the trials the committee enlisted the services of Mr E. J. Dingwall of the Society of Psychical Research to see if he could detect any trickery. Such procedures presaged those often used in paranormal research today. None was observed in a repeat of the experiments that were again spectacularly successful. Horder believed that the key to success, and the reason why earlier tests failed, lay in the extensive screening used, and there was a possibility that tests on Abrams' system often failed because of an absence of screening.

The committee commented on the fact that the subject appeared to be working 'in an entirely automatic, indeed almost perfunctory, manner, and it was easy for the investigators to hear the change in percussion note produced by the insertion of the test substance into the hatch.' Horder and Heald could also feel an alteration in their abdominal muscles as specimens were inserted or withdrawn from the hatch without their knowledge.

The investigators were happy to announce that 'something does happen' when using the technique and concluded 'That certain substances, when placed in proper relation to the Emanometer of Boyd, produce, beyond any reasonable doubt, changes in the abdominal wall of the "subject" of a kind that may be detected by percussion. This is tantamount to the statement that the fundamental proposition underlying, in common, the original and certain other forms of apparatus devised for the purpose of eliciting the so-called Electronic Reactions of Abrams, is established to a very high degree of probability'. Unfortunately they could not recommend its use in practice, as there was no demonstrable correspondence between the 'reactions' found and known pathological states. Indeed there had been 'no contribution to pathology by electronists after 10 years practice.' This is unfair, as the tests were not designed to test for disease states; indeed no clinical tests were ever conducted. But the lack of correlation between the findings made on the box and pathological states did prove a problem for at least some practitioners trained in conventional medicine.[39] The committee summed up, probably unfairly in the light of the tests conducted, 'The conclusions arrived at in this Communication leave the position of the practising electronist as scientifically unsound and as ethically unjustified as it was before. They give no sanction for the use of E.R.A. in the diagnosis or in the treatment of disease. Nor does there appear to be any other sanction for this kind of practice at the present time.' This was a very negative conclusion for a very positive series of experiments, the conduct of which would stand well with modern experimental research. It is probable that the conclusions were a sop to the medical establishment as evidently Horder was by no means unsympathetic to Abrams' theories as he told his son: 'I hesitate to talk about vibrations, since so little is known of these things, but there is something of that about it all.'[83] He evidently felt rather guilty about not following up the findings of his report. Years later he told the novelist Beverley Nichols that he had 'rather a guilty conscience about it' and gave him the impression that he was personally interested in raising funds for a further investigation.[78]

Much literature has, not surprisingly, been published mocking and deriding radionics. From its earliest days radionics, and particularly Albert Abrams and later Ruth Drown, has been the brunt of attacks both personal and professional.[6,7,14-17,45,49,51,52,79,107] Abrams was described in *Hygeia*, a popular publication of the American Medical Association, as 'the most finished medical charlatan of our time'.[86]

In more recent times the world wide web has seen a number of sites dedicated to the 'quackery' of radionics[86] as well as plenty supporting the concept, although a number of these do seem bent on selling expensive equipment, courses or treatments. There can also be no denying that in the past unscrupulous operators have entered the field, attempting to frighten people into parting with large amounts of money for their services or deterring others from seeking prompt medical advice in serious conditions such as cancer.[50,63,98,107] Thankfully, such cases are rare and today potential clients are protected by a strict code of ethics which apply to members of professional radionic organisations.

Explanations of how radionics works have tended to rely on pseudo-scientific concepts which have ultimately done more harm than good. The Horder report[60] states 'but it is instructive to note that the alleged "explanations" proffered by Abrams consisted in the main of a medley of technical terms adopted indiscriminately from normal electrical practice and so misused as inevitably to invite the most pungent criticism.' 'Jargon characteristic of charlatanry' is a phrase used by the otherwise sympathetic Horder committee.[60]

Regrettably, much of the criticism of Abrams' and Drown's techniques was justified, as the notes in the *Journal of the American Medical Association* testify, and rarely did the actions of the practitioners help their cause! Abrams used one of his devices in court in a paternity case, and he also claimed to be able to identify the religion of patients.[62,92,107] The Horder report points out that '... the task of those anxious to discredit the Abrams technique was greatly facilitated by the profusion with which the inventor advanced more and more claims of an increasingly remarkable nature.'[60] The sometimes strange prejudices of the pioneers also did not help. Drown, for example, apparently believed that jazz music caused cancer which could be dissipated by more soothing music.[97] Also she believed that people should look after their magnetic fields and weak patients should not take showers as the patient's magnetism would be washed with the water through the drain, leaving him depleted.[44]

Practitioners often have had unwarranted faith in their ability to diagnose and cure and this has led to spectacular failures in controlled trials of their methods or where 'diagnoses' have been checked by conventional means. Both Drown's and Abrams' techniques have come off particularly badly.[10,107] With the wisdom of hindsight we can appreciate the potential of radionics in the spectrum of health care and its complementarity to other forms of treatment. One would not attempt to use radionics to stop bleeding in a nicked femoral artery, as Drown did in one trial, when more appropriate conventional methods are available.[17] With the training modern practitioners receive we should not see a woman diagnosed with prostate problems, as Drown did in one of her tests, or to make claims to cure or prevent just about every major disease.[17,107] As with many new therapies the enthusiasm of the early practitioners sometimes overrode common sense and the fallout of these humiliating failures and, as the US government with justification claimed, 'nonsense' written by the promoters of these methods, is still with us today.

References

1. Abrams A. (1914) Human Energy. In: *Spondylotherapy*, 5th edn, pp. 45-101 (of the Supplement 'Progressive Spondylotherapy 1914'). Philopolis Press, San Francisco.
2. Abrams A. (1916) *New Concepts in Diagnosis and Treatment*. Philopolis Press, San Francisco.
3. Abrams A. (1917) The electronic reactions of Abrams. *International Clinics*. 1, 93-103.
4. Abrams A. (1921) The electrical nature of man. *Medical Record*. 99, 862-864.
5. Anon (?) *Investigations of the Electronic Reactions of Abrams*. Borderland Sciences, Bayside, CA.
6. Anon (1922) Abrams "Oscilloclast". Some of the lessees of this alleged therapeutic device. *Journal of the American Medical Association*. 79, 1626-1628.
7. Anon (1922) Albert Abrams, A.M., M.D., LL.D., F.R.M.S. "Spondylotherapy," "Electronic Reactions," the "Oscilloclast," the "Electrobioscope," Etc. *Journal of the American*

   Medical Association. 78, 913-914.

8. Anon (1922) The marvels of Abrams and Yergin. *Journal of the American Medical Association.* 79, 743.

9. Anon (1922) Two electronic diagnoses. The reactions of a guinea-pig and a sheep to the Reaction of Abrams. *Journal of the American Medical Association.* 79, 2247-2248.

10. Anon (1923) Another electronic diagnosis and treatment. "Everything clears up" – but the patient dies. *Journal of the American Medical Association.* 81, 317-318.

11. Anon (1923) Two more electronic diagnoses. *Journal of the American Medical Association.* 80, 1317-1318.

12. Anon (1924) Announcing a great invention: The Patho-oscillograph. *ERA-Rays,* No. 1, 16.

13. Anon (1924) The autoclast. The electronic therapy machine supreme. *ERA-rays,* No. 1, 6-15.

14. Anon (1925) Dr. Abrams and his box. *The Spectator,* Jan. 24th, 112-113.

15. Anon (1925) The inquiry into Abrams "Dynamiser" and similar apparatus. *Discovery,* March, 107-110.

16. Anon (1941) Drown laboratories submerged in pseudo-science. *Journal of the American Medical Association.* 116, 888.

17. Anon (1950) The Drown technique fails. *Journal of the American Medical Association.* 142, 506-507.

18. Anon (2000) Heil Eugene Crum and the Indiana Supreme Court. www.mtn.org/quack/amquacks/crum.htm. (Accessed 15/02/01)

19. Bailey D. M. (1978) The rise and fall of Albert Abrams, AM, MD, FRMS. *Oklahoma State Medical Association Journal.* 71, 15-20.

20. Barr J. (1925) *Abrams' Methods of Diagnosis and Treatment.* Heinemann, London.

21. Bell A. H. (1946) Dr. Abrams and his discovery. *Radio-Perception (Journal of the British Society of Dowsers).* 6, 367-381.

21a Beutlich, R.E. (2003) The story of radionics. *10th Annual Conference of the Radionic Association of India (Souvenir programme)* pp. 70-76.

22. Boyd W. E. (1925) The Boyd emanometer research and the related physical phenomena. *British Homoeopathic Journal.* 15, 346-386.

22a. Boyd W. E. (1927) The emanometer research and homoeopathy. *Transactions of the Ninth Quinquennial International Homoeopathic Congress, London,* Part 1, 691-721.

23. Boyd W. E. (1930) Electro-medical research and homoeopathy. *British Homoeopathic Journal.* 20, 299-330.

24. Boyd W. E. (1930) Polarity and the emanometer. *The Homoeopathic World.* 65, 24-25.

25. Britz D. (2002) Comment following 'Precognition and telepathic waves', a letter from Georges Sassoon. *Journal of Scientific Exploration.* 16, 253-254.

26. Cave F. A. (1922) *The Electronic Reactions of Abrams.* Health Research, Pomeroy, WA.

27. Cave F. A. (1922) The electronic reactions of Abrams. A scientific interpretation. *Pearson's Magazine.,* July 1922. (Reprinted by Borderland Sciences, Bayside CA in *ERA The Electronic Reactions of Dr Abrams,* pp. 17-20).

28. Colson T. (1936) *Introduction to Electronic Therapy.* College of Electronic Medicine, San Francisco (1989 reprint by Borderland Sciences, Bayside, CA).

29. Colson T. (1951) Effects on living tissue of chopped or pulsed energy. *Electronic Medical Digest Fourth Quarter* (Reprinted by Borderland Sciences, Bayside CA in *ERA The Electronic Reactions of Dr Abrams,* pp. 73-76).

30. Colson T. (1960) Abrams contribution to electronic medicine. *Electronic Medical Digest,* Special edition. (Reprinted by Borderland Sciences, Bayside, CA).

31. Colson T. (1960) Electronic disease classification. *Electronic Medical Digest* (Reprinted by Borderland Sciences, Bayside CA in *ERA The Electronic Reactions of Dr Abrams*, pp. 70-72).
32. Colson T. (1960) Oscilloclast energies. *Electronic Medical Digest* (Reprinted by Borderland Sciences, Bayside CA in *ERA The Electronic Reactions of Dr Abrams*, pp. 53-58).
33. Colson T. (1960?) The electronic test. *Electronic Medical Digest* (Reprinted by Borderland Sciences, Bayside CA in *ERA The Electronic Reactions of Dr Abrams*, pp. 59-69).
34. Colson T. (?) *Electronic Therapy*. Electronic Medical Foundation, San Francisco.
35. Colson T. (?1960) Abrams' oscilloclast rates...frequency characteristics. *Electronic Medical Digest*. (Reprinted by Borderland Sciences, Bayside CA in *ERA The Electronic Reactions of Dr Abrams*, pp. 45-52).
36. Constable T. J. (1961) The work of Dr. Ruth Drown. An outline on a thumbnail. In: *Radionics. The New Age Science*, pp. 69-76. Borderland Sciences Research Foundation, Garberville, CA.
37. Constable T. J. (1976) Criminal or Genius? In: *The Cosmic Pulse of Life*, pp. 233-255. Neville Spearman, Sudbury, Suffolk.
38. Crabb R. H. (1991) Interview with Dr. Leonard Chapman on the operation and use of radionic equipment. In: *Radionics. The New Age Science*, pp. 25-35. Borderland Sciences Research Foundation, Garberville, CA.
39. Crimp G. L. (1924) Electronic reactions of Abrams (Letter). *The Lancet*. 206, 415.
40. Denning R. M. (1989) Dr Ruth Drown and her work *and* Radionics and the mystique of esotericism. *Radionic Quarterly*. 35 (1/2), 28-31. See also *Memorandum of Fundamental Radionic Principles as Developed by Dr. Ruth B. Drown*. R. Murray Denning, Little Chalfont, Bucks; 1983.
41. Dower L. (1971) Abrams and Drown in retrospect. *Radionic Journal*. 18 (1), 10-13.
42. Drown R. (1938) *The Science and Philosophy of the Drown Radio Therapy*. Ruth Drown, Los Angeles. (Reprint by Borderland Sciences, Garberville, CA).
43. Drown R. (1991) Radio-Vision. Scientific milestone. In: *Radionics. The New Age Science.*, pp. 77-102. Borderland Sciences Research Foundation, Garberville, CA.
44. Drown R. (?) *The Drown Radio-Vision and Homo-Vibra Ray Instruments and their Use*. (Reprinted by Health Research Books, Pomeroy, WA.)
45. Edwards H. (2001) Radionics, good for everything. From *Australian Skeptics* (Vol. 13 No. 1). (Available on line at www.skeptics.com.au/journal/radionics.htm.) (Accessed 16/01.2003)
46. Ellis F. C. (1923) *Report on "Electronic" Diagnosis and Treatment of Disease*. 32pp. Electronic Research Laboratories, Chicago.
47. Ellis F. C. (1924) *Operating Instructions and General Working Principles of the Indicator and Intensity Gage in Diagnosis and Electronic Wave Analysis*. 11pp. Electronic Research Laboratories, Chicago.
48. Evans C. W. (1992) A practitioner's thoughts on Ruth Drown's centenary. *Radionic Quarterly*. 38 (4), 4-7.
49. Fishbein M. (1925) The quackery of the Abrams box. In: *The Medical Follies*, pp. 99-118. Boni & Liveright, New York.
50. Flaxman N. (1953) A cardiology anomaly; Albert Abrams (1863-1924). *Bulletin of the History of Medicine*. 27, 252-268.
51. Gardner M. (1957) *Fads and Fallacies in the Name of Science*, 2nd edn. Dover, New York.
52. Gibbes J. H. (1925) Quacks and quackeries. *The Scientific Monthly*. 21, 533-550.
53. Goodavage J. F. (1973) The incredible Hieronymus machine. *Radionic Journal*. 19 (3), 12-24.

54. Gray K. (2000) Brief history of White Light radionics. www.geocities.com/wlradionics/03/page6.html. (Accessed 15/03/2002)

55. Hart F. J. (1941) The college. *Journal of Electronic Medicine*. 25 (6), 3-4, 28-29.

56. Hart F. J. (1942) Short wave and disease control in dairy herds. *Journal of Electronic Medicine*. 26 (3), 5-10.

57. Hieronymus T. G. (1946) Report on electronic research. *Journal of Electronic Medicine*. 30 (2), 11-15.

58. Horder T. (1925) Electronic Reactions. *The Lancet*. Jan 24th, 177-181.

59. Horder T. (1925) The Electronic Reactions of Abrams. *British Medical Journal*. Jan 24th, 179-185.

60. Horder T. (1925) *A Preliminary Communication concerning the "Electronic Reactions" of Abrams with Special Reference to the "Emanometer" Technique of Boyd*. John Bale, Sons & Danielsson, London.

61. Hudgings W. (1923) *Dr. Abrahm's Electron Theory*. www.svpvril.com/Abrahm.html (Accessed 29/01/01)

62. Humphris F. H. (1924) The "Electronic Reactions" of Abrams (E.R.A.). *The Lancet*. 206, 176-178.

63. International Hahnemannian Committee. (1926) *Certain Body Reflexes in their Relation to Certain Radiant Energies and a Third Report of the International Hahnemannian Committee on the Abrams Method of Diagnosis and Treatment*. 46pp. International Hahnemannian Association, Derby, CT.

64. Kocher G. (2002) More on the Hieronymus machine (letter). *Journal of Scientific Exploration*. 16, 480-481.

65. Lab Radiants. (2000) Radio Disease Killer. http://radiantslab.com/quackmed/rdk.html. (Accessed 29/01/2001)

66. Laurence K. (1985) *A Study in Vibronics and its Relationship to Pathometry in Health and Dis-ease*. Ken Laurence.

67. Lescarboura A. C. (1924) Our Abrams Investigation - VI. A study of the late Dr. Albert Abrams of San Francisco and his work. *Scientific American*. 130, 159, 207, 210-212, 214.

68. Lescarboura A. C. (1924) Our Abrams Investigation - VII. Queer adventures and queer people met in our quest of the E.R.A. truth. *Scientific American*. 130, 240, 278-281.

69. Lescarboura A. C. (1924) Our Abrams Investigation - VIII. The report of a test on localization of abscessed teeth through handwriting. *Scientific American*. 130, 313, 361-362.

70. Lescarboura A. C. (1924) Our Abrams Investigation - X. Two more blood specimen tests and a new offer of co-operation from the electronists. *Scientific American*. 131, 16, 64-65, 69-70.

71. Lescarboura A. C. (1924) Our Abrams Investigation - XI. The treatment end of E.R.A. and a study of testimonials and the oscilloclast. *Scientific American*. 131, 96, 140-142.

72. Lescarboura A. C. (1924) Our Abrams verdict. The Electronic Reactions of Abrams and electronic medicine in general found utterly worthless. *Scientific American*. 131, 158-160, 220-222.

73. Lindemann P. A. (1991) Build your own radionic tuner. In: *Radionics. The New Age Science*, pp. 57-60. Borderland Sciences Research Foundation, Garberville, CA.

74. Lindemann P. A. (1991) Radionic analysis: a theoretical approach. In: *Radionics. The New Age Science.*, pp. 61-64. Borderland Sciences Research Foundation, Garberville, CA.

75. Maby J. C. (1946) A note on Dr. J.W. Wigelsworth's "Pathoclast" (for radionic diagnosis and treatment). *Radio-Perception (Journal of the British Society of Dowsers)*. 6, 358-367.

76. Marky A. (1922) A challenge. *Pearson's Magazine*. July 1922. (Reprinted by Borderland Sciences, Bayside CA in *ERA The Electronic Reactions of Dr Abrams*, pp. 3-5).

77. Monroe J. (1998) Radionics, psychotronics and electronic medicine. Quantum leaps, dead ends, and new ways of thinking. *Strange Attractor*. 1. (Available on line at www.newscience.santa-fe.nm.us/strange2.htm) (Accessed 15/03/2002)

78. Nichols B. (1966) *Powers That Be*. Jonathan Cape, London.

79. Orbison T. J. (1923) Certain electrical diagnostic and therapeutic methods from the standpoint of a neuropsychiatrist. *Journal of the American Medical Association*. 81, 2057-2059.

80. Parkes O. and Perkins E. (1930) *The Detection of Disease*. Sampson Low, Marston & Co., London.

81. Perkins E. (1987) The original concepts of the late Dr. Abrams. *Radionic Quarterly*. 33 (2), 14-21. (First published in *Radionic Therapy* 2 (5), 1-27 (1956))

82. Perkins E. (1987) The original concepts of the late Dr. Abrams. *Radionic Quarterly*. 33 (3), 14-19. (First published in *Radionic Therapy* 2 (5), 1-27 (1956))

83. Pound R. (1967) *Harley Street*. Michael Joseph, London.

84. Radionist, The. (1991) The history and development of radionics Part 1. In: *Radionics. The New Age Science*, pp. 1-16. Borderland Sciences Research Foundation, Garberville, CA.

85. Rae M. (1985) Theory and practice of radionics. *Radionic Quarterly*. 32 (1), 20-24.

86. Raines K. (2000) Dr. Albert Abrams and the E.R.A. http://ny.observer.org/raines/abrams.html. (Accessed 29/01/2001)

87. Raines K. (2000) The Electronic Radio Biola. www.premier1.net/~raines/biola.html. (Accessed 29/01/2001)

88. Reyner J. H., Laurence G., Upton C., and Souter K. (2001) *Psionic Medicine. The study and treatment of causative factors in illness*. C.W. Daniel, Saffron Walden.

89. Richards G. (1934) *The Chain of Life*. John Bale, Sons & Danielsson, London.

90. Rogers H. J. (1936) *The New Radionics*. Missouri Printing & Publishing Co., Mexico, Mo.

91. Russell E. W. (1986) Radionics: a science for the new age. In: *Psychotronics Book 1 A primer on instruments using variable capacitor tuning* (ed. P. J. Kelly), pp. 74-85. Interdimensional Sciences, Lakemont, GA.

92. Scofield A. M. (2003) Albert Abrams and Sir James Barr – the correspondence in the Radionic Association archives. *Radionic Journal*. 48 (3), 6-12 .

93. Senseman M. I. (1931) Affinity remedies by radionic test. *The Homoeopathic World*. 66, 323-331.

94. Sinclair U. (1922) Albert Abrams. A defense by Upton Sinclair. *Journal of the American Medical Association*. 78, 1334-1335.

95. Sinclair U. (1922) The house of wonder. *Pearson's Magazine*. June 1922. (Reprinted by Borderland Sciences, Bayside CA in *ERA The Electronic Reactions of Dr Abrams*, pp. 6-14).

96. Sinclair U. (1934) *The Book of Life*, 2nd edn. T. Werner Laurie, London.

97. Smith R. L. (1968) The incredible Drown case. www.chirobase.org/12Hx/drown.html. (Accessed 12/02/01)

98. Smith R. L. (1969) At your own risk: The case against chiropractic. Chapter 5: The gadgeteers. www.chirobase.org/05RB/AYOR/05.html. (Accessed 15/03/02)

99. Strong F. F. (1922) Disease: its cause and cure. *Pearson's Magazine*. August 1922. (Reprinted by Borderland Sciences, Bayside CA in *ERA The Electronic Reactions of Dr Abrams*, pp. 26-27).

100. Swayze B. W. (1922) The Abrams method in practice. *Pearson's Magazine*. August 1922. (Reprinted by Borderland Sciences, Bayside CA in *ERA The Electronic Reactions of Dr Abrams*, pp. 22-26).

101. Tansley D. V. (1982) *Radionics: Science or Magic?* C.W. Daniel, Saffron Walden.

102. Van Vleck R. (1999) The electronic reactions of Albert Abrams. www.americanartifacts.

com/smma/abrams/abrams.htm. (Accessed 29/01/2001)

103. Van Vleck R. (1999) The Radio Disease Killer. ERA quack diagnostic instrument. www.americanartifacts.com/smma/abrams/rdk.htm. (Accessed 29/01/2001)

104. Westlake A. (1985) The genesis of radionics. *Radionic Quarterly*. 32 (1), 13-19.

105. White G. S. (1929) *The Finer Forces of Nature in Diagnosis and Therapy*. Health Research, Pomeroy, WA (reprint).

106. Wilcox J. O. (1960) *Radionics in Theory and Practice*. Herbert Jenkins, London.

107. Young J. H. (1967) *The Medical Messiahs*. Princeton University Press, Princeton, NJ.

Gillian Lowe

The Chronic State of Disease – a Radionic Approach to Treatment

3

The Victor
Man is spirit – that is all man needs to know; and spirit is
triumphant over matter.

From 'The Quiet Mind – Sayings of White Eagle'

What is a chronic state of disease?

A chronic state of disease is defined as one lasting a long time (Gr. chronikos – time) or being deep-seated. This, to a radionic practitioner, indicates that there may be a great number of causes which, over the years, have been ignored/suppressed to allow this state to pervade.

Here I will represent the development of a chronic disease state as seen from a more conventional viewpoint and from an esoteric stance (Fig. 3.1 and 3.2).

From a more conventional medical viewpoint the development of a chronic condition is illustrated in Fig. 3.1. The baby is fed on cow's milk to which he, unfortunately, is sensitive. As a result he may not sleep well and, during the time he is having his vaccinations to various diseases, develops a poor gut flora and eczema. This, along with a reduced zinc intake in the processed foods of today, will make him more prone to repeated infections, upon which occurring he may be given antibiotics repeatedly. The recurring throat/ear infections may result in tonsillectomy and a further decline in gut health as the child develops, leading to constipation and a build-up of toxins, or even appendicitis. At the very least there is likely to be a case of irritable bowel disease but unfortunately arthritis or some forms of cancer are also possible.

A radionic practitioner may be asked to intervene at any of the above

41

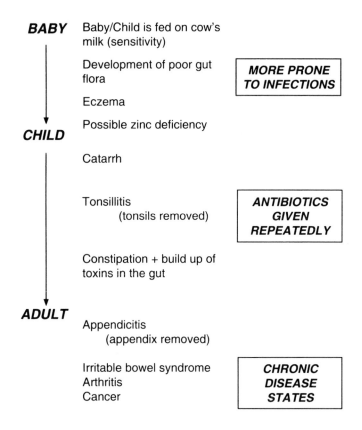

Fig. 3.1 Possible development of a chronic disease condition – Physical

stages, with the latter stages inevitably needing longer term treatment, but if they are only worked on at a physical level, without any change in lifestyle or diet, little lasting benefit can be expected.

From the approach of a holistic healer the development of a chronic disease pattern can be seen in rather a different way (Fig. 3.2) which allows for a variety of alternative methods of treatment.

At a mental level of consciousness, that is understood as a mind level above and free from emotional sidetrack, a message is sent from the higher self which can be dealt with in one of two ways. Either it can be noted and absorbed, bringing about a realisation in the person involved and a raising in consciousness with minimum disruption or, on the other hand, the personality input of the individual may resist any changes finding them too painful

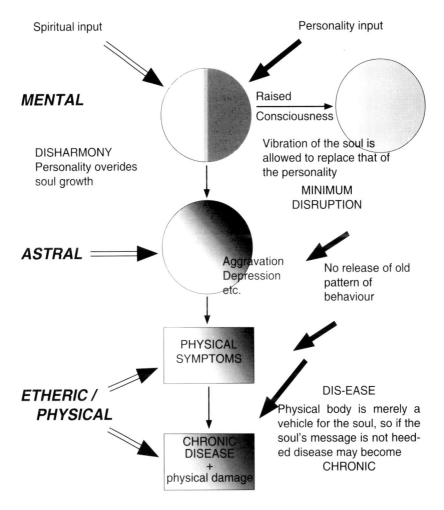

Fig. 3.2 Development of a chronic disease from an esoteric viewpoint

or too fear-invoking to implement. After a period of time this resistance will bring about disharmony at the astral level/emotional level resulting in negative traits such as aggravation or depression. The personality is in denial. If further attempts at spiritual input are denied repeatedly dis-ease will result in the etheric and physical levels as well and will be felt as pain such as headaches, stomach imbalances, skin disorders etc. If this situation continues without rectification or recognition it may lead to a chronic state of health with physical damage occurring.

The radionic practitioner aims to act as a catalyst for change

The work of a radionic practitioner is more effective if he is able to stand back and observe the whole situation for the patient from a mental level. This is not easy when a patient complains of a myriad of physical symptoms and may be in great pain both mentally and physically. It is his job though to find the key to unlock negative energy states and act as a catalyst for change. Through a radionic analysis can be seen the overall picture of subtle bodies, chakras and physical structures, the patterns of miasms and the significant causes. Then in treatment using energy to shed light, even for a glimpse initially, the door may be slowly opened. Radionic practitioners are very privileged in their work to be able to see through the opaque areas that could not be accessed by more conventional medical approaches.

The next section is written from the point of view of a practitioner being faced with the task of trying to help patients who are chronically ill.

Is the patient ready to be healed?

A chronically ill patient rings up and asks for help. He has been in a constant state of anxiety for years, he may live alone and has suffered from a great many symptoms for a long time. He may be suffering from asthma, eczema or multiple allergies, he can't sleep, he can't eat and he is afraid. Remember though that he asked for help.

As radionic practitioners we must go about our routine, not be afraid ourselves and not be too self-assured to assume that we can help this man. With as little emotion as possible we approach the problem with empathy not sympathy. We need to ask a few questions by dowsing initially before we dive into a radionic analysis (See Fig. 3.3).

If the patient is found not ready to be healed radionically we can dowse to see if we can change this perception by another means (left hand side of diagram). If 'no' is still produced, even though we may wish to help, we should not attempt to go any further. Going to the 'yes' box can open up a great number of possibilities, some of which have been given as examples.

What is the limiting factor?

I have proposed internal and external limiting factors but in effect the only ones that exist are internal because external factors can be overcome by an internal attitude to them. It would still be beneficial to find the source of limiting factors. We may then try to find where the most significant subtle energy block is situated (in a subtle body, chakra or etheric structure) which would

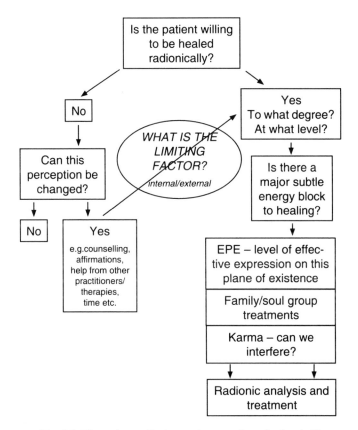

Fig. 3.3 Flow chart – Is the patient ready to be healed?

also come out in the radionic analysis.

EPE – The level of effective expression (of the patient) on this plane of existence

This is a reading I take when I am first introduced to a new patient and at many times during treatment. I find it to be particularly relevant for ME patients and those with eating disorders.

The idea is that the patient cannot be healed unless he is fully functioning on this earth because he cannot effectively learn the lessons intended for him. This may be interpreted as a reading of the level of his incarnation (incarnation being the embodiment of physical form). Readings (EPE) are often initially as low as 40 or 50 (out of 100), so the rest of the patient's energy pattern must be functioning elsewhere. The aim is to increase this level to 90+ i.e. to give treatments to bring the patient more fully into consciousness and functioning strongly on this plane of existence. I have had many times when people say they feel 'out of themselves' or 'not fully grounded' and I have developed radionic treatments designed to help them correct this, if it is appropriate, and to hold them more firmly onto this planet to give them a chance to experience all that they need.

One of the main treatments in this case is to strengthen the whole aura of the patient. This can be done with radionic command and by giving colour and/or gems and gem essences into the aura. The treatments may need to be repeated at regular intervals until the EPE reading increases. Also I find it to be effective to give co-ordination into and between the subtle bodies and into and between the chakras, particularly linking the upper and lower chakra pairs (i.e. base and crown, sacral and throat, solar plexus and heart.)

Family/soul group treatments

When working with the chronically ill it is more often than not indicated that it would be beneficial to work with the family or soul group. This does not mean treating all members of the family as individual patients but to treat their interaction with the patient. We may be talking about siblings, parents and marital partners, children and close friends, workmates and, in the case of children, treating the peer group is especially important. It may also be important to note here that some of these members may not be alive any more but are still having an effect, having left an imprint that needs to be recognised and dispersed or balanced. It is also necessary to recognise repeating patterns over generations. For instance, one may be treating a grandmother, mother and daughter with an echo of a similar problem which may have already lead to a chronic physical disease in the older generation/s. I think it is possible to clear a negative programme like this but it may be necessary to go even further back, to say 5 generations, but that would need to dowsed out.

Karma – can we interfere?

Different people have differing views and understanding of what is meant by karma. Nevertheless it may be a significant factor for consideration in some cases of chronic disease.

'The word karma means 'action' and karma is both the power latent within actions, and the results our actions bring' (from *The Tibetan Book of Living and Dying* by Sogyal Rinpoche). For every action there is a reaction and, as energy follows thought, for every thought there is a reaction. We must work on being aware of our thoughts and their effect and the effects of our actions. Karma is that realisation. It is our aim as healers to create this realisation in ourselves and in all the people we deal with. In saying this I am aware that I have not answered the above question but I am also aware that the answer is probably beyond my understanding at this present time! It is nevertheless thought provoking as karma, or realisation, and raising of consciousness, are in effect the same thing; so isn't that the aim of healing?

When treating the chronically ill it is very easy to get into the doldrums, the initial ideas are running out and treatments you have found to be effective elsewhere or earlier are being found to be ineffective. After six months or longer a shake up is needed, a reassessment of the situation. It is then useful to return to the diagram of 'Is the patient ready to be healed?' (Fig. 3.3) Redowse and reanalyse the whole thing and it may found that it would be beneficial for another practitioner to take over, to throw new light on the scene. It is often the case that one practitioner, having done all the spade work, comes to a point of no movement with a patient, then when another practitioner takes over everything falls into place quite quickly.

On the other hand there are some patients who have had a disease for many years and for whom many years steady treatment is needed from one practitioner with whom they feel comfortable and trust, although we should be wary of a state of dependency developing. Time should not be a limiting factor but levels of payment are, and this should be thought about very carefully.

Conclusion

Speaking from the perspective of a radionic practitioner I would like to say, in conclusion, that while working with the chronically ill there is no reason that we cannot be as effective as with any other patient with an acute condition. We must bear in mind that there are always new aspects to our approach to healing energies emerging through radionic therapy and we must be open to them and so hold the feeling that all can be achieved, although the result may not always be in the manner we had originally envisaged.

Finally, in order to work with people with long term illness it is even more necessary **to face realities in ourselves as well** in order to be able to help the process of lifting the veil in our patients. With dowsing, which is our essential link with our intuition and a knowledge of the infinite, a transformation may be allowed to take place through radionic treatment.

Case Histories

Patient 1

A woman aged 50 who had had many vaccinations throughout her life for foreign travel. Hay fever annually. Chronic candida infection, gynaecological problems, very low energy levels for many years.

    Initial EPE 55

    Damage to aura 45

    Lack of co-ordination etheric/astral 20

    Treatment time 3 years.

    Initial treatments were aligning of subtle bodies and chakras and repairing the aura with colour and gems. At this time the patient was also menopausal and I note a treatment during the first month *'To give estrone into the ovary'* but interestingly, once it had been indicated that this treatment needed additions, I dowsed out the complete purpose of the treatment which was: *'to give complete grounding and integration with this reality'*. The two were closely connected. Also in the next week *'to give acceptance of existence at a physical level to the etheric body'*.

    During the first year of treatment there was little effect on the allergy response to various trees which started in early February. There were repeated treatments during the first and second years *'to give co-ordination between the subtle bodies mental/buddhic'* and much clearing out of toxins from all levels and physical structures. EPE readings in the 2nd year were around 75. By the 3rd year energy levels were generally much improved (EPE 90 –95). Time will tell if there will be a decreased response to the tree allergy in the long term, although I have found that a radionic desensitiser is perhaps a little quicker to work each year.

    Generally this patient is much more in control of her own life and there are very few distressed 'phone calls these days.

Patient 2

Female aged 38. Severe ME, bedridden, unable to feed herself or even speak at times.

    Analysis showed aura damage 60, original EPE 35, lack of co-ordination between all subtle bodies, a radiation miasm expressing primarily through the spleen chakra.

    The first treatments were to restore the aura with appropriate colours and then to give co-ordination between astral and mental bodies and to eliminate vaccination toxins in the mental body. Also the Gurudas gem essence, *Star Sapphire,* to alleviate the effects of the radiation miasm on the spleen chakra.

After one month EPE reading was up to 50. Treatments then included *'to release and eliminate ME toxins from the astral body'* and *'to give co-ordination between the spleen chakra and other main chakras including the throat sacral and heart'.*

By 3 months aura damage was still found to be 55 but EPE was up to 60.

At 6 months I started working on geopathic stress in the house and brought the patient's carers into the healing plan.

After 6 months EPE was, one day, suddenly found to be 90 but was generally around 70/80 and it was at this time that the patient showed a few signs of improvement. Her main concern was lack of sleep due to too much mental activity. For this it was indicated to apply the Schupbach flower patterns, *Willow* and *Privet,* which are generally used to break the habit of smokers; I realised that poor sleep patterns are habitual too.

After this time the patient continued to improve very slowly. Sometimes there were setbacks but she was much more positive in herself mentally, able to do a little bit more for herself and generally taking more of an interest in life.

After 1 year I was directed to give this treatment quoting from Emmanuel's Book: *'You are here to live your life*
My function, through my love
Is to shine the light on areas
That will direct you to your inner light' into the solar plexus chakra

And then a command *'to perceive the connection between the inner world and the outer world'* using the Bach flower remedies, *Olive* and *Clematis,* which are interpreted so well in the *Bach Flower Book* by Mechthild Scheffer. *Olive* is described with the signature 'to give the understanding that in order to gain strength and vitality we may rely completely on inner guidance to restore etheric energies'. For *Clematis* the potential following transformation is described for the individual gaining control of the thought world and daily finding new interest in the real world, because the connection between the different worlds, and the deeper meaning behind them, is understood and accepted.

Progress is being made very slowly, with some setbacks, but now, after 14 months of treatment, I do feel that radionics is possibly the best therapy in this sort of case when the physical body reacts so adversely to any herbal or homeopathic remedy. At present EPE readings are more or less constant at 85–90 and the aura is virtually complete at 95+, so I hope we have reached a point where the treatments given radionically will have an increased effect.

References

Scheffer, Mechthild (1990) *Bach Flower Therapy.* Thorson, Wellingborough.
Rodegast, Pat & Stanton, Judith (1987) *Emmanuel's Book.* Bantam New Age Books, New York.
Rinpoche, Sogyal (1992) *The Tibetan Book of Living and Dying.* Rider, London.

Alan Gwilt

Terminal Illness and Post Mortem Treatment 4

> 'All is flux, nothing is stationary.'
>
> Heracleitus 513 B.C.

> 'All is new and always the old. Nature is forever changing
> and in her there is nothing standing still in a single moment.
> Each of her manifestations a most isolated concept and yet all
> comprises only ONE.'
>
> Goethe.

Treating a patient who is dying causes one to be reminded not only of the mortality of your charge but also of the transience of your own tenure in this physical world. One of the most poignant and powerful interactions one can experience with another human being is to perform in the role of practitioner accompanying him in the finale of his human life experience: one is participating in a service of the most profound kind and there is no greater act of love than to help a fellow being to die well, and the healing discipline of radionics provides a uniquely comprehensive system with which to accomplish this.

In a very real sense there is no difference between terminally ill and terminally well, both conditions are destined to culminate in our recurrent transformation of consciousness from material world existence back again to our spiritual-world and home: and this, of course, incorporates what we call death. By its very nature this physical life is fatal. The so-called difference really is a matter of emphasis and focus during the ongoing process of Life.

We enter into the physical world where death is as much a part of life as is the event of birth itself. Both polarities of our material plane existence are but specific pulses in an enduring rhythm in an indescribable and recurring phenomenon that is intrinsic to our state of being. We are born into a world that demands death as the means whereby we are enabled to return to our spirit-world where we merge again, in Oneness, with the essence of the higher world of spiritual existence. However, except in cases of the very aged, all too often the general view is that death is seen as a sort of defeat whereas in reality it provides the return ticket from the excursion that is this most recent human world experience.

The role of a practitioner of radionics, as well as functioning as an agent in healing interaction with his patient, is more profoundly that of a spiritual being caring for another during the time their individual journeys in the physical world require mutual collaboration. In participating in his patient's healing the practitioner too experiences healing at a subtle or spiritual level of consciousness, although this is never his conscious motive in being engaged in this kind of work.

In day to day practice the greater amount of time spent by a practitioner in a healing role is in focusing on the needs of the physical body; we are more aware of our sensory bodies' disharmonies because of their everyday impingement on our consciousness. We are more familiar with our lower-self characteristics and know a good deal about physical anatomy and the physiological consequences of injury, illness etc.; our super-sensory forms are immensely more mysterious for all their profound influence on our physical-world lives.

Our physical bodies have been the focus of investigation for centuries in efforts to understand how they work and as time progresses so too does our knowledge but still we are faced with large areas of incomprehension; for example, although we know something of some of the component parts of the human cell we have no idea of how the mind of that cell functions. How much more awe-inspiring then is the wonder of our own existence in which birth and death are but cyclical incidentals in the continuum of Life.

After twenty years of study and work in the field of radionics I am led to the clear understanding that the active force motivating 'healing' through this truly holistic system is fundamentally one of a spiritual nature. The accessing of this force is dependent upon the inclination of the practitioner who, while observing historic principles and radionic techniques, applies them through personal sensibilities. The interaction between patient and practitioner takes place at a higher level of consciousness where mutually stimulated responses are orchestrated by sympathetic non-carnate spirit-world beings who provide a subtle environment whereby 'healing' is effected. This process is incomprehensibly mysterious and operates in a realm beyond the grasp of our conscious minds.

Treatments to everyday physical problems are routine. Even so during these one is sometimes called upon to administer to subtle or spiritual needs, as well as physical, thus invoking spiritual or extra-sensory responses to physical manifestations of disharmony. Where physical disharmonies are of the kind that appear very likely to culminate in the physical demise of the person concerned the practitioner must be alert to the potential presenting and so be very aware of the truth manifesting in his patient's entering into the act of dying and, with an open mind and more comprehensive view of things, see his patient in the light of what is really happening.

Treatment after clinical death is no more extraordinary than treating the physical vehicle of the person concerned, it is merely a shift of emphasis. There is no place for anxiety or worry in the mind of the practitioner; if there is then he is not witnessing the manifestation of a perfect wisdom and has no business working with someone who is dying. His patient is expanding into an eternal truth and is doing so with the aid of the practitioner who, while remaining detached, bears happiness in his heart for his patient is undergoing the most profound act of healing in his physical life experience. Any negative responses on the part of the practitioner can only hinder his part in the process of the miraculous transition which is taking place.

Birth and death should not be seen by the radionic practitioner as the extremes of human life but as moments in an on-going phenomenon. Death is of divine origin: the act of processing the dismissal of the human body is a joyous event and once fear is overcome it facilitates re-entry into the spiritual domain that is our enduring reality.

In the world of duality fear of death is understandable and that part of the spiritual being responsible for maintaining the focus of consciousness in the material plane is conditioned to preserve that status even though the higher self may be expressing the desire for transformation. (It is not unusual for the radionic practitioner to witness the conflict of wishes taking place in the spiritual realm of the person concerned as one part of that spiritual being desires to maintain physical plane focus while a superior dimension is advising transformation). What is occurring is an altering of consciousness and this should not be seen as though one is standing on the edge of an abyss but merely as taking another step in the ongoing process of one's evolution.

If death is understood for what it really is it is difficult to comprehend the tenacity with which someone will cling to a decaying and useless form when joy and light await his emergence from the material plane. All too often the motivating force prolonging physical life experience is fear.

It behoves the practitioner always to carry in his mind the awareness that when he goes to treatment he is treating a spiritual being at present utilising a physical body. Each one of us is a spiritual-being in a human-being state of consciousness, and for a limited term only; we need always to remind ourselves of that inescapable fact. Part of our super-sensory consciousness is on an expedition into the material world and is, compared with the enduring reality of our spirit-life, a brief journey, Shakespeare's, 'Poor player who struts and frets his hour upon the stage', and one thing is for sure we hold a return ticket for this excursion – our return home is guaranteed.

It pays to ponder on this before going to treatment. It helps one re-evaluate the nature of this life and encourages reflection on what we are about in our work as radionic practitioners. It helps us adopt the perspective of seeing what death is. It is the means whereby a spiritual-being is enabled to dismiss the produced physical vehicle which has provided the means for physical-world experience and which is now no longer appropriate; this is necessary in order to re-attune with his spirit-world self and there to begin the next chapter in his on-going journey in Life.

Death should be seen as no more than that!

When one is confronted with a patient who has been diagnosed as clinically terminally ill what should be the response of the practitioner? To get in there and do all one can to prove that death is not after all inevitable in this instance? To set out to do all one can to prolong as much as possible his or her term in the physical dimension? The answer is, of course, in acquiring an attitude of mind where one goes to treatment with all opinions and forecasts about death suspended as one enters into the blessed and precious relationship with the patient that is the prerogative of our profession and, 'Mind fixed but else made vacant'[1] one becomes, in innocence, part of a channel for healing directed to that individual just as it would be if he were going through the experience of birth into this world and it were the practitioner's role to help in this. In a state of spiritual openness he allows the treatments 'given' to come without any preconception or intrusion on his part and in a state of surrender to the needs of his patient he passes to him joyfully that which he is directed to do, remembering he is in higher-self communication with the spirit-consciousness of his subject. Hesitation and doubt on the part of the practitioner hinders the fluent interaction between those attending the dying person and those non-carnate ones engaged in the healing process of his death. One is part of a team of others, non-carnate, who are there to assist him just as the practitioner is the subject of care and attention by those spiritual ones who attend to and care for him. Love and happiness make fluid the connection between the practitioner and patient and those supersensible ones in attendance, and in due time encourages the patient to decide, at a spiritual level, whether or not it is the time for transformation to take place, just as we all too, in our subtle realms, will one day make this decision for ourselves.

It does not matter how old or young a person is chronologically. When the higher self and soul edict deem it no longer appropriate for that part of itself to remain focused in the material plane the process to effect transformation is initiated. And transformation of consciousness is the all important thing that is happening! One is privileged to participate in the continuing evolution of this spiritual being. You cannot transform and also take your physical body with you; its role is for the physical world and the material-plane body must be shed. That is the positive function of death.

Using creative imagination one learns to see the so-called doorway of death not solely from an humano-centric viewpoint but also from the spiritual perspective and to view that doorway from the spiritual dimension and to look back and through that 'doorway' to the physical world now no longer relevant to the needs of your charge. One visualises from one's higher-self viewpoint the scene unfolding and dispassionately observes the indescribable miracle taking place.

It is a joyous and wonderful event to be going home so treatments are carried on a flow of happiness and love, for your patient is going to a blissful state where the process of spiritual evolution continues in a higher realm. One enters into treatment objectively but with joy in one's heart; having emotions of sentimentality or sadness cause obstacles to your patient's progress. The practitioner's conscious mind-state also influences his higher self and can adversely affect the state of harmony there, 'As you conduct yourself in your everyday human life so there is a reciprocal influence in your higher self.'[2] To fulfil effectively the role of a member of a team of helpers for your dying patient during times of treatment it is necessary to suspend entirely all ideas and beliefs by which you direct your own personal life and to surrender to absolute selflessness in service to your patient and the spiritual brethren attending him. Even when you think of him outside of a treatment session have in mind this message psychically transmitted to me for occasions such as this, 'One way to be of help in the divine plan for the experience of death for X and X's consequent transformation of consciousness is for you to maintain thoughts of his crossing the threshold of unlimited consciousness in a higher spiritual world'.[2]

Dealing with the grief of those no longer having the physical presence of the loved one is a two-fold requirement, for not only is compassion for those suffering bereavement a natural response by the caring practitioner but much more important is the need for the principal in this momentous event as much as possible to be spared the negative influence of anguish and distress caused by his dismissing his physical body.

The following excerpt from Alice Bailey's *Esoteric Healing* is remarkably germane to the work of a radionic practitioner and also to his mental posture with regard to the mind states of particularly close friends and relatives of the dying or recently deceased individual. There is, after all, a very meaningful interaction between them and their dear one at a higher level of consciousness. Almost certainly they will need attention unless the contrary is clearly expressed.

Support for Carers and those passing into the Light
Alice Bailey

'Aid at the time of the "passing into the light" depends largely upon two things:

'Firstly:- the amount of close contact between the dying person and the one who watches over and also the level upon which that contact is strongest.' (i.e. the level of contact needs to be very substantially spiritual not emotional or physical.)

'Secondly:- upon the capacity of the carer to detach and dissociate himself from his own feelings and to identify himself, through an act of pure unselfish will, with the dying person. None of this is really possible when

the bond between the two is purely emotional or based upon a physical plane relationship. The contact must be deeper and stronger than that. It must be a personal contact upon all planes.'

(This is precisely the quality to be found in a competent radionic practitioner. The deeper and more selfless the bond the more effective the role of the practitioner. Buckmaster Fuller coined the expression 'Less is Greater', an aphorism never given more meaning and utility than in the discipline and practice of radionics).

'Where there is true soul and personality contact, there is then little problem. But this is rare to find. Nevertheless I have here given you a hint.'

(This is not so rare among those spiritually attuned through the discipline of daily practice in radionic methodology. It is, after all, routine for one to enter into this spiritual attunement with one's patient and it is to be found in the higher level of consciousness contact existing between patient and practitioner. Daily work in radionics is indeed a profoundly spiritual education in one's committed but detached union with one's patient).

'There should also be as little definite thought process as possible on the part of the carer. All that is required and possible at present is simply to carry the dying person forward on an ever deepening stream of love.'

(e.g. 'Mind fixed but else made vacant ...') [1]

'Through the power of the creative imagination, and not through intellectual concepts, no matter how high, must the dying man consciously be aided in discarding the outer garment in which he has been encased and in which he has laboured during his physical life. This involves an act of pure self-forgetfulness, of which few as yet are capable.'

(Practising such self-forgetfulness is a liet motif of radionics and is entered into frequently by committed practitioners, each one approaching and endeavouring to attain this state of consciousness in his or her own way through the meditative procedure central to this healing discipline. I personally was given the following advice by one of my spirit-world counsellors: 'When you prepare for work in your present healing role you are engaging in a form of meditation, therefore enter into feeling loss of the present and direct your consciousness into feeling profoundly dissolved in forgetting who you are and focus on what your just being eternal is. You are seeking to find and, within your deep inner-self, come to compatibility with the understanding of Perfect Love'.[2] Every time I pass this instruction through my mind I wonder at and ponder on the deep significance of what is being put before me).

'Most people are swept by fear, or by strong desire to hold the beloved person back, or are side-tracked in their aim by the activities involved in assuaging pain and deadening agony; they are dismayed also by the depths of their ignorance of the 'technique of death' when faced with the emergency. They find themselves unable to see what lies beyond the doors of death, and are swept by the mental uncertainty which is part of this great illusion.'

(The sensitive radionic practitioner is very much aware of important aspects of the 'technique of death' and its role in on-going spiritual evolution and it is a spiritually educated act of wisdom to see through 'death's door' from the spiritual viewpoint).

The following are selections from case histories in my own practice and provide examples of the interaction between patient, practitioner and those non-carnate who are intrinsically involved.

Patient A

Sam Saunders became a patient shortly after his stroke which had left him badly paralysed in his left arm and leg plus pronounced slurring of speech. The hospital prognosis was that Sam was not expected to recover indeed that his death could not long be delayed.

Treatments to his physical body included those directed to his cardio-vascular and autonomic nervous systems as well as to endocrine glands where improved co-ordination was called for between depleted adrenals and the thyroid. But to his extra-sensory self was prescribed: *'Have peaceful reflection on your ceasing to resist your premonition of approaching transformation of consciousness'*. This was prescribed to that dimension of spiritual consciousness we label the mental body.

Later that day: *'Seek to accept with positive thought your need for transformation of consciousness'*. This was given to an even more profound realm of super-consciousness called the buddhic body. To his wife, as well as her receiving balancing treatments to her nervous system, was also pre-scribed: *'I accept with selflessness and honesty in allowing Sam to transform consciousness.'* This was administered to her mental body, a spiritual dimension associated with intellectual activity and the ability to think dispassionately. To his daughter such treatments as: *'Have strengthened your foreseeing his (Sam Saunders') physical demise'*. This was passed to her astral body (a dimension of spiritual consciousness largely concerned with feelings and emotions) and, also: *'Positively affirm contentment at his transformation of consciousness'*, to her mental body.

After some seven days of pre-death treatments to Sam, in the vein similar to those of the first day, I received at the close of a healing session the following message given me by my spirit-world counsellors and directors:

'With regard to Sam Saunders, you are witnessing the experience of his transforming his focus of consciousness while he is still in the light of his physical consciousness, therefore learn from this.' i.e. that although in a comatose state but still in physical-world-focus of consciousness preparations were being made for his transition and his compliance was being sought. The instruction 'learn from this', was to emphasise to me the omniscience of our spiritual selves and the profound effect of their influence over our physical selves.

To his daughter that day the prescribed treatments included: *'Release, in love, your father Sam Saunders'*, directed to her astral and mental bodies.

The following day, with Sam still in deep coma, he received the treatment: *'Seek to understand that those from the world of spiritual being, now apparent to you, are to help and guide you'*. This was directed to his buddhic body.

Later, to Sam: *'Positively affirm your confidence in those non-carnate attending you'*, also to buddhic body.

To his wife: *'Have the realisation with positive affirmation that in this time of your depression and sadness you view this event as one of Sam's joyous reunion with the world of spiritual light of all blessed ecstasy for Sam.'* This was directed, via her astral, mental and buddhic bodies, to her nervous and urinary systems (where her physical treatments included: *'Expel toxins from apprehension and sadness from urinary organs'*).

Two days later he achieved clinical death. I had understood from his family that Sam knew that life continued after death but on the first day of posthumous treatment it was clear that there was an obstacle blocking his moving on. The problem was vividly identified from the treatments presenting for him e.g. *'Dismiss your ideas of what happens when you leave the world of your physical body. Have trust in those with you who wish to formulate truly what is to happen to you in the process of your transforming back to the spirit world'*. This was directed to an aspect of his buddhic body.

Later: *'Do realise positively that your physical-world-learnt-ideas of the stages of transformation of consciousness are misconceived'*, also directed to buddhic body. Further: *'Discontinue your self-indulgence and inflexibility'*, directed to mental body. Later still: *'Do believe the truthfulness of what those helpers are saying to you'*, directed to buddhic body.

Clearly Sam was arguing with and even, it seems, contradicting the advice being given him.

Gradually the treatments presenting for Sam indicated his lessening resistance and his mind state graduated from initial challenge to those attending him and rejection of their offer of help, until, by degrees, we followed his progress through stages marked by:- defiance, then forbearance, curiosity, interest, consideration and finally acceptance.

One always asks if it is appropriate to go to treatment with any given patient (sometimes it is in his/her best interests that the practitioner's assistance is withheld on that particular occasion and the practitioner, as always, unquestioningly accepts such instruction). Ten days after his physical demise, on what proved to be his final day of post-mortem treatment (from me that is, further healing clearly continued but on a plane of spiritual consciousness inaccessible and unavailable to me), Sam's mind-state now indicated full preparedness to conform to the wishes of his spiritual helpers. The spiritual being we knew as Sam Saunders was expressing:- 'Sincere desire to understand in honesty' – then, becoming 'Extreme happiness and ecstatic rejoicing and exaltation in fulfilment of transformation of consciousness.'

I have come to recognise that once the subject receiving posthumous treatment presents a mind-state displaying expressions, like, 'blissful', 'ecstatic', 'supreme joy' etc. my assistance in his transformation is no longer required and I am dismissed by the non-carnate carers attending him.

Some days after my role in his post-mortem treatments had ceased I learned from a relative that at some time in his earthly life Sam had been a lay preacher in a particular religious denomination and had expressed very dogmatic opinions about 'life after death.'

Intrinsic spiritual activity during the process of physical death is clearly demonstrated in this next case history.

Patient B

The subject was young middle-age, physically very active and to all intents and purposes perfectly fit and well. On this occasion he had retired to bed in the usual manner but the following day did not wake up. He had died during the night.

After two autopsies no clinical explanation was established as the reason for his physical demise and the death certificate recorded as the cause, 'Adult Cot Death'.

Although an acquaintance he was not a patient of mine, but in the circumstances I offered to enter into posthumous treatment. This was contraindicated by my spiritual advisors (my participation was not required) but I was given permission to ask questions. The answers were given me in the usual familiar manner, i.e. I am directed to certain books wherein I find the vocabulary necessary for the psychic communication to be transposed into manageable English grammar. The resultant rather odd syntax is peculiar to nearly all messages from the spirit-world.

Question: What caused the death of Kenneth Ovey?

Answer: 'His dying is the realisation of the power of soul practising fulfilment of a need in his higher realm of consciousness.'

Q: Do you mean, as we would say in the physical world, 'His time was up?'

A: 'Yes.'

Q: - and without disease or design to end his physical world experience (e.g. suicide?)

A: 'He had no disease or design.'

Q: What please, more precisely, caused the termination of life in his physical body?

A: 'Dense ether was repelled from the etheric body on "instruction" from a realm within what you call the buddhic body of your fellow human-being. This caused distortion and disharmony in the integrity of fluids within his adrenal medulla. This effected cessation of physical life vitality.'

The next question was prompted by a fellow practitioner to whom I had reported the foregoing.

Q: Does terminal illness serve a positive function?

A: 'Yes, firstly it is a cleansing experience within what you call the buddhic body and this contributes to the on-going need for a state of wholeness and balance within that body.

'2. It activates awakening of a particular function within the ethers. This function becomes discerning in the healing process that forms the act of transformation of consciousness i.e. your human death.

'3. Terminal illness expresses the buddhic body's desire for fulfilment with regard to it's ongoing self-expression of heavenly (spiritual) evolution and vitality.

'4. It provides the premonition of understanding by the person concerned that their human-world-form is required in love to begin the act of transformation from a physical focus to again that of a spiritual one.'

Q: Why did Kenneth Ovey die without prior illness?

A: 'The power of soul creates, indescribably, a living body and it also creates light throughout and around that physical body. Your fellow spirit Kenneth Ovey in his physical form had received not only created physical tissue but also the light (or condition) of that which dispels the tissue of material life. There is a reason why he died without physical ailment but you may not know that reason other than that which you already have been told.' (Clearly I was being privy to a certain amount of information but no more than was appropriate for me because my spiritual communicants then continued with, 'You see here outworking in the affairs of the Life of Kenneth Ovey that which is working towards the continuing evolution of Life's spiritual path for your fellow being. Now, you cease further questions.')

In pursuance of this I refer now to information given me direct from a spiritual communicant not associated in particular with Kenneth Ovey, but in a more generally philosophical sense, nevertheless relevant to what profoundly happens when we as human beings enter into clinical death.

Spiritual Communicant:-

'With regard to your human-world death as part of the process of transformation of consciousness.

'The change of consciousness takes place through the on-going will of Soul. Before that change takes place things emanating from your higher consciousness must, by Divine Law, relate to the path indicated by particular codes. These codes have a complementary relationship with your higher consciousness. These codes manifest in the physical body as malfunctions e.g. your human-world illness, what you call accidents etc. You also have a personal relationship with others non-carnate who know the cards in your hand.

'Every human person is to find the code which will decide the manner of their discontinuing the human-life experience. They find causes and reasons by which the accomplishment of death is to realise their transformation of consciousness and also the manner in which Divine Law accomplishes a loving manifestation of disorder in the physical body. "Help" is the function of your others non-carnate in order to reflect your higher consciousness' intention to achieve that which is in truth the Love of God.

'The creation of the codes for the creatures in question is part of the consciousness that you presently love as the physical world. These codes are developed in yourselves in an aspect of your consciousness which is specifically aware of the Self's need to effect a change of consciousness in the ongoing phenomenon of Life.

'Manifested dysfunction in the physical body becomes the joyous demise of that physical state of a spiritual being and, if understood, should be without fear, depression and negative mind states generally. The consequent joy and peace achieved through this transformation should not be tarnished by human-world emotions of anguish and grief.

'Human-kind overlooks the fact that the higher consciousness has the foresight of knowing the true nature of what is, in fact, your spiritual beingness.'

It appears that in this terminal life the preparation for what is to become terminal illness can manifest years before clinical symptoms demonstrate to the extent that the person concerned feels the need for medical or other help. For example: with regard to patients C and D in the following cases, where both of whom are continuing in reasonably good health, we may be witnessing the implementations of the codes referred to above through our being made aware of subtle anatomy requirements presenting in the spiritual realms of the subjects in question (apparently well in advance of physical symptoms considered to be those which would lead to death) as well as other treatments directed to their physical bodies.

As on all occasions when the practitioner is 'called' to treatment his responsibility is to assist in providing the best possible quality of life to his patient whether the problem be one concerned with approaching transformation of consciousness or, as in the routine order of things, merely acute or chronic physical conditions and their associated mind states which pose no apparent life threatening potential.

Patient C

Symptoms: '... horrible weakness persists – nearly every day – well, a good part of every day, lasting approximately four hours – irregular – hampers decision making and gives me periods of wakefulness during night.'

Cause: Spiritual: 1. (As 'dictated' to me): 'Need to cultivate the intention of transformation of consciousness within the buddhic body and also to effect the commencement of entry into spiritually surrendering to orders from co-ordinating buddhic body.'

Cause: Physical: 2. Virus in autonomic nervous system.

Treatment – selected examples:-

Spiritual: 1. *'Have the realisation that your world of human experience is illusory'*: this was administered to effect co-ordination in the buddhic body.

Physical: 2. Maximise assimilation of vitamins in liver and central nervous systems.

Physical: 3. Balance discord in fluids within nervous system.

Some days later:

Treatment – selected examples:-

Spiritual: 1. *'Look unconditionally (i.e. without any prejudice) at needing to know that your material life body will interact with the will of your higher self to effect eventual transformation of consciousness'*. This treatment was directed to effecting harmony in the mental body.

Physical: 2. Balance harmony and interaction between endocrine glands.

Physical: 3. Maximise assimilation of vitamins in nervous system.

Patient D

Symptoms: '... dull pain mid-chest worsening every ten minutes then easing and then gone in about twenty five minutes ... like a large bubble ... coming up as a burp ... felt sweaty ...'

Cause: Spiritual: 1. 'Fundamentally the opportunity for D to observe the beginning, in love, of the process of transformation of consciousness.' The purpose of this was to help in establishing harmony within the complex spiritual frequencies that constitute the super-sensory realm called the buddhic body.

Cause: Physical: 2. Varicosity coronary artery at thirty percentage degree severity.

Cause: Physical: 3. Physical stress toxins in lower self: associated with many previous occasions of dealing with difficulties concerning problems to do with professional responsibilities causing nervous stress which adversely affected the nervous system – especially nerves of renal capsules.

Treatment - selected examples:-

Spiritual: 1. *'Have thoughts of surveying your world of human-life task in connection with the furtherance of (your) being spiritually being attuned to thoughts of Soul advancement.'*

Physical: 2. Transform to positive function nervous stress toxins: in cardio-vascular tissue.

Physical: 3. Dissolve blockage impeding assimilation of vitamins: to CV vessels.

Physical: 4. Enhance assimilation of nutrients: into arteries of CV system.

Some months later:

Treatment continued

Spiritual: 1. *'Have progress in learning to behold the approaching phenomenon of your transformation of consciousness'*, directed to effect harmony in the buddhic body.

Spiritual: 2. *'Involve yourself in light of thoughts of your path and task known as fostering feelings of brotherhood, thus expressing your essentially needing to perfect the spiritual plan of your initiation into healing work'.*

Spiritual: 3. *'Open your mind to new opportunities'*, to mental body.

Physical: 1. Realise tranquillity in nervous system.

2. Liberate congested energies in nervous system.

3. Disperse congestion in para-sympathetic nerves: directed to nervous system.

So here we see running concurrently treatments to two spiritual beings presently in the physical plane, and also indications of what is happening in their physical bodies to conform, as I understand it, to the wishes of the higher self of each with regard to their approaching transformations. A reminder of not who we are but of what we are. Not simply Mrs C, Librarian, and Mr D, Company Director, but spiritual beings with the personalities and material plane bodies of Mrs C and Mr D.

These examples also remind us that the space-time continuum that governs our consciousness in the physical world does not apply in our higher spiritual domain where there is a state of eternal simultaneity. Einstein remarked that, 'Human-kind having a finite brain cannot conceive the infinite.' Our present concept of time has no relevance in our spiritual-world.

Once it is brought to your notice that there is a desire in the higher realms of your patient (i.e. buddhic body) for transformation of consciousness one must understand that it might be years of human-world time before this demonstrates in the physical body as clinical death, so the practitioner needs to be prepared for this. However, it might well be that the person will effect discarding his physical body sooner; indeed the moment for initiating transformation may even be imminent. One allows for treatments addressed to the physical condition of the subject, of course, but also the practitioner holds himself open to those treatments which may be directed to spiritual needs for the forthcoming event, part of which includes his physical death. Healing treatment will, I understand, certainly continue after his fulfilment of transformation of consciousness.

After clinical death is established the role of the practitioner is, as ever, to function in support of his patient in assisting the provision of the best possible service to his subject. In posthumous treatments what is sought after is that the person concerned attains fulfilment in the miraculous process of transition. After shedding the physical vehicle, attention to which is obviously now irrelevant, treatment is usually called for to help ensure that the process of fully balanced re-attunement to his spiritual-self takes place as harmoniously as possible. Fear and uncertainty manifesting in the mind of the deceased on confronting his 'new' circumstances very often cause mistrust, even distrust, of those non-carnate ones who are endeavouring to make fluent the process of transition. The practitioner, although still in an incarnate state, is privileged to be part of this compassionate team and as such may be called upon to assist for, in my experience, anything up to thirty-eight physical-world days after the subject's physical body had died. In this particular instance the person concerned when incarnate had held fervently the view that this earthly life ended in complete oblivion. It was disturbing to witness the tormented state of mind of this individual when realising that 'she' was still living and fully aware of the different world 'she' now inhabited and which 'she' was viewing through the distortion of her long held earthly life prejudices. The most rapid transition to fulfilled re-integration with the spiritual self is, in my experience, three earth-world days; I have never encountered a shorter period. Remember, there is no sense of chronological time in our spirit-world; the referred-to 'days' of radionic treatment should be seen in the context of that the amount of input requested of the practitioner in assisting the spiritual team attending his patient's transformation.

Each time treatment is entered into in the manner and circumstances I have described, little by little and according to one's own evolutionary pace, one is granted deeper understanding of one's patient's spiritual as well as physical needs and consequently by personal reflection one becomes increasingly aware of the role played by one's own Super-sensible Self. With this dawning awareness there develops a growing sense of indebtedness and responsibility not only to this loving presence but also to other spiritual beings who watch, guide and use one as a member of a group functioning in a healing capacity. To be so used in this work is, for the practitioner, to undergo a profound self-healing in his spiritual self, which unlike his physical life is not terminal, and where labels like 'Terminal Illness', 'Death', and 'Post Mortem' are recognised for what they are i.e. merely transitory moments in the ongoing performance of the eternal Oneness of our spiritual being.

This piece is an accurate witness to my personal experience in radionic practice and should be understood as such and not necessarily as a definitive concept held by all registered practitioners of the Radionic Association.

References

[1] Walter de la Mare, 'The Snowdrop'.
[2] Spirit-world Communication to A.G.
Steiner, Rudolph (1976) *Knowledge of the Higher Worlds*. Rudolf Steiner Press, London.
Bailey, Alice (1953) *A Treatise on the Seven Rays Vol. 4 Esoteric Healing*. Lucis Press, London.
Sogyal Rinpoche (1992) *The Tibetan Book of Living and Dying*. Rider, London.
Rodegast, P. & Stanton, J. (1989) *Emmanuel's Books*. Bantam New Age, New York.
White Eagle (1972) *The Quiet Mind*. The White Eagle Publishing Trust, Liss, Hants.

Nick Franks

<table>
<tr><td>5</td><td><h1>A Study of the Miasms for Radionics</h1></td></tr>
</table>

'It is essential that holistic health practitioners understand the profound impact miasms have on chronic diseases. Underlying miasms contribute to making one susceptible to various acute illnesses. What usually happens today is that the client is treated with natural remedies, yet the underlying problems are not even considered or examined ... effectively treating the miasms is essential if the holistic health movement is to reach its full potential of restoring people to health in mind, body and spirit.'

Gurudas, *Gem Elixirs and Vibrational Healing Vol II*, p. 82

The concept of *miasm* was introduced by the founder of homeopathy, Samuel Hahnemann (1755–1843) and was initially proposed in *The Chronic Diseases*. Perhaps the most fundamental concept in homeopathy is that of the *Vital Force*, also referred to as the *Dynamis* or *Life Force*. The Vital Force [2] is inseparable from the physical body and entirely contiguous with it, and its free flow throughout the physical organism is absolutely essential to health. Any sufficiently strong impingement of the Vital Force will produce observable symptoms. These may present on the physical, emotional or mental levels and can consist of functional or pathological disturbances, or both:

'When a person falls ill, it is initially only this spirit-like autonomic life-force (life principle), everywhere present in the organism, that is mistuned through the dynamic influence of a morbific agent inimical to life. Only the life principle, mistuned to abnormality, can impart to the organism the adverse sensations and induce in the organism the irregular functions that we call disease.' [3]

Careful observation showed Hahnemann that some disease conditions would persist in spite of him giving well-chosen remedies from his existing Materia Medica; acute symptoms would disappear, but a true and ongoing state of good health and vitality would not be achieved. This led him to believe that chronic illness results from an underlying condition which permanently and progressively impairs and ultimately breaks down the Dynamis. In short, the miasm is a hidden and insidious pollution of the Vital Force; it is in effect an occult presence which cannot be removed by any external or material means, medical or otherwise, and externalises in a progressive symptomology which ultimates in premature death:

> '... a miasmatic, chronic nature ... that after it has once advanced and developed to a certain degree can never be removed by the strength of any robust constitution, it can never be overcome by the most wholesome diet and order of life, nor will it die out of itself ... it is ever more aggravated, from year to year, through a transition into other and more serious symptoms, even till the end of man's life ...'[4]

If we accept Hahnemann's thesis then identification and proper treatment of miasms must be a priority for the radionic practitioner diligently wishing to bring the patient to a higher state of health. Miasms present, in many cases, such a considerable problem that they can hardly be ignored.

A general overview of the three classical miasms

Hahnemann's principal miasm is denoted *Psora*, which he describes as the *itch-disease*. In fact the eruption on the skin is the sign of the inner action of the otherwise invisible psoric miasm on the Dynamis. It is *suppression*[5] of the eruption by unwise methods which then drives the Psora deeper into the organism and forces it to manifest through a more serious set of symptoms. Thus the Dynamis always attempts to keep symptoms as far away as possible from important vital organs such as the heart and brain. Suppressive treatment may force it to retreat from its best defensive position thus causing the intensity of the miasm to increase. This may eventually result in a more concerted attack on the organism. In Hahnemann's words:

> 'Psora is that most ancient, most universal, most destructive *and yet* most misapprehended *chronic miasmatic disease which for many thousands of years has disfigured and tortured mankind, and which during*

the last centuries has become the mother of all the thousands of incredibly *various (acute and) chronic (non-venereal) diseases ... Psora ... is ... the* oldest *and* most hydra-headed *of all the chronic miasmatic diseases.'* [6]

Hahnemann states that Psora is highly contagious and that it is devolved from leprosy, i.e. that leprosy was its original form of *physical* manifestation:

> *'... let no-one think that the Psora, which has been thus mitigated in its local symptoms, its cutaneous eruption, differs materially from ancient leprosy.'* [7]

In Hahnemann's view Psora may be considered to account for about 90% of all chronic diseases, but his two remaining fundamental miasms are also important: *Sycosis (the fig-wart disease)*, the miasm resulting from suppressed or improperly treated gonorrhoea, particularly where condylomata and other skin excrescences such as warts accompany the discharge; and *Syphilis (the chancre disease)*, where improper removal of the initial ulcer-like eruption leads again to suppression of the disease and its subsequent devastating consequences. Thus it may be noted that each miasm has its initial presenting symptom as a form of eruption on the skin – in other words, far from the vital centres – and it is the suppression of this eruption which leads to the complication of the miasm, driving it deeper into the interior of the organism, enabling it to develop into more ominous and threatening forms. These forms are the many and various diseases described by orthodox medicine.

Since Hahnemann's time many efforts have been made to explain the miasms. Many books and articles have been written describing its symptomology in encyclopaedic detail, and this wealth of literature is freely available. However, the essential characteristic of each miasm can be summarized in a single keyword. Psora is the miasm of *deficiency*; Sycosis, that of *excess*; and Syphilis, that of *destruction*.

With an additional 150 years of research into human physiology and pathology – not to mention genetics – since Hahnemann's death, this viewpoint may seem ridiculous. So let us turn to an expert assessment of miasms by a modern doctor:

> *'Unfortunately, because the idea, as propounded by Hahnemann, is so patently, in our modern eyes, merely a beginning, the germ only, of a real understanding of the nature of disease, it has given rise to two equally irrational attitudes in recent times. There are many homoeopaths who take the view that the original thesis cannot be improved upon ... there*

are also others who, by reason of its obvious incompleteness, dismiss the whole thing as nonsense ... Despite the foregoing remarks, it is striking that the described characteristics of the original 'three' nonetheless do correspond with the three fundamental types of manifestations of disease, namely: – overproliferation of tissue (Sycosis), destruction and ulceration (Syphilitic) and functional depletion and imbalance (Psora) and regarded in this light, the theory is indeed a monument to Hahnemann's genius and acuteness of observation.' [8]

Identifying the miasms in radionics

When analysing the patient, the practitioner should separate the miasms by type and attempt to determine their effect on the condition being treated. As stated the miasm may only be a potentiality and even though a high reading may be obtained it equally may not be necessary to give any treatment in the initial stages. What is important is to determine which miasm or miasms are active in the patient and the order in which they should be treated.

It must of course be borne in mind that there are numerous other causative factors which will appear in the analysis. Some of these include, by way of example, congestion, overstimulation, unco-ordination, dislocation, hypersensitivity, toxins, damage, infection, shock and so forth. These may have to be dealt with prior to treating any miasms; or miasms may be the priority. Thus the problem, especially in complex cases, is actually not at all simple. The prioritisation of treatments and the order in which the *layers* are removed is usually central to success. The practitioner may imagine or presuppose that certain treatments are desirable but unless they accord with the (at present largely not understood) mechanics of how the subtle bodies interact and how they interface with the physical body and the personality consciousness, then treatments will be ineffective or only effective in the short term.

What must clearly be understood is that reducing or removing the impact of miasms is not a universal method or panacea any more than treatment of chakras is the *ne plus ultra* of treatment. The practitioner has to be entirely open in his or her approach to the problem; there is a framework, there are a range of possibilities, but there are few hard-and-fast rules.

For simplification miasms may be grouped into certain categories which are briefly described below.

Acute miasms

These can be looked at from two angles, firstly as a presenting illness and secondly as after-effects or *sequelae* (*post-infective dyscrasia*). Thus in the first instance we find an acute infectious disease which takes the same general form from patient to patient particularly in a specific epidemic. Thus in this category can be found diseases such as influenza, chicken pox, measles, mumps, whooping cough, glandular fever, cholera, typhoid, smallpox, anthrax and so on. A current example is the SARS virus.

In the second instance we find a miasmatic inhibition particularly of the physical-etheric body which is a result or after-effect of the acute episode. In homeopathy this is sometimes categorised as NBWS, 'never been well since'. A typical example is where the after-effects of measles may linger for years or for life. The situation can be complicated by two further factors; the effects of an acute episode may also be seen inter-generationally, so that a person may exhibit some symptomology resulting from, for example, smallpox in a parent or grandparent even though they personally have never had the disease.[9] In addition the powerful effect of an acute may be sufficient to activate or entangle with an underlying chronic (classical) miasmatic state. If this situation is seen then the practitioner will almost certainly be obliged to deal with the classical miasm(s) involved.

Articulated miasm

The articulated miasm is a new concept and may be considered to arise when the classical miasms have become activated. The concept is most particularly applicable when serious physical pathology has emerged and is advancing. The word 'articulate' means to express, and therefore the articulated miasm is the particular expression of the miasm or miasms in the form peculiar to each individual. The miasmatic expression may further be complicated with toxic and many other layers in the subtle bodies, chakras, aura and nadis to give an extremely complex illness.

In order to differentiate this further:

'... *the disease's essential esse* (the dynamic, self-subsisting presence which is the disease) *is invariable. Miasms are collective diseases in that everyone who manifests the disease* (in whatever form) *has the same disease ... the wesen* (nature) *of a miasm ... always remains the same. This is true both of the acute miasms* (e.g. the measles) *whose disease manifestations are limited and fairly invariable, and the chronic miasms* (e.g. Psora) *whose disease manifestations ... vary greatly; all miasms, no matter how variable or how fixed their disease manifestations, always remain the same as their wesen.'* [10]

In contrast the articulated miasm in the individual will be peculiar to that individual and will reflect in a chronic pathology that is specific to that person in the same way that the personality is specific. Generally, if an articulated miasm is present, this will probably need to be dealt with very soon in the order of treatment if progress is to be made.

Classical miasms

In addition to the Psora, Sycosis and Syphilis of Hahnemann, Tuberculosis and Cancer are now considered miasms of fundamental importance. Traditionally, Tuberculosis is seen as being predicated on Psora, and hence an alternative name for it in homeopathic terminology is *Pseudo*-Psora. Cancer is predicated on Sycosis, since this miasm covers the disorganized and uncontrolled reproduction of cells. Some basic general symptoms of the five major miasms will be listed. To start with,

Psora (Deficiency): Vitamin, nutrititional and catalyst (enzymes etc.) deficiencies of all types. Impaired immune response. Skin eruptions and itching. Functional disorders. Excessive response to slight stimuli. Anxiety, fears, restlessness, neurotic states. Fear of poverty. Basic feeling of weariness. Existential anxiety. Symptoms aggravated at any time of day or night.

Sycosis (Excess): Overgrowth of tissues, cancers, warts, condylomata etc. Chronic catarrhs and mucous discharges. Obsessive mental states and fixed ideas. Deceitfulness and other aggressive attitudes covering up lack of self-confidence. Control freaks. Sexual perversions. 'Night people'. Symptoms generally ameliorated evening and night, worse day.

Syphilis (Destruction): Destruction and necrosis of tissue; ulcerations; neurological diseases; congenital disorders; systemic breakdown. Depression, suicide, murder, breakdown of mental function, psychosis, paranoia, alcoholism, violence. Symptoms generally ameliorated day, aggravated evening and night.

Tuberculosis is the miasm of *dissatisfaction* and *exhaustion*. Romantic longings, the desire to live at maximum intensity,[11] inexpressible yearnings for the unattainable,[12] feelings of burning up, 'burning the candle at both ends', grudge-bearing, easily offended, many forms of respiratory complaints, chronic dry cough, bone and endocrine diseases, profuse night-sweats, excessive sexual desires etc. As a disease tuberculosis was rampant, slowly-developing and inevitably ended in death. It was introduced as a main miasm at the end of the 19th century and its taint is widely indicated even today, some 50 years after effective drug treatment was introduced.

Cancer, the miasm of *adaptive failure*. Perfectionism, sympathetic and sensitive, conscientious with great sense of duty, easily offended, love for animals, nurturing. Ailments from domination and repression, especially in childhood; too much responsibility too early in life (e.g. children of alcoholic parents). Suppressed emotions, mild-mannered, yielding. Sensitive to reprimands. History of severe childhood diseases especially glandular fever and frequently-recurring inflammatory illness. Multiple allergies. Difficulty falling asleep. Moles and naevi. Cancers of all types.

Gurudas miasms

During the 1980s Gurudas published a number of books, particularly on Gem and Flower essences. The books contain a great deal of channelled material, some of which relates to miasms, homeopathy and various associated topics. In these books Gurudas introduced the concept of four 'new' miasms which can be related to pollution of various types. These miasms are *Radiation, Petrochemical, Heavy Metal* and *Stellar.*[13] According to Gurudas the first three of these miasms, like the classical miasms, can be inherited (as opposed to acquired, as in the case of, for example, acute miasms). If this is correct then new general symptom pictures will eventually be created as studies and case histories are built up, so that the diversified results of these impacts can be known and understood. Briefly,

> 'the Radiation Miasm is associated with the massive increase in background radiation ... it contributes to premature ageing, slower cell division, deterioration of the endocrine system, weakening of bone tissue, anaemia, arthritis, hair loss, allergies, bacterial inflammations (especially in the brain) ... cancer ... hardening of the arteries and the full spectrum of heart diseases ... this miasm is mainly focused on the molecular level.'

Practitioners should note that patients subjected to X-ray and other imaging devices may also give readings for the presence of some form of radiation and appropriate steps should be taken to neutralise this.

> 'the Petrochemical Miasm is caused by the major increase in petroleum and chemical-based products in society ... some problems ... include fluid retention, diabetes, hair loss, infertility, impotence ... stress and

psychosis ... autism ... overexposure to petrochemicals ... may lead to schizophrenia and wildly erratic emotional behaviour patterns, especially those associated with allergic states.'

This generally speaks for itself, given the ever-increasing statistics for disturbances in the behaviour of children, the increase in autism and other syndromes such as ADD (attention-deficit disorder). It should also be remembered that Hahnemann devoted considerable space to the strongest criticism of the methods of his contemporaries, notably concerning their excessive use of strong toxic medicines in so-called heroic doses and the deleterious effects that resulted. The petrochemical miasm may not be so new after all.

'the Heavy Metal Miasm is cross-indexed with other Miasms. For instance Radioactive isotopes often latch on to heavy metals ... the symptom picture of this developing Miasm includes allergies, excessive hair loss, excessive fluid retention, inability to assimilate calcium, susceptibility to viral inflammation ... senility.'

The dubious effects of aluminium have long been noted in radionics and the effects of dental amalgam, gold and mercury have been the subject of controversy for many years – and in some people, the toxic source of many symptoms.

'the Stellar Miasm (note: stellar background radiation, or cosmic radiation) ... constant low vitality ... an overall sense of loss. The loss seems unconnected to the forces that bring an individual into existence, as if they are being told to go back to sleep, leave physical existence, or stop what they are doing. Such people will feel this as a general malaise ... It is important to understand that stellar background radiation is an important energy that can transform people ...'

The stellar miasm is said to particularly affect the five higher chakras which are located in the subtle bodies above the crown chakra.

Miasm-like parasitic fields

The practitioner should also be aware that certain factors exist which may have a similar effect or presence to an acquired miasm. Three particular categories spring to mind which should be tested and treated if necessary. These are electromagnetism, geopathic stress, and the detrimental effects of vaccination.

Electromagnetic stress, or electrostress, can result for example from living near power lines or cellular phone masts, or using computers and mobile phones. Various studies suggest that cancers and other tumour formations may be stimulated or aggravated by this phenomenon.

Geopathic stress is the effect of earth energies, usually on the nervous system. It can be caused by a number of factors such as underground streams, discontinuities in rock strata and so forth. These may create a negative or damaging field in the patient's residence or place of work. As a consequence geostress, often manifesting as an energetic blockage or disturbance in the central nervous system, may be an important reason why many treatments fail to produce results. Thus steps should be taken to identify and remove it early in treatment.

The same comments may well apply to vaccination effects. These can be detected in most people; controversy over vaccination has existed since the introduction of vaccination itself. Contemporary arguments over the alleged deleterious effects of the MMR (measles – mumps – rubella) vaccine are but one example of this ongoing story. Negative effects from vaccines also may be detectable as acquired or inherited miasms but in either case the practitioner needs to pay close attention to them.

Brief comments on treatment

Discussion of methods used to treat miasms must be reserved for a further article as the matter is complex and must be done by an experienced practitioner. There is a range of possible approaches. Apart from the homeopathic Materia Medica, which contains at least several thousand remedies, there are a large number of gem, flower, colour and radionic treatments (radionic commands and related methods) which may be relevant.

A small table (Table 5.1) is appended listing some qualities of the miasms and some remedies which may be useful. However, to automatically assume, for example, that Psora will be removed by giving homeopathic Sulphur is an error. Each case needs to be assessed on its own merits and appropriate selections made accordingly.

An esoteric view of the miasms

Radionics in particular is concerned with the elucidation of certain esoteric ideas and their application to healing. Many of these ideas have their origin in the work of Alice Bailey, and were transposed into radionic methodology by Tansley. [14] This transposition was integrated with the existing methodology, which analysed and treated physical symptoms through their vibrational patterns. Consequently the underlying principle

MIASM	RAY PHYSICAL-ETHERIC BODY	RAY ASTRAL BODY	COLOUR PHYSICAL-ETHERIC BODY	FLOWER ASTRAL BODY	GEM PHYSICAL-ETHERIC BODY	HAHNEMANNIAN CLASSICAL REMEDY	HOMEOPATHIC NOSODE
PSORA	1	6	ORANGE	AGRIMONY	AMETHYST	SULPHUR CALC. CARB	PSORINUM BOWEL NOSODES
SYCOSIS	1	2	RED	BIRCH; GREAT LEOPARDSBANE; CRAB APPLE	AMAZONITE	THUJA	MEDORRHINUM
SYPHILIS	1	1	ORANGE	CRAB APPLE KAHILI GINGER	AZURITE ALEXANDRITE	MERCURY	SYPHILINUM
TUBERCULOSIS	6	1	BLUE	POPPY	DIAMOND	STANNUM CALC. CARB	TUBERCULINUM
CANCER	2	4	ORANGE (GREEN-ASTRAL)	ASPEN	AZURITE	STAPHYSAGRIA CONIUM	CARCINOSIN
ACUTE	1	/	ORANGE	/	CARBON STEEL	/	/
ARTICULATED	1	6	ORANGE	VINE PANSY	COAL	/	/
HEAVY METAL	1	/	YELLOW	/	CLAY	ALUMINIUM METALLICUM	/
PETRO-CHEMICAL	3	/	GREEN	/	BRONZE COAL	SILICA TERRA	/
RADIATION	7	/	INDIGO	/	CACOXENITE MALACHITE	X-RAY	/
STELLAR	7	6	GREEN	/	DIAMOND	HYDROGEN	/
GEOPATHIC STRESS	1	5	RED	ZINNIA; BLUE FLAG; GOLDEN YARROW	QUARTZ	MAGNETIS POLI AMBO	/
VACCINATION	1	2	RED	CREOSOTE BUSH	CLAY AMETHYST	THUJA	VACCININUM
ELECTRO-MAGNETIC	5	/	VIOLET	/	FIRE AGATE ELECTRUM	GERMANIUM METALLICUM	/

Table 5.1 The qualities of the miasms

is that the energetic expression is prior to the physical manifestation. This was originally set out by Abrams, Drown and others and can be broadly compared with the fundamental concepts proposed by Hahnemann. The radionic model, however, encompasses not only physical and physiological concepts of symptomology and pathology but also the experiential and existential arena of subtle energy, consciousness and its effects on the physical vehicle. This extended model of the subtle energy system is not found in homeopathy. Thus, while radionics is able to – perhaps even must – use homeopathic ideas such as miasms, it may also look at them from a different angle.[15]

Thus Psora, Sycosis and Syphilis as the three fundamental miasms form a good start to a consideration of the matter of the problem of illness as an energetic phenomenon because they equate with the three fundamental destructive forces which tend to rein in the ignorant, arrogant and destructive tendencies within man and humanity.

The Psora concept identifies the slow erosive force which permeates the entire cellular fabric of the individual and in its most easily identifiable form presents as *ageing*. Thus Psora is ever-present in the run of things and at the physical level may not be entirely eliminated; otherwise the laws governing life and death themselves would be subverted and that which belongs to Nature and the Nature-governed organic processes would be compromised. [16] Thus Psora applies itself as a parasite to the incoming pranic force which energises the physical-etheric body and its various and related structures. Like the incoming tide, its process is inexorable, even though one may build barriers to attenuate its strength and delay its more undesirable actions. Psora may then be considered as an external *natural* field which is drawn into the orbit of the living organism under Law, which is to say, the Law of Nature.

It may not truly be said that Psora affects the astral and higher bodies or vehicles but the various characterisations provided by the homeopathic philosophers serve in effect to identify what may, for convenience, be called Psora, which means in essence a shortfall in, or excessive, response to stimulus. This has its deepest roots in the problem of enlightenment and of being as it were cut off from the highest source, not only *God* (it may be said) but also the highest aspect of the Self. Thus Psora descends as an invisible fog around the soul and its vision and creates the delusions which find form in the astral and mental vehicles as reactions which may be considered *inadequate*; although such a simple characterisation is far from *adequate* when contemplating the vast array of psychological states, both reactive and compensatory, which are described by the psychiatrists and psychologists.

Experience nevertheless points to the fact that these perceived inner states also exist as disturbances of the vibrational patterns which characterise the subtle vehicles. Such disturbances may be rectified or cancelled out by the application of an appropriate form of subtle energy such as the homeopathically- or radionically-introduced quantum. This in turn suggests that removal or reduction in intensity of any miasm not only brings about an eventual improvement in the physical and other symptoms but also in the personality conditions. Thus by alleviating or eliminating psychological stressors, treatment may also allow for an incremental increase in the Soul's light as experienced by the individual.

This is not to suggest that such therapeutic means can bring enlightenment as such; in the end it is down to the individual, his or her experience, and inner desire and need to grasp and wield some portion of the perceived higher purpose, to bring this about. This desire emanates from what may be termed the higher Ego or causal body, whereas psychological problems and disorders almost inevitably manifest through the personality typically expressing itself through astral and emotional bodies. [17] Soul consciousness at its own level is purity incarnate but each step towards manifestation in a lower vehicle brings about an added complexity and possibility for error and confusion, and hence the idea of the Fall. [18] The essence of the matter is not however Sin, but *confusion* resulting from the discrepancy between Soul in its pure form and that same Soul attempting to apprehend reality through the density of manifested existence. This problem is clearly compounded when many such Souls are incarnated simultaneously and all are trying to solve the same problems of being and essence at the same time.

This then brings us to Sycosis. This may be considered the delusional state *particularly* related to social conditioning as a means by which feelings of inadequacy are induced in the individual; as a result compensatory emotional and mental states are produced. Hahnemann's choice of gonorrhoea as the paradigm of Sycosis is useably acceptable when considered in the purview of the idea of excessive response. At the physical level the characteristics are well-known e.g. overproduction of faulty tissue in warts, growths and cancers; and discharges of many kinds. Correspondingly the psychological nature of Sycosis is to try and hold its position and fix itself in its own form of reality and hence the delusions and obsessive states which may characterise the emotional and mental pathology. Psora may be equated with neurosis, with anxiety as the core phenomenon; in Sycosis the condition has deepened its grip and complexity and is not typified by the immediate and excitable response of Psora, hence obsession and fixation are typical.

Syphilis may be considered the epitome of *destruction* and in its activity as the disease of the negative participle of the destroyer Ray One, [19] mercilessly plies its way through the organism, breaking down all form and demanding chaotic disintegration as its right, thus ending in destruction. The situation in the subtle vehicles is also basically well-understood by the homeopaths even though, again, it is the energetic paradigm or field and not the disease itself which, as it were, infects the astral and mental vehicles. [20] The destructive and chaotic states in the subtle bodies which typify this final stage of disease mirror the conditions found in the physical body. Murder, insanity, self-destruction, alcoholism, addiction, suicide, unjustified rage and anger, violence, theft, greed and so on are all markers for the syphilitic state where the inner sense of order and rationality have been submerged under the deluge of lower destructive passions resulting from a depleted sense of self-identity permeated with chaotic and uncontrollable feelings, thoughts and impulses.

It scarcely needs to be said but that each miasm may exist to a greater or lesser extent in each of the physical and subtle bodies. They may in addition co-exist and become as it were entangled, thus making the therapeutic process more complex.

It becomes clear that this vast topic concerns an important aspect of the very essence and ontological problem of the nature of incarnation and the processes of physical existence.

The astral body and the miasms

The astral body so-called is a mechanism which enables the individual to relate to the group. Bailey teaches that it is a chimera, in the sense that it is a projection of desire or, as it is also known, the desire-mind or *kama-manas*. Thus it is impossible to actually treat the astral body directly. The treatment must access another energy centre which is the source of the cloud or emanation known as the astral body. But the astral body is neither essential nor essence; it is, in fact, the result of the need for a means of communication and a communality of experience and reaction with the group. Nevertheless it also exists as a powerful layer of illusion and delusion and as such is a kind of electro-force field held together not only by the crystallised desire-mind of incarnated humans but also by the desire-mind of the masses of humans and other beings[21] who have ceased to occupy the physical worlds yet cannot as yet escape the need for some form of externality for their consciousness. The phenomenon of the 'second death' is also described in some esoteric literature, where the astral sheath is abandoned in favour of the more exalted, higher and truth-enabled mental plane, which is stated to be an essence and a reality. Suffice it to say that what passes for thought in most humans is in fact the verbalised expression of emotional patterns into some kind of apparently logical form, hence the expression *desire-mind.*

The totality of expression of the desire-mind is contained within the solar plexus chakra area but is not entirely the same as, and contiguous with, this chakra. Neither can it be identified with the *dan-tien* or, as it is also known, the *hara*, of the oriental system. This desire-mind is like a coating or layer which envelops the greater part of the chakra and has a type of cloaking effect on it. This coating is an ever-changing vibrational field which is often, or even always, linked into that of many others, even thousands or millions of others, in some of its parts. This then is the group astral body which is so responsive to mass manipulation and persuasion, to group control, to delusion, to memes, to the willingness to surrender personal truth to mass glamour and hysteria, and so on.

It is thus also incorrect to say that each chakra has, as it were, a layer or component which is astral in nature. Each chakra certainly has an etheric layer and some have essences from the mental and certain other bodies. It can be stated that the truly awakened heart chakra produces an energy which is not astral in nature; the truly awakened throat chakra produces an energy which is not astral in nature; and so on. Each chakra, and in fact also the many minor chakras, have their own exceptional qualities and characteristics. The actual study of the chakras, how they work and interact, and their function and purpose, seems to be as yet at its smallest beginning even in spite of the much that can already be found, both written and taught.

Stripped of its astral coating, the solar plexus chakra can then start to be understood in another way which is also concerned with connectivity and emotion but of a more rarefied type; the feelings for example of connection with nature, with the animal and plant kingdoms. Often, that which creates art and artistic self-expression on the second ray of love energy essence comes from the true solar plexus realisation. This is different from the negative astral energy aspects such as individual and group anxiety and fear, selfish emotion and grasping love which proceed from and paralyse the solar plexus area. These also lead to many physical and psychosomatic complaints in the abdominal region. Misuse of, and false – one-sided – religious teachings are also aimed, consciously or unconsciously, at paralysing the systematic circulation of energy throughout the personal macro-energetic system and at congesting this astral energy area. False psychism and many spectacular but false psychic phenomena also result from manipulation and abuse of astral solar plexus energy.

Thus the astral centre can be considered to be an energy centre which originally developed to enable group ritual expression. It is located in the region of the solar plexus chakra. It produces an energetic cloud as both an individual and a group phenomenon. As the mental powers develop in the individual it becomes proportionally attenuated, allowing the 'natural' function of the solar plexus to come to the fore if needed and appropriate to that individual's mode of self-expression.

It is entirely appropriate, however, for the practitioner to treat the astral centre, as it may more appropriately be called, with the various means at his or her disposal. This centre can be considered, by way of analogy, as a type of 8-layered globe with the inside three (denoted 8, 7 and 6) or *core* layers being the most important and the most profoundly impacted and impinged by emotional events. Dislodgement of these layers or their pollution by crystallised vibratory qualities which present, for example, as obsessions, neuroses, fear, anxieties, phobias and a general sense of existential dislocation can thus be considered as miasms. But miasms in the astral centre are an entirely different matter from miasms in the etheric body, which may rightly be identified as the Dynamis of Hahnemann.[22] For convenience of understanding we use the terms Psora, Sycosis, etc. but the meaning attributable to these artefacts in the astral context cannot be directly equated with any particular disease form. It is only the manifestations of the artefacts which allow some classification with what has been observed and categorised in the homeopathic symptomology, just as they may be equated with the terms of psychology and more particularly psychiatry. There *is* for therapeutic understanding a wholeness and compatibility of expression between these arts but it has scarcely been explored.

Expression of the miasms

Normally miasms lie dormant in the subtle fields of the person although the physical form, as expressed from birth, may bear numerous and various marks of miasmatic expression, many of which can be identified by the trained observer. However, at this point the miasm has expressed itself through the DNA or genetic formation or, it might be said, deformation, for it is axiomatic that the physical form is built up by biochemical process from the DNA pattern and is only informed and energised by the etheric body and other subtle fields. That one is entirely congruent and coterminous with the other is only a moot point.

The inheritance or acquisition of miasms in the subtle bodies comes not from the physical levels but through a different and esoteric process. The *results* of miasmatic activity and, in particular, the activated miasm become imprinted into the DNA, and the expression of the DNA consequently bears the imprint of the miasm, but the DNA is not the miasm itself.

It is, however, entirely consequent that efficient and effective removal of an articulated miasm, and to a lesser extent the precipitate or classical miasms, may lead to changes in the DNA functioning and even structure, since the DNA is bound to follow the condition and conditioning of the physical-etheric body or Dynamis. This not only *is* so but accords exactly with Hahnemann's fundamental proposition that the state of the physical body accurately reflects the state of the Dynamis. What was missing from Hahnemann's exposition was the understanding of the means by which this could take place and also a fuller comprehension of the real depth and meaning of the Dynamis and also the profundity of what and how impingements could impact it.

Thus the adoption of miasms by the individual is, to some extent, determined by karma and, to some extent, by the desire of the Higher Self to expand and extend its range of experience; how and in what form the miasms are expressed and used depends upon the individual. Whether or not they are triggered into action is dependent upon the many stress factors at play. As Hahnemann understood, there is a considerable difference between *latent* Psora and *expressed* Psora, and thus, generally, between latent and expressed miasms. Miasms also have their positive aspects. Many of the greatest works of art, for example, are the result of the struggle to overcome inner miasmatic forces and to gain a closer understanding of truth; many existential struggles depicted in the arts are actually showing the conflict produced in the individual between the negative aspect of the miasm and the aspiration to greater understanding. Thus miasms may bring energy and fire and stand opposed to complacency and stagnation. Hence miasms have both positive and negative qualities. Careful control and use of the forces they ignite may hasten the way to a deeper understanding and quicken personal evolution.

On a mass level, as has been described, miasms are mainly a phenomenon of the astral body. However, contagious epidemic diseases in particular may spread through contact between the individual etheric body and the etheric field in general i.e. the energy pattern of the disease inhibits the individual Dynamis and the infectious agent appears later, since the internal environment has been prepared for it. [23]

Group astral phenomena are entirely present and pervasive throughout the modern world, particularly since the ideas involved may spread very quickly through the mass media. Thus for example:

'A good number of people in the world today are in a Sycotic state. There is a *sense of inadequacy and inferiority, of having a tough time with the self in the struggle for existence. The growth of psychotherapy, self-improvement techniques, etc., are all in response to this rise in Sycosis. Unfortunately, however, most such methods manage to achieve the opposite because they only bring about a better adjustment to fixed ways of thinking and living. These are only ways of coping with the same feeling of inferiority rather than a true diminution of the feeling.'* [24]

or perhaps even more trenchantly,

'The value of the nosodes of human disease products lies in the fact that each one in a different relationship possesses the sum total background of racial miasmatic development. In this connection I offer a suggestion in the social study of the much-discussed psychology of 'mob action', often syphilitic in its brutality and unreasonableness, sycotic in action and persistency, and psoric in the welding of many persons from various social strata toward a unified purpose. The explosive element represents the release of the suppressed miasmatic accumulation, producing an effect entirely against the routine of long-established custom.' [25]

Thus it is suggested that miasms not only function in the life of the individual but play an important role in the life of society and in historical development. Mass consciousness, mass hysteria, aspects, elements and artefacts of the subconscious and unconscious life of humanity can be attributed to group astral activity and reactivity and hence can be related to this problem of the miasms, *not* as energetic primitives creating illness in the physical body in the classical Hahnemannian sense but as emotional *delusional phenomena creating the conditions* for miasms in the physical-etheric body to be activated.

Notes

1. This title was used by John Da Monte for his contribution to *Chakras Rays and Radionics* by David Tansley. I may only hope that I have come anywhere close to being as useful.
2. It is arguable that the Vital Force can be identified with such concepts as ch'i and prana. The main and perhaps fundamental distinction is that, as far as I am aware, all non-Western forms of medicine, traditional or otherwise, be it acupuncture, Ayurveda, Reiki etc. are essentially *vitalist* i.e. they assume there is a life force or life energy. This concept was eliminated from the Western model used in orthodox medicine. There is consciousness, the object of psychology and psychiatry, and there is physiology. But the level of energy or vitality, so far as it is considered, is thought to be entirely a function of various biochemical processes in the body.
3. §11, *The Organon of Medicine* by Samuel Hahnemann (see book list). There is no fundamental book of method comparable to this in radionics and it should be essential reading for every radionic practitioner. Why? Because it is the most complete and thorough treatise

on the causes and treatment of illness as an energetic disturbance that is available.

4. *The Chronic Diseases (Theoretical Part)* by Samuel Hahnemann, page 35.

 I will give a simple analogy which may help with the idea of miasms as fixed pollutions of the Vital Force. Every house has a cold water tank into which water flows from the main supply. Let us suppose there is something in the cold water tank which always stains the water brown. The water will therefore always flow out of the taps discoloured brown. There may be blockages in the pipes (congestion) which can be cleared; there may be excess water pressure which needs adjusting (overstimulation); there might be air bubbles in the pipes which means the water flows in an irregular fashion (unco-ordination); defective structures in the building might press on the pipes (stress), leading to fracture (damage) or breakage (cleavage) and so on. But none of these will stop the water flowing out discoloured brown. The only way that can be done is by removing whatever it is in the tank which stains the water. By analogy, that something is the miasm. This is a little simplistic; but the important point is that there are other conditions which affect the Dynamis such as congestion, overstimulation, unco-ordination, energetic toxins etc. which can also produce serious symptoms. These however are not miasms. But they may be entangled with miasms or may even be the result of miasms, hence untangling the problem may require a great deal of care.

5. Hahnemann's view is that since diseases result from an impingement of the Vital Force i.e. diseases are Dynamic in nature, they can only be removed by correcting the problem at the dynamic level with a suitably homeopathic potentised (i.e. dynamic) remedy. In radionics we go a step further, since we broadcast codes, which represent the remedy, to the patient. Whether these codes are mnemonics which draw the appropriate energy out of the etheric field or actually are energy artefacts identical to the quantum they represent – or both – is at present unknown. This method however produces the same phenomena described by Hahnemann and others, e.g. aggravations, return of old symptoms, and so on.

 Suppression therefore occurs when external symptoms are removed without a corresponding correction of the disturbance of the Dynamis, creating conditions whereby this disturbance may be forced to manifest at some later time in further and more serious symptoms.

6. *The Chronic Diseases (Theoretical Part)* by Samuel Hahnemann, page 35.

7. Ibid., page 40, Note.

8. Miasms – A Review by Dr Farley Spink. *Journal of the Psionic Medical Society*, Volume XVI, No 38, Spring 2000.

9. See *Homoeopathic Links*, Volume 15, Winter 2002: Variolinum, Vaccininum and Malandrinum – the powerful smallpox nosodes and their therapeutic use by Erika Scheiwiller-Muralt.

10. *The Organon of Medicine*, Glossary, page 328.

11. 'The light that burns twice as bright burns half as long. And you have burned so very, very brightly, Roy. Look at you. You're the prodigal son. You're quite a prize!'
 Eldon Tyrell to his android creation, Roy, in the film *Blade Runner* (1980).

12. 'This is the end – beautiful friend,
 This is the end, my only friend, the end
 Of our elaborate plans, the end
 Of everything that stands, the end
 No safety or surprise, the end
 I'll never look into your eyes again – the end
 Can you picture what will be

> So limitless and free
> Desperately in need of some stranger's hand
> In a desperate land
> Lost in a Roman...wilderness of pain
> All the children are insane –
> All the children are insane
> Waiting for the summer rain.'

– Jim Morrison, The Doors, '*The End*' (1966). This was also used as theme music to Francis Ford Coppola's *Apocalypse Now* (1978) which in turn was based on Joseph Conrad's novel *The Heart of Darkness*.

The 19th century was the era of tubercular art. Many major artists succumbed to the disease e.g. Keats, Chopin, Paganini, Chekov, Schiller, Aubrey Beardsley, Schubert, Emily Bronte – it was a constant and ominous threat to the life of all. Thus the Romantic period may be considered a response to tubercular miasmatic forces. Note that Schoenberg, the quintessential 20th century composer, sought to impose order on his internal passionate feelings by inventing the rigid compositional method of the tone row (12-tone music). Thus tubercular emotionalism gave way to sycotic control. We may ask if 20th century compositional music recovered from this?

13. See particularly *Gem Elixirs and Vibrational Healing Volume I*; there are numerous references to these 'new' miasms.

14. See for example *Chakras, Rays and Radionics*. The principal source is *Esoteric Healing*, by Alice Bailey.

15. It is possible that Hahnemann was aware of these concepts in some form. He may have had certain esoteric knowledge which he chose to omit from his writings. Compare for example §225 of *The Organon*, '...there are certainly a few emotional diseases that have not simply degenerated from somatic disease...with but little infirmity it develops outward from the emotional mind due to persistent worry, mortification, vexation, abuse, or repeated exposure to great fear or fright...emotional diseases of this kind often ruin the somatic state of health to a high degree.'

   As an example of the early relationship between homeopathy and radionics, Abrams noted that homeopathic *Mercury* offset the reflex reaction to syphilis in his test subject.

16. While such processes may be temporarily set aside they may not ultimately be abrogated i.e. everyone dies. Eternal life, should it exist, is presumably not for the physical form. The view presented here is clearly very different from that set out by Hahnemann but it may be no less true or useful.

17. Gurudas (see bibliography) proposes that we can divide the astral body into astral and emotional bodies. The astral body is more part of a group or collective emotional field whereas the emotional body is the personal emotional response.

18. i.e. The Fall from Paradise as described in The Bible. This is to do with the idea of original Sin, but here we have the idea of original Confusion, which might be a more workable concept for post-20th century humanity.

19. Bailey proposes that everything in the universe is built up through the action and interplay of the 7 rays and their cycles. These are divided into 3 rays of Aspect (Rays 1 – 3) and 4 rays of Attribute (Rays 4 – 7). To give some ideas about ray qualities, very briefly:

Ray 1	WILL
Ray 2	LOVE
Ray 3	ACTIVE INTELLIGENCE
Ray 4	ART AND HARMONY THROUGH CONFLICT

Ray 5   SCIENCE AND CONCRETE KNOWLEDGE
Ray 6   IDEALISM OR DEVOTION
Ray 7   ORDER OR CEREMONIAL MAGIC

It should be noted that the dominant ray throughout the Piscean Age was Ray 6 and as we now pass into the Aquarian Age the transition to the dominant Ray 7 energy is taking place.

Each ray has positive and negative aspects and also 7 sub-rays.

20. Bailey tells us in *Esoteric Healing* that only about 5% of all human illness develops from the mental body. This is because diseases of the mind are actually mis-named and misunderstood, since they in fact have their source in the astral body. The causal body (Higher Self or Ego) is also, as it were, at one of the levels of the mental plane.

21. 'Other beings' – for example animals which have started to develop a differentiated consciousness.

22. It seems to me that the emotional and mental symptoms of homeopathy are primarily somatic in origin, i.e. they result from impacts to the Dynamis which affect the nervous and endocrine systems in particular. If this is correct it reinforces my opinion that the Dynamis is most closely identified as the physical-etheric body. See also Note 10 above, where Hahnemann clearly differentiates between emotional diseases resulting from impacts to the 'emotional mind' as opposed to emotional diseases 'degenerated from somatic disease.' He does not elaborate on what the 'emotional mind' is but as noted, it is possible that Hahnemann was aware of esoteric concepts which he chose not to factor explicitly into his writings.

23. In *Esoteric Healing* Bailey also refers to the three planetary diseases, syphilis, cancer and tuberculosis. '….. *They are planetary in scope, present in the substance of which all forms are made, and are responsible for producing a host of lesser diseases which are sometimes recognised as affiliates but are frequently not so known.'* (p. 199)

Space does not permit me go further into this here, nor do I have sufficient knowledge at this time!

24. *The Substance of Homoeopathy* by Rajan Sankaran, p. 26.

25. Quoted in *Synoptic Materia Medica II* by Frans Vermeulen, p. 126. This section concerns homeopathic remedy *Bacillinum*, a nosode of tuberculosis. The quote is attributed to 'Waffensmith, 1929'.

Bibliography

Bailey, Alice (1953) *Esoteric Healing*. Lucis Press, London.

Dormandy, Thomas (1998) *The White Death: a History of Tuberculosis*. The Hambledon Press, London.

Gurudas (1986) *Gem Elixirs and Vibrational Healing, Vol II*. Cassandra Press, San Rafael, CA, USA.

Hahnemann, Samuel (1993) *The Chronic Diseases*. B. Jain, New Delhi, India. (Other versions are available.)

Hahnemann, Samuel (2000) *The Organon of the Medical Art*. Edited by Wenda Brewster O'Reilly. Birdcage Books, Redmond, Washington, USA . (Other versions are available.)

Reyner, J. H. (2001) *Psionic Medicine*. C W Daniel, Saffron Walden, Essex.

Sankaran, Rajan (1994) *The Substance of Homoeopathy*. Homoeopathic Medical Publishers, Bombay, India.

Sherr, Jeremy Yaakov (2002) *Dynamic Materia Medica: Syphilis*. Dynamis Books, Malvern.

Tansley, David (1984) *Chakras, Rays and Radionics*. C W Daniel Company, Saffron Walden,

Essex.

Vermeulen, Frans (1996) *Synoptic Materia Medica II.* Merlin Publishers, Harlem, Netherlands.

Studies of Carcinosin (the nosode of cancer) and post-vaccination syndrome can be found on the website of Dr Tinus Smits http://www.tinussmits.com/english/ (Accessed 19/5/2003).

Cathy Marshall

Extending the Energy Centres in Radionic Work

6

As healers radionic practitioners are familiar and comfortable working with the seven chakra system positioned in line with the physical spine. For most practitioners the system is a major focus of their work and a source of ever expanding information about how the human energy field functions. To this system can be added various minor chakras that may benefit from treatment, for example, those positioned in the palms of the hand or the soles of the feet.

The seven major chakras govern not only specific physical locations but our emotional well being and our mental health and balance. Much has been written about the seven in the past ten years; a search through most bookshops will offer a wide choice of interpretation of the seven chakra system. While considering the chakra system we should remember that the word 'chakra' is sacred in many eastern religions. It is in the very sacredness of the nature of the centres that we learn more about ourselves and about the individual journey that each of us follows on the earth.

If we take each of the seven chakras individually or in groups we find that they have counterparts further out in the auric space which are natural extensions of the seven chakra system (See Fig. 6.1). These are the extended chakras. They contain an explanation of the potential for growth inherent in each individual. From an understanding of their role we are able to enrich our interpretation of a patient's subtle energy field.

Established healers have been working with extended systems for some years and each has developed a system that works well for him. Because this work depends on the healers' own knowledge, interpretation and understanding, extended systems will vary in content. This is why confusion has arisen for some healers as they try to make sense of the various systems available.

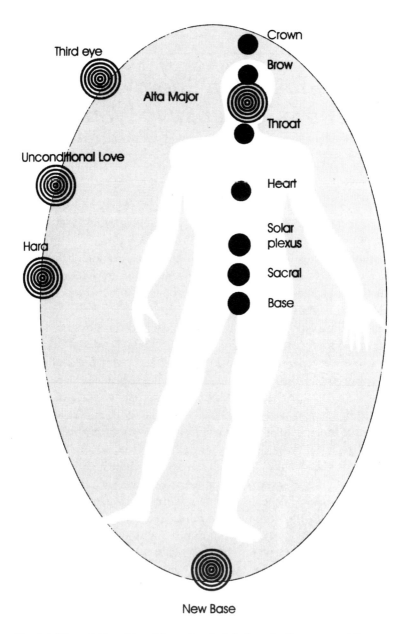

Fig. 6.1 The relationship of the extended chakras to the aura and the seven
spinal chakras

The system to be considered here is inspired by the work of Ruth White and Gill Pichler and applied to radionic practice. It began as lively discussion and a generous sharing of ideas with Gill for which I remain very grateful. It is not offered as the only system and will by its very nature be found to overlap with other systems. For example, interpretations of hara energies occur in martial arts and yoga literature; Peter Dawkins gives three alta majors in *The Grail Kingdom of Europe* and Aquarius Flower Remedies literature include extended centres. For me, Ruth White's system, as given by her guide Gildas, and introduced in her book *Working with Your Chakras*, has been tried and tested over some years and extends the seven chakra system, as used in my radionic work, bringing a greater relevance to practice.

So let us first consider how the major chakra system (as introduced by Alice Bailey in *Esoteric Healing* and David Tansley in *Radionics and the Subtle Anatomy of Man*) extends itself within the subtle anatomy.

The base chakra extends to an awareness of the new base centre.

The solar plexus, sacral, base and minor chakras positioned in the lower abdomen extend to an awareness of the hara centre.

The heart chakra extends to an awareness of the unconditional love centre.

The crown, brow and throat chakras (sometimes known as the head centres) extend to the third eye centre.

All seven major chakras, and in particular crown, sacral and base, extend to an awareness of the alta major centre. In this case the alta major is less of an extension, more of a vehicle for bypassing the existing system so that the etheric body can respond with speed and confidence in challenging situations. We will look at this in more depth later on.

At this point it should be emphasised that these are not 'new' chakras. The 'equipment' of the subtle anatomy includes many possibilities, some of which are active and of which we are aware and others that are currently quiescent. These hold potential and may or may not be called upon to play a part in this lifetime, depending on the lessons learnt or opportunities offered and accepted by the incarnate soul.

For example, many of us know that we aspire to love unconditionally in our day to day life but we know this is not easy for us and that we have to work at it. We know that we may not reach our full potential for loving unconditionally in the near future but that does not stop us making tentative efforts to catch a glimmer here and there of what it is like to know and work through our unconditional love centre. Issues associated with this centre are of enormous importance for each of us as individuals as well as for many of the patients who come to us for help. So often a patient approaches a radionic practitioner at a time of crisis in their personal life. The crisis may be expressing itself with a multitude of physical problems, for which we can offer help, but the underlying cause may come from a deeper issue and this issue may well be found within those relating to extended centres.

Unconditional love, the extension of the heart chakra, shows us that extending the chakra system is about considering man's highest aspirations. Within the extended system we have a counsel for perfection, or the opportunity of sainthood if looked at from a Christian point of view. This idea holds great promise for the future of the world, for peace and harmony on the planet, for mankind's responsibility for the state of the earth and his ability to work harmoniously within 'the group'. Thus we can see that the extended system will lead us towards group consciousness, and group consciousness is one of the lessons that the Aquarian Age brings. If mankind is to flourish in future years, we are going to need to develop some of the strengths offered by the extended centres. If we understand a little about the qualities these chakras bring we may move nearer to achieving group awareness.

I have heard it said within radionic circles that we do not need an understanding of the extended chakras because we never use them. For me this is far from true. It is my belief that we are in fact using them frequently, not in straightforward treatment intentions such as 'to normalise the hara', but in the wording and combination of treatments in day to day work for our patients. Initially it may not be obvious to the practitioner that he is in fact being asked to treat the extended chakras. Other than the alta major, extended chakras are not normally included on analysis sheets. Yet the more I work with the chakras the more certain I feel that I am dealing with inner struggles, concerns of spirituality, sense of purpose, attitude to others and to the state of the earth which are part and parcel of daily life. These underlie the very fabric of our existence and it is an enormous privilege to gain glimmers of awareness, either of self or of others, through this process.

I find the clue that an extended chakra may be involved comes when I am asked to look repeatedly at one or two of the seven chakras for a particular patient, perhaps by treating the same chakra in a variety of different ways, and when certain issues or key words come up within treatment. In fact we are assisting our patients handle their key life lessons with ease and equanimity. I hope to show in the following pages how these centres are at work in our lives and practices and how, through the chakras and the lessons they bring, each of us can move forward with whatever is asked of us at this present time on earth

Let us start by extending the base chakra.

The new base centre

The essential need of the base chakra is material security. Initially our parents provide this for us; as we grow up we start to take responsibility for our personal needs. We clothe ourselves, feed ourselves and provide a roof over our heads. Security is the foundation of the first major chakra of the seven. Its symbol is the square: a square has four corners, it stands four square rather like the drawing of a small child's house. By developing a secure foundation on earth in the early years of life we are able to take care of our physical needs as adults which enables us to grow and develop our talents and our awareness.

When we were conceived it is thought that certain choices were made by the incarnating soul. During the time in the womb these choices were clarified so that by the time we were born there was purpose to our incarnation. The obvious initial choice was that of our parents, but factors that will have been considered will have been the year we were born, the astrological influences at the time and the place where our parents lived. Such considerations as town, country, climate, wealth or poverty, other members of the family (including siblings) will have been taken into account, even though normally there is no recollection in adult life of having made these decisions

If we extend our understanding of the base chakra back to the time *in utero*, a new view of our life and purpose will start to emerge. We had choice: are we prepared to consider that now? We accepted this incarnation as being best for our individual needs: are we still fighting it? We chose to live in this place, in this century: are we able to see why? If we don't like how we live, had we considered changing it? Can we accept that this life is the best learning experience for us right now? When life is considered in this light it takes on a very different meaning. It may bring a feeling of greater contentment, liberation, renewal or acceptance when facing particular problems.

If treatments are needed for a patient that involve assurance, trust, peace or acceptance given to the base chakra, the radionic practitioner is almost certainly touching the new base centre. One patient came to me with skin irritation that had started in his second year of life, after receiving childhood vaccinations. Dowsing showed he had suffered pre-birth shock, birth shock, a Psora miasm that was blocking his crown chakra, a miasmic pattern from childhood illness (probably scarlet fever), and an alta major chakra that was low and blocked. There were issues concerning cell renewal and tissue regeneration. I found discontent with his situation in general and I suspected deep irritation with many aspects of life in particular. In fact this was a strong reaction, the message being 'I'd rather not be here, I am thoroughly irritated by it all.'

I did not consider it appropriate to discuss in depth with this patient his struggle with his place in life. Much of the work to heal, strengthen and reconnect this patient with the new base could be broadcast as radionic treatment. The one difference was that I held in mind that the purpose of these treatments was to assist in the healing of early traumas.

To contact the energy of this centre means taking various things on trust. Though we may have difficulty coming to terms with some of these ideas, no one can deny that a good relationship with the earth will ease our path in this lifetime. The patient whose physical body has difficulty accepting many aspects of modern living (for example, allergies or sensitivities to chemicals) may, in fact, be manifesting deeper problems accepting his incarnation. These are issues associated with the extension of the base chakra, issues that raise the question of what can be done to assist the patient through this crisis?

When treating any patient with these problems I ask whether it is appropriate to give flower remedies for the time when the patient was within the womb. Bach remedies may be indicated and so, too, might be the range of Lunar and Moon flower remedies from Aquarius Flowers. *Moon Water* in particular assists in clearing trauma from the time *in utero*. Treatments may be given 'to harmonise with the earth experience' or 'to harmonise with present place'. The adrenal glands, the chromaffine tissues, the base chakra and the autonomic nervous system are treated to assist the physical body. In some instances it may be appropriate for patient and practitioner to consider various aspects of lifestyle and discuss whether there is particular resistance or unwillingness to embrace the earth experience.

I am very careful about what I discuss with a patient. Occasionally it may be indicated that the time is right to suggest to the patient that he chose to be on earth at this present time, that it could be viewed as a privilege to live in the first world and to have the benefit of scientific, medical and technological research. Mostly I reserve this information, allowing it only to be held in mind as I treat the patient. I find that many seemingly less pleasant aspects of life become more acceptable when viewed and treated in this light.

The hara centre

Below the diaphragm in the lower abdomen are three major chakras – solar plexus, sacral and base – and various minor chakras, including two that support the adrenals. At times they work in combination, and in order to develop a strong hara it is of great importance that all these chakras are in balance.

I know little about Zen practice but I understand that Zen masters place great emphasis on the practice of stillness and breathing in certain positions. Karlfried Graf Durckheim, in his book *Hara the Vital Centre of Man*, describes how much of Zen teaching comes from within, from a lower centre of gravity within the trunk of the body that is accessed through specific exercises. Japanese culture values the inner calm and stillness that springs from strengthening the hara. I understand from those who sing and ride to professional standards here in the West that they too access this seat of power and inner calm so that their work becomes virtually effortless and their energy greatly increased by 'effortless effort'.

The hara chakra is able to provide the body with a huge reserve of power. This is not mental strength, though it may lead to mental calm and stillness and will require an ability to still the mind in order to achieve strength. Rather it needs to be seen as an extension of all that is best within the lower chakras. So what exactly might hara energy involve? There will be qualities of 'fire in the belly' from good digestion and a healthy solar plexus. There will be ability to relate well to others either as individuals or groups as an extension of co-creatorship within the sacral chakra. There will be security and strong foundations from the base chakra. There will be an ability to withstand fear from the two minor chakras near the adrenals. There will be an ability to nurture self.

As each of these chakras extends it emphasises the hara qualities.

Hara energy may be somewhat alien in our view of the world but that does not mean that we do not need it. In the West we place great emphasis on intellectual activity and achievement and in an energetic sense we are often found to be top (or head) heavy. In radionic analysis this may be found as great mental activity with over-stimulated brow or throat chakras and a dullness or lack of energy below the diaphragm. By contrast in the Far East hara qualities are valued. The ideal is the big-bellied Buddha who is well nourished both physically and spiritually. He is calm, contented and centred and has a power point deep within himself that nothing can unsettle.

As the Piscean age draws to an end there is a re-emergence of ancient energies that have been dormant for millennia. The goddess cult, so firmly repressed first by aggressive civilisations and then by the Christian church, is re-awakening as women regain their power and position in society. The search for a balance between the masculine and feminine energies is on. As women take up roles of authority in society do men feel threatened? Who is empowered? Are women seeking to usurp men's roles rather than re-discovering their own? Who has become disempowered? Where is the patient to find a point of balance when society changes dramatically within a generation?

Hara energies need to be treated with the greatest respect. Out of balance they can send a person into great disharmony. These energies are not to be trifled with, over-stimulated or contacted irresponsibly. Our frameworks are vulnerable. We have not been brought up in disciplined eastern practices, and I believe most of us will be only slightly aware of these energies in our lifetime. I would encourage those drawn to martial arts; they are learning the discipline in a formal setting required to start to touch the hara energies.

The clue that the hara is out of balance is when the radionic practitioner is asked to treat extensively the energy framework below the diaphragm. If a patient is struggling with problems of power or position it is likely that this is the focus of the problem. The hara brings tremendous forces for regeneration and healing, both for self and others, but when out of balance I find it is frequently associated with 'burn-out'. The patient who has embraced a career as a carer or therapist and has become overworked may reach a point of total exhaustion and collapse. Frequently this results from a lack of care of self, a need to take time out, nourish self and recharge batteries. In my experience I have found that the hara chakra highlights the importance of caring for self properly before we take on the care or healing of others.

One child I treated had had repeated infections. His digestive bacteria had been severely disrupted by antibiotic use. I searched for a flower remedy to break this pattern and assist him regain balance and health. Dowsing indicated the Pacific Essence *Snowdrop*. The description given by Sabina Pettitt in her book *Energy Medicine* showed me that the route to healing for this child could be *via* the hara chakra. I was surprised that this was the case in a young person. Yet it made sense, the snowdrop pushes up through the hard winter earth to reach the sun, it is an enormously resilient bulb. It is said to embody the qualities of personal power and leadership. It acts on the base chakra, the solar plexus chakra and the crown chakra and brings healing by restoring the flow of Qi energy within the body, restoring vitality. Treatments to all the chakras in the lower abdominal area were given to assist in the healing process.

I feel that in no other instance is it of more importance to 'restore to perfect balance and harmony' or 'normalise' when giving radionic treatments which involve energies associated with the hara because I have no wish to upset the balance within this area. Strength and stability combined with protective treatments will assist the process of regeneration. In some instances I find an adult patient can be greatly helped by breathing exercises which provide balance and inner calm.

The unconditional love centre

Now to extend the heart chakra. For me this chakra has always stopped me in my tracks. I find the task of putting something relevant into words daunting. I see this chakra as the pivotal point for all the subtle anatomy, the centre of the centres. Most of us are blessed because we have or have had some experience of love in our life; we know something of the tears and joy it brings. Yet the true mystical experience that causes a deep ache within and unites with the universe is elusive. It was known as 'ecstasy' to the Christian saints and is experienced through tremendous joy or enormous suffering. The very first love in a life may bring a taste of this experience. A shared horrific experience may also bring this response which etches on each individual a memory that can never be broken. These are the experiences that mature the heart chakra.

When the heart moves out to experience unconditional love it brings wisdom and integrity. This is not necessarily the mystical experience. Wisdom and integrity do not necessarily go hand in hand with mysticism. I believe that one experience of love is not necessarily a prerequisite for the other.

What I can offer are some questions that give a flavour of working with the unconditional love chakra. How detached can we be in a potentially emotive situation? Can we be true to ourselves at all times? Can we temper judgement with mercy and not criticise or condemn other people?

Unconditional love knows when to say 'no'. A small amount of chocolate may be acceptable for a child, the whole bar may make him sick. We usually know when enough is enough in cases like this but can we bring the same discrimination to complex relationships? Are we able to love even when we receive nothing in return? How often does our love come with strings attached: if I do this for you, will you do this for me? Unconditional love does not count the cost or expect a return, but it does know when to say 'no' and when to care for ourselves first.

We could ask who, among the thousands of household names familiar to us in the past decades, show qualities in their life or work which demonstrate true unconditional love. Each of us may choose a different selection but here are a few as a starting point. Mother Theresa working with the poorest of the poor in Calcutta; Archbishop Desmond Tutu for his work with the Truth Commission in South Africa; Dr Elizabeth Kubler Ross for making the subject of death and dying acceptable in society; Pope John XXIII for bringing a fresh impetus to Catholicism; Wallenburg for assisting hundreds of Hungarian Jews escape deportation during the Second World War. More names are mentioned under the next centre and some will be found to overlap with qualities of unconditional love.

Working with, or meditating on, the element given by Ruth White for the extended heart may clarify the picture. 'Seawater' flows everywhere, it knows no boundaries as it flows between continents. The sea is ever changing, rough and dangerous one day, calm and milky the next. It supports a whole ecosystem, plant and animal life, much of which is still unknown to us. Its tides and currents control the migration of a multitude of sea creatures as well as maintaining the temperature of the planet.

The patient who needs help with energies extending from the heart chakra as it develops to unconditional love may be facing challenging decisions, possibly associated with their way of handling those they love.

Physical symptoms may be manifesting in the form of lowered immunity, tension in the chest or thoracic area, long-term infection or asthmatic problems. There may have been devotion taken to a point that can no longer be sustained without making a change, or devotion taken to the point of sacrifice to a cause. There may be great suffering ahead or a need for wise decision making. Only the patient knows what is right in this situation; the practitioner's task is to provide a framework of healing support during this time.

To assist this centre I would support the heart chakra with some of the treatments that bring a higher vibration of love. Many gems and crystals bring these qualities because they act as amplifiers. For example consider rhodochrosite, which come in a variety of shades of pink to red. Melody explains in *Love is in the Earth* that this gem brings a strong vibration of love combined with healing energies for the Mother Earth. It balances, attunes and expands awareness bringing calm emotions and clarity of mind. Pink coral or pink carnelian both amplify love. Each or all of these stones used in combination with the heart chakra will assist in providing the safe protected environment the patient needs in order to work with the energies of unconditional love.

I would also look to the Pacific Sea essences that combine the quality of the element 'seawater' with a variety of plant and animal life. Sabina Pettitt gives a wealth of information on each of these remedies including the associated signature, challenges, key words and affirmations, each of which may be invaluable when included in radionic practice. These essences are gentle in their action and ideally suited to the extended centres. Many are indicated for use with the sacral chakra, which is the centre through which we initially start to learn to work with others. For the heart chakra to move out to the unconditional love centre consider *Surfgrass, Barnacle, Diatoms, Sea Palm* or *Dolphin*.

The third eye centre
Vision

Civilisation has been shaped not only by the might of the sword but by kings and princes, writers, orators, philosophers, scientists, architects, artists and musicians. Many of those who made their mark had insight and inspiration beyond the present circumstances and were able to reach further into the future with the consequence of their thoughts and actions. Music, art and literature delights us but certain names from earlier centuries offer mankind much more than entertainment.

Those men who were inspired to encourage the building of the great cathedrals of Europe wanted to create a heaven on earth, a place that would last forever. Their work stands as testimony to the mediaeval mind and its conviction of a life hereafter. John Bunyan had a vision of religious piety that was embraced by the English speaking world for 250 years. The political dream of Machiavelli, the vision of Joan of Arc, Thomas Moore's Utopia, Martin Luther and the Protestant Reformation: all saw further than the world that immediately surrounded them.

In the last century we have those who have fought for causes which have an immediate impact on our lives. Emily Pankhurst and the suffragette movement gained the vote for the women of England. Marie Stopes pioneered birth control. Albert Schweitzer became a symbol of colonialism with a human face.

Here we do well to consider Dr Edward Bach. He may not spring to mind as the most obvious choice for qualities of vision, but as healers we owe him an enormous debt. In the *Collected Writings of Edward Bach* there is a wealth of information. Ridiculed by his profession for turning his back on conventional medical practice this was a man who pursued a course which has resulted in the enormous outburst of flower essences which are now available to people world-wide. During the First World War he had been responsible for a ward of four hundred wounded men. As they slowly recovered he was able to observe the wide range of emotions which were suffered and which he noticed had great influence on the healing process. Before the use of antibiotics and other modern medicines, recovery and rehabilitation was a lengthy process. Anxieties, discontent, fears and uncertainties were shared by most of the patients and it was these that Dr Bach wished to address.

He was convinced that it was better to heal the outlook for the patient and that if a mother had the means within her hands to improve the mood of the sick child physical symptoms would lessen. This was the vision that drove him to develop his essences, treating the country people generously and devising the system from which all flower, gem and animal essences result today.

The twentieth century has seen a struggle for Indian independence with Mahatma Ghandi, a change in politics in South Africa with Nelson Mandela, and Lech Walensa and the Solidarity movement in Poland in the 1980s. Vaclav Havel with the Charter 77 movement stood publicly against the communist regime in Czechoslovakia. Martin Luther King stood up for equality and racial tolerance in the United States of America. Two names stand out from Soviet Russia: Andrei Sakharov for his strong anti-nuclear lead and Alexander Solzhenitsyn for exposing the repressive nature of the Soviet regime. I believe each showed qualities of third eye vision.

Finally there is the Dalai Lama. For almost half a century he has kept the spirit of Tibet alive maintaining respect and integrity as a religious leader in exile. He is a constant thorn in the side of the Chinese who occupy Tibet, and Tibetan Buddhism is alive and well and embraced by greater numbers world-wide than ever before.

Where are the common threads? Each one of these people sees further than their own personal life. All set their minds on greater things for the good of mankind. Often, but not always, their own needs are suppressed by the greater goal. Difficult circumstances are turned into challenging situations. The dross of life is turned into gold.

We may not think that these high ideals have too much to do with our everyday work. Yet each of us has the glimmer of opportunities here and there in life and the third eye energies ask us to think about what we do with opportunity, what will we make of our vision?

I find it almost impossible to isolate particular instances in practice when I am asked to assist third eye energies. There is still much work to be done on my part. Perhaps those who are working with this chakra no longer need radionic help; probably I am not ready to treat them. Certainly I do not have the clarity myself to see what I am doing in this area. I know that developing qualities of watchfulness, observation and detachment from given situations engages the brow and crown chakras and provides the stillness needed to make wise or measured decisions. I hope at some point in the future I will gain an understanding of this centre. I feel whenever I use 'Gold' as a treatment there is almost certainly a link with this energy. Other treatments that may give a clue include words like 'awareness, clarity, understanding and justice'.

The alta major

Here we have the eighth chakra on the radionic analysis sheet. It is wrong to think of it as a new extended centre, unless we consider it 'extending' in terms of our own personal awareness. This is a very, very old chakra. Probably it is the original chakra that came before all others when all that concerned the living creature was survival. Survival is not really a major issue now for most of us in the Western world. We know where the next meal is coming from, we have a roof over our heads, and we are not living on our wits!

The alta major is our 'early warning' system. I believe it can override the major chakra system in times of emergency so that the physical body can step up a gear or move into an altered dimension. There are times when we do not have time to think, we just have to act. That is when alta major energy emerges. By treating the alta major and allowing it to function freely we facilitate a greater degree of self-healing and access energies which resonate with the earth. This is why the alta major responds so very well to flower, gem or animal essences. Within each is a powerful devic energy and this is the energy of the planet, the resonance of life on earth, the old energy that has been denied, overridden and negated so often in the name of civilisation or progress.

Working with the alta major demands that we look at a variety of aspects. Starting at a physical level there is the base of the skull and the delicate balance of the cervical vertebrae. A whiplash injury will almost always result in shock to the alta major. This is the point where the upper portion of the spinal cord enters the brain; here too are the cerebellum and brain stem. This is the oldest part of the brain that evolved over 500 million years ago, sometimes known as the reptilian brain. It is made up of all the nerves from the spinal column as they link into the brain. Also in this area is the carotid body which maintains the oxygen content in the blood and helps to regulate breathing.

Key issues of the alta major are balance, duality, instinctive reaction, intuition, spontaneity and improvisation.

The exoteric qualities of this centre are that it provides a balancing mechanism for the body through breathing, control of blood pressure and emotional response; it also provides the body with an ability to cope with perceived danger, because it links us back to earlier survival skills needed by man or animal living in the wild. It is the healthy alta major that stops us from states of panic and gives us the ability to act promptly in emergency. It also acts as counsellor to the etheric, a wonderful bonus being that once it is functioning well patients start to know what is right for them, for example what foods to eat, what supplements to take and what lifestyle changes to make. Instinct starts to play a valuable role in their life.

Esoteric qualities of the alta major are that it aligns us with the elemental worlds. There is the possibility of a deep attunement with the kingdoms of nature and the element 'wet earth' (given by Ruth White). When treating animal patients this chakra is found to be of immense importance. Both cat and dog are nearer to their wild ancestors than humans, and their fine-tuned response to energetic changes within the earth's magnetic field shows us what we, as humans, with our material lifestyle, have lost. When the hairs stand up on your dog or cat's neck with fear you are seeing the outward manifestation of alta major energy!

Negative emotional response within this chakra will be fear, anxiety, worry, inability to cope, inability to listen and trust instinct, being out of touch with issues relating to the nature kingdoms, inability to care for oneself resulting in confusion and bewilderment and in a badly blocked alta major you may find blind panic. Asking the simple question of a patient 'how do you feel you cope in an emergency?' will give an initial clue to the state of this chakra. If the alta major is found to be blocked or sluggish simple suggestions such as walking barefoot in the garden, visiting parks or seashore, or taking up gardening on a regular basis combined with radionic treatment will help to initiate change.

Positive responses within the alta major are trust, both in oneself and in the universe, fast response in an emergency, an awareness of the rhythms of nature and an ability to draw strength from the kingdoms of nature. There is an ability to take care of oneself by just knowing what is beneficial for the body.

Because the alta major is attuned to devic energies it responds particularly well to flower remedies and gems; the choice is great and I offer some of my favourites. I have used those listed below repeatedly with this centre:

- Bach *Scleranthus* is used for its balancing qualities. It addresses the issues of duality within this centre, whether manifesting at a physical level in areas of ill health or an unconscious level as confusion with the experience of life on earth.
- Bach *Rock Rose* is for panic states. It is the remedy for extreme states in particular terror. It may be used alone or in combination as *Rescue Remedy* which includes four other Bach remedies *Star of Bethlehem, Impatiens, Cherry Plum* and *Clematis*.
- Bailey *Foxglove* is for confusion. It restores calm so that the

patient knows how to care for himself, encouraging him to worry less. It restores that contact within that allows the alta major to become the counsellor to the physical body.

• *Terra* is an emergency combination from Bloesem Remedies of the Netherlands. It is a wonderful earthing balancing remedy for use in extreme situations.

• Boji or Pop stones come in pairs. They can be male, female or androgenous. They have great grounding properties and enhance the telepathic link between man and plants and man and animals. They balance the subtle energies and are sometimes found with rainbows on the dark brown surface. Holding a pair in your hands often brings an awareness of the depth and mystery buried deep within the earth. I find most people have a very positive response to Bojis!

• Jasper, in particular tan, red, brown or green, is a sustaining balancing stone. It offers a high degree of protection and keeps one well grounded.

• Tiger's eye, especially the type that looks like a humbug, is said to bring together the energies of sand and sunlight on the earth. This is the stone to help one become aware of one's personal needs.

To conclude this work on the chakras I must add that others are working with extended centres. I am certain that we will hear more from them in the future and that we have much to learn. I feel that my personal journey of exploration of this topic is just beginning. Some healers find centres extending above the crown chakra, while others have centres positioned elsewhere in the aura. It is exciting to look forward to what we are about to discover and embrace. I hope that, in the spirit of discovery, I can look to a future where I can embrace a little more understanding of our own subtle anatomy.

Bibliography

Bach, Edward (1994) *Collected Writings*. Ashgrove Press, Bath.
Bailey, Alice (1953) *Esoteric Healing*. Lucis Publishing Company, London.
Bailey, Arthur (1996) *The Bailey Flower Essence Handbook*. Bailey Flower Essences, Ilkley.
Dawkins, Peter (1995) *The Grail Kingdom of Europe*. The Francis Bacon Research Trust, Warwickshire.
Durckheim, Karlfried Graf (1962) *Hara the Vital Centre of Man*. George, Allen and Unwin,

London.
Kaminski, Patricia & Katz, Richard (1986) *Flower Essence Repertory*. The Flower Essence Society, Nevada City.
Melody (1995) *Love is in the Earth*. Earth-Love Publishing House, Wheat Ridge, CO.
Pettitt, Sabina (1993) *Energy Medicine, Healing from the Kingdoms of Nature*. Pacific Essences, Victoria, Canada.
Tansley, David (1972) *Radionics and the Subtle Anatomy of Man*. CW Daniels, Saffron Walden.
White, Ruth (1993) *Working with Your Chakras*. Judy Piatkus, London.

Flower Remedy information:

Aquarius Flower Remedies catalogue available from 01626 852309 or 01434 606286 (UK)
Bloesom Remedies of the Netherlands available from The Flower Essence Repertoire 01428 741572 (UK)

Ina Manzoor

<table>
<tr><td>7</td><td>*Radionic Rates*</td></tr>
</table>

'All things are numbers'

Pythagoras (c. 580-500 B.C.)

'Whatever there is in all the three worlds, which are possessed of moving and non-moving beings, cannot exist as apart from the 'Ganita'' (Sanskrit: calculation).

Mahavira

Albert Einstein said that God does not play dice, and, indeed, there is order in the universe. The building blocks of creation are not a meaningless jumble, assembled at random – order emerges from apparent chaos. If there were no order, scientists would never be able to unravel any of the mysteries governing our existence. And this order is based on numbers.

In ancient times, religion and science had close ties – philosophers were at the same time scientists. Pythagoras, the famous Greek mathematician and philosopher of the 6th century B.C., was the founder of a college of higher learning that was known in all the civilised world as the central assembly of the learned of Europe. To him we have to look to appreciate the science of numbers in their mathematical and esoteric nature.

Pythagoras taught what he himself had learnt from the Hierophants of Egypt, the Oracle of Delphi, the Brahmins of India and the Kabbalah of Hebrew Rabbis. He is known for his 'Harmony of the Spheres' and his doctrine of the 'Transmigration of the Soul' – today's reincarnation – but much more important for the history of philosophy and science was his doctrine that 'all things are numbers'.

The select members of his Pythagorean brotherhood had to obey strict rules. On entering the brotherhood, they had to pass a five-year period in silent contemplation. They were also required to be celibate, vegetarians and were not permitted to record in writing any of the secret tenets they were to become familiarised with. This is why we are today dependent on whatever information was handed down from Pythagoras' followers or critics after his death. Since we are particularly concerned with the eso-teric interpretation of numbers, it might be suggested that, when looking for publications dealing with this subject, to make sure that the authors have based their work on Pythagoras.

When dealing with the interpretation of numbers, I do not rely on so-called numerology books. Although they were part of my early interests, I soon realised that the study, which leads you to keenly work out dates of birth and names, can easily become obsessive, particularly if you try to re-arrange your life around numbers! This phase of my life was a thing of the past when I came into radionics – but, numbers came back into my life, this time on a higher level. Dr Aubrey Westlake said in one of his addresses 'In ordinary scientific work the moral character of the experi-menter does not, as a general rule, affect his experiment or its results, but in work with the supersensory forces it matters very much what he is in himself and the motives, conscious and unconscious, which underlie his activities.'

Personally I think that we are having proof nowadays that even other experimenters should be of excellent character and that their motives mat-ter very much. In recent times, it seems that a distinct and ever widening split is developing between the spiritually oriented and some branches of the scientific establishment – touching here on the subject of the bio-technology dramas that are being enacted regarding gene manipulation etc. Instead of being philanthropic as the Pythagorean brotherhood was, today's industry is mostly governed by greed and unconcern and this is an infallible recipe for disaster.

Einstein was a scientist who admitted that his profoundest insights came through intuition – in his words 'no problem can be solved from the same consciousness that created it' and there are even today many who still respect and believe in divine guidance, particularly in the field of cosmology. So at least this is good news.

Exactly a year ago, in February 2002, I watched a 'Horizon' programme on 'Parallel Universes'. It was a summary of scientific work carried out over a long period of time and dealt with scientists continuing from where

Einstein had left off. As cosmologists were struggling to match Einstein's 'Theory of Everything' with their newly developed 'String Theory' which showed that the universe really consisted of very fine strings and was being played like a harmony, they discovered 'Parallel Universes'.

There were apparently also a number of existing dimensions in the universe. Einstein had suggested that 'time' should be the 4th dimension (we live in three dimensions). Some scientists said that space should be the 5th dimension. According to the 'String Theory' however there should have been a total of 10 dimensions (nine spatial and one time-oriented). Then it was found that there were 11* dimensions in total! Again, everything is based on numbers. Next, they discovered that all the matter of the universe was connected to one vast structure – a membrane. They now formulated the 'M-Theory' (Membrane Theory). And, yes, you can imagine that I was thrilled to hear the physicists who were interviewed commenting that the 'M' could easily stand for Mother, Magic, Mystery, Majesty … !

It was even more interesting to hear what methods they used to arrive at their conclusions. At one time, three of the pioneers of the 'M-Theory' were free-associating together while sitting on a train to London, asking questions, finishing each other's sentences – they simply let their imagination roam freely. Within the space of an hour, they had solved the 'Singularity' puzzle, which had obstructed the equations for the 'Big Bang' for such a long time. On another occasion, a young female scientist was on an indoor leisure climbing pursuit and in the midst of that had an extremely important brainwave which dissolved the problem of 'Super Gravity'.

Letting intuition take over, I find, brings the most gratifying results. It is an intentional and non-prejudicial expansion of consciousness, which can apparently cope with any problem. And this extends of course also to the field of radionics where we have to, mostly, if not all of the time, let ourselves be guided by intuition. Of course we must not deny logic and intelligent reasoning. In fact, it is greatly to our advantage if we allow both left and right brain hemispheres to play an equal role.

In preparing for this chapter, I have just discovered a most interesting fact. I wrote down, on a sheet of paper, a selection of interesting treatment rates as they came to mind, which I was then planning to explain and weave into the text. Later, while consulting Mme Blavatsky's *The Secret*

---

* '11' is one of the two master numbers (11 and 22). It stands for equilibrium and is a symbol of attainment. The numbers of 11 and 22 vibrate to all the 7 tones of the musical scale. They also respond to the entire planetary octave.

Doctrine, I came across what she termed 'the famous numerals 13514' and their anagram 31415.

In Vol. I, p.114 of *The Secret Doctrine* we read that 'the Kabbalistic circle of the Elôhîm reveals, when the letters of the Hebrew word for Alhim or Elôhîm are numerically read, the famous numerals 13514, or by anagram 31415 – the astronomical π (pi) number, or the hidden meaning of Dhyâni-Buddhas, of the Gebers, the Gibbôrîm, the Kabiri, and the Elôhîm (*the Sons of Light and Life),* all signifying "great men", "Titans", "Heavenly Men" and, on earth, the "giants".'

She also mentions (*The Secret Doctrine* Vol. 1, p. 114,) that the same numerals, expressed in geometrical form as $\triangle$ I $\square$ I $\star$, which equals of course 31415, are inscribed in the trans-Himâlayan Chakra. These sets of figures appear in various parts of *The Secret Doctrine* and their esoteric importance is stressed every time without fail. In Stanza IV of the Secret Book of Dzyan (*The Secret Doctrine* Vol. 1, p. 89), the same is repeated '... then the three, the one, the four, the one, the five – the twice seven' (3+1+4+1+5 = 14, or 2x7). 'And these are the essences, the flames, the elements, the builders, the numbers, the Arûpa (*formless),* the Rûpa (*with form),* and the force of Divine Man – the sum total. And from the Divine Man emanated the forms, the sparks, the sacred animals, and the Messengers of the Sacred Fathers ...'

Blavatsky then explains: 'This relates to the sacred Science of the Numerals; so sacred, indeed, and so important in the study of Occultism that the subject can hardly be skimmed, even in such a large work as the present. It is on the Hierarchies and correct numbers of these Beings, invisible (to us) except upon very rare occasions, that the mystery of the whole Universe is built ...' (*The Secret Doctrine* Vol. 1, p. 89).

I couldn't believe what I had just read. In front of me I had the sheet with the treatment rates and among them the rate for congestion of the etheric body: 13514, the very set of numerals gone into with such emphasis. Then I found its anagram in the rate for brain integration: 314151! What more proof do we need that through radionic treatment we are purifying our physical and subtle bodies and balancing our brains to become spiritual 'giants'? Although the rate for brain integration (harmonising both hemispheres) has one more digit, the figure one, in addition to the 31415, this is only because the meaning of this '1' is: to harmonise; it is the command for the 31415 to be harmonised!

This same harmonising '1' occurs in many other rates, as e.g. in the rate for the 10th chakra, which is 06181. This 10th chakra, when functioning correctly, ensures harmony between micro and macrocosm, powerful interaction and flowing of energies. '6', which represents, among other things, the macrocosm in its perfection, is harmonised with the divine, most perfect number 1, which is God manifest, having emerged from 0, the unmanifest. The number 8 in this rate, stands for the intellect, perfect rhythm and the plus as well as minus effect of all the elements of the micro and macrocosm.

At this point, I want to mention that I have never 'constructed' a rate with a view to obtaining certain results. I simply dowse the numbers with the pendulum and only later, on completion of the rate, do I contemplate its meaning. I let the rate speak to me. This language of the rates is, however, a reciprocal process. Not only do the rates speak to us if we let them, but also are we using this language to communicate with the subtle realms, to pass on our requests, our demands. In Atlantean times, it is said that the magic of the priests consisted in addressing their gods in their own language 'The speech of the men of the earth cannot reach the Lords...' and the ancient priests' language was explained thus: 'It is composed of sounds, not words, of sounds, numbers and figures.' The same also applies to the mantras, yantras, tantras and chanting sounds of Hindu lore.

I was pleased to learn that Ruth Drown had used the same method for rate making. She also examined the rates only after she had made them by drawing on kabbalistic interpretations (see Chapter 2). This is the only way one can understand higher truths. The mind has to be unprejudiced and open to instruction.

Examining her atomic element and cranial nerve rates, however, I find that Ruth Drown had for this purpose, at least to some extent, used a system of progression based on rationale. The cranial nerves are all prefixed by 10.1 and end in 44. The numbers in between have a vertical progression. I explained to myself the reason for the 10.1 and 44 as follows. 10.1 is the rate for the skin; 44 the rate for the medulla oblongata. Since all the nerves enter the spine, and therefore the body, via the medulla oblongata, it stands to reason that 44 was used for all the cranial nerves. Also 10.1, the skin, has nerve endings which receive from and send sensations back to the cranial nerves and the brain. An orderly system was produced, but most probably prompted by the pendulum and intuition. Where the vertical progression is concerned, I could be wrong, maybe she was not even aware that this was happening. The reason why I say this, will be made clear when I explain the following.

When I produced the rates for the various kingdoms, which are meant to harmonise us with them, I didn't realise what the outcome would be:

Elemental kingdom	247985
Mineral kingdom	463717
Vegetable kingdom	456167
Animal kingdom	375616
Humankind	275612

I have intentionally staggered the rates in the above table so that one can see more clearly an emerging vertical pattern. Leaving aside the elemental kingdom for now, we look at the four kingdoms below. The rate for the mineral kingdom, which is inanimate, has nothing in common with the animate kingdoms except a similar pattern at the end, the 717 – the next two kingdoms have 616. But, strictly speaking, it is not really correct to say that there is nothing these four kingdoms have in common, they do – the '1', the divine spark, which resides in everything.

Vegetable and animal kingdoms and humankind have one core in common and that is 561. The animal kingdom and humankind have, in 7561, one further digit in common – they are capable of expressing the '7', love and harmony, along with their life energy '5'! It was strange that I noticed these relationships only at a much later date. Taking up the elemental kingdom rate now, we are given the following insights:

247985	elemental kingdom
765624	co-operation between low/middle/high self (Kahuna)
479524	electro-magnetic balance
8479	nerve tissue

I find the above extremely revealing when examined. The Kahuna rate, we can separate into '76' as representing the high self (76 is also the rate for the fire element which is divine), '56' as the middle self (refer to the rate for humankind with 56 as the core), and '24' for the low self, the unihipili (24 is also in the rate for the elemental kingdom and the unihipili belongs to the elemental realm!).

479524, the electro-magnetic balance, has 479 and 24 in common with the elemental kingdom, and the nerve tissue along which our electro-magnetic life energy flows contains 479 as well as the 8 of the elemental kingdom.

The '8' in nerve tissue, 8479, is representative of universal conscious-ness, the connecting link with the essence, the Christ plane, the healing plane. It is through this connection that we receive healing via our nervous system, that we are connected with the Anandamaya kosha, the sheath of bliss! The elemental kingdom rate also has this '8' and in Kahuna lore it is said that if we are not in harmony with our unihipili, it will block our connection with the high self – it will block our '8'.

Some years ago, Gordon Smith gave me a few sheets with interpreta-tions of numbers channelled by a Victoria Bridges. Although I have never found out who she is (I think she may be American), I respect her highly, because using her information to interpret my rates, I have received con-firmation that as healers who use the sacred system of numbers, we are all tuned into the One Source.

When we look at the kingdom rates and interpret them with Victoria's channelled information, we find that the '5', which since ancient times has been called the cordialis, the heart of the decade, is with her the 'door' that allows the universal force to enter. '5' has always been the number of manifestation, the root cause of life energy in all its expressions, but in her document this is expressed in words that open up further vistas. Since Victoria is apparently working with the mentally handicapped, it is explained to her that with the vibrations of the '5', all bodily systems, including the mental, blend together to operate as one. A blending of these systems is very much needed with the mentally handicapped and the '5' is the 'core of being', the cordialis.

Going to the next digit in the kingdom rates which they hold in com-mon, '6', her interpretation is that it is a command number with its own forcefulness, a producer of thought, it is a backbone. Interesting, because even the mineral kingdom has a number 6 and thought begets feelings. If we look at Mother Earth as a sentient being, how can earth and rocks not be part of that sensorium?

Since we have looked at the number '5', there is another interesting observation I made some years ago in relation to this (see Table on next page). At the time when my children were still very young, the only quiet time I had to myself was when they were asleep, so I used to meditate sitting upright in bed just prior to falling asleep myself. I had been doing

Radionic Rates

this regularly until one day, when I suddenly felt nauseous on going into the silence. The deeper I went into my heart as it were, the worse it felt, so I had to give up. Of course, at the time, I couldn't understand what had happened and the puzzle was only solved when I discovered much later on, radionically, that my subtle bodies had not been aligned properly with my physical body.

ear �⟩ ear

7910.55	alignment subtle bodies/physical
7910.	semicircular ducts/canals in ear
7910.8	emotional maturity
910.75	neck
57910.	auto-intoxication
55	right atrium
2555	ventricles of heart

I think the diagram and the adjacent rates tell their own story. The semicircular ducts/canals in the ear are the organs of balance – their rate is 7910. (in my book on physiology by McNaught, they do not differentiate between ducts and canals). The right atrium in the heart is 55, the ventricles 2555. When you connect the ears and complete the connection down to the heart, we get the rate 7910.55 for subtle bodies/physical body alignment. If I had already been trained in radionics at that time, it would have been easy to rectify the problem!

The other rates that I gave with the diagram, for autointoxication, neck, and emotional maturity – due to their similarity of vibration with the alignment rate – present an obvious conclusion as to what else could have needed treatment. An interesting aside: not so long ago, I listened to a programme on BBC Radio 4, in which a heart surgeon spoke and he said that when they operate and sometimes touch a certain part of the heart – the Bundle of His – they jokingly say that they have touched the soul of the patient! They are right of course, because the Bundle of His, which is in the right ventricle, is precisely the seat of the Monad.

The use of numbers in magic and healing goes back a long time, spans all the continents and was common to nearly all ancient religious systems. We know from the Western and Indian occult systems of the use of magic squares which are ascribed to the planets and subdivided into 9 smaller squares containing numbers which, when added up, whether horizontally, vertically or diagonally, always show the same result. Just to give an

113

example of a square, the one for Saturn is reproduced below.

When added up, the sum remains always 15. This particular planetary talisman is said to protect its bearer against danger of death from

4	9	2
3	5	7
8	1	6

apoplexy, cancer, poisoning, or violence. The remarkable coincidence, if one can call it this, is that the rate for the cancer virus is 51, and cancer cells are 0510.510. The fact that rates are sometimes like anagrams, does not matter (we saw that earlier on from the comments in *The Secret Doctrine*), the same energies are involved and the different arrangement simply allows us further insights.

The rates for the congestion of the astral body, 91915, and the mental body, 88815, have both a '15' in them and we know that these two bodies are very often the cause of disease. If you look again at the above square, you can even see the figures 9, 5, 1 in one vertical line. Looking at my radionic rate for harmonising with the planet Saturn, which is 65432, I can see that these numbers are also contained in the square in a certain order. Saturn is a hard taskmaster, but he does lead us back onto the right track, that's why we have to retrace our steps sometimes: from 6 to 5 to 4 to 3 to 2!

Many years ago, I had occasion to experience the effectiveness of such magic squares on myself. I was very young and lived for about three years in the Indian subcontinent, when I suffered a prolonged bout of sleepless nights. I would go to sleep all right, but then wake up very soon afterwards through the pounding of my own heart. When I mentioned this to one of my Muslim friends, she decided to take me to someone who could help. She was convinced that it wasn't a case for the doctor, luckily. After all, this was my first introduction to healing with numbers!

I was taken to a remote area, to the only brick-built house amidst tin huts, in a shantytown. The house was also very simple and had mud floors. A woman greeted us and when my friend explained my problem, she got busy preparing a long black thread. It had to be measured according to my height, then it was cut, folded a few times and the ends secured with tight knots. I had to measure this three or four-fold thread against the span of my hand – it was about 7½ spans long. Then the woman took the thread, rolled it into her cupped hands and mumbled a few words over them – I presume they were prayers – whereupon I had to measure the thread again. I had to do this three times and every time the thread had been quite a bit shorter. This was a sign for the woman that all was not well on the psychic front.

When we finally left, I was equipped with three pieces of paper that had squares and numbers in Arabic written on them in black ink, two small, flat, earthenware dishes and a few folded-up pieces of paper, secured with thread. My instructions were that, for three days, before going to sleep at night, I had to place one of the papers with the squares in a glass of water, shake it so that the writing dissolved and then drink the water. From the very first night on, I slept very soundly. I also had to report back to the woman what I dreamt in those three nights – they were the clues as to what had gone wrong.

My further instructions were to place one of the earthenware dishes by the seaside, where the waves could wash over it, and the other one by a river. They both had numbers written on them. Of the small folded-up papers, one was to be hung from a sweet-fruit tree and one was to be buried underneath it. Another had to be burnt. It was obvious that the healing intent was to harmonise me with all the elements. Different from our radionic treatment – but effective!

The numbers orthodox Muslim healers use are representative of certain Sûrahs from the Qurân. The Qurân is like a healing manual to them. Even the short protective prayer of 'Bism'illah er Rahman er Rahim' (In the name of the merciful and compassionate God) is translated into '786' and every believing Muslim will place this figure at the head of any letter to be written or utter the words before beginning any important task.

In Burma the healers who use healing by numbers are called 'Isle makers' – the isle being the equivalent to the magic square. Nowadays, of course, radionics, as we know it, has already penetrated Asian countries, but the old methods will continue to exist side by side with the new. Their instruments based on the same principles may be unsophisticated, less well made and inexpensive, but nevertheless equally effective, especially as the practitioners are able to draw on a vast amount of ayurvedic or homeopathic experience.

Radionics is the modern equivalent to ancient magic. In this technical age, the human mind is attracted to technical innovations: computers, electronics, moving visual displays, and radionic instruments change with the times. We have to keep our enthusiasm up – whatever 'turns us on', will make us better healers. But having said that, we wouldn't actually need any expensive equipment in order to be effective, it depends entirely on our own individual belief system. Frank Moody, a very successful Australian radiesthesist and homeopath, wrote in the June 1980 *Journal of the British Society of Dowsers* that he had helped many people by broadcasting (without an instrument) Anchor 0400 (grey) stranded cotton to balance their chakras! He wasn't joking.

Now a small example of how, through contemplation and inspiration, symbols and numbers can lead to revelations.

The triangle on the left represents the sacred 'Tetraktys' of Pythagoras, his name for the decad.

$$4 + 3 + 2 + 1 = 10$$

Tetraktys means approximately 'fourness' and this reminds us of course immediately of the pyramids with triangular sides on a square base, which are in themselves ancient sacred symbols.

In its symbolism, this triangle shows the number 4 as its base, which stands for created matter and therefore here also for Man. Man, in reaching upwards to spiritual heights (symbolised by the upright triangle, whereas divinity's descending power is shown by a downward pointing triangle – the two then forming the six-pointed star), goes through the levels of 3 and 2 to reach his status of 1 – as one with divinity, in self-realisation. Created Man, as the 4, has to be raised and united on all 3 levels of body, mind and soul, in order to find balance, 2, but must overcome even this 2, for it represents duality. Only when he has gone beyond duality, will Man return to his origin in full knowledge of himself as heir and son of the Creator.

A basic list of the meanings of numbers can be given herewith, but it is just a general guideline, for this listing can be extended by everything that one can find in the many publications on numbers and their esoteric meanings. Every author seems to be specialising in a different application of the numbers. What we are doing in effect, by collecting the various interpretations and, if we are so inclined, experimenting with them in our daily treatments, is creating a computerised source of information in our subconscious. This subconscious computer spills out at the right moment, in a given situation, and on being presented with a keyed-in problem, the appropriate information leading to the solution. What I am trying to say by this is that one and the same number will never be interpreted in the same manner – it depends entirely on the concept or situation under review.

This is just a brief outline. Also, it must not be forgotten that every positive aspect has a negative opposite, therefore when interpreting rates for negative conditions, the meaning has to be changed accordingly.

No.	Planet	Possible Interpretations
0	Pluto	the unmanifest; the circle in which all things live and move and have their being; the origin of everything; the largest and the smallest (e.g. cosmos v. atom)
1	Neptune	God made manifest; the Monad; omnipotence; unifying, harmonising principle; will-power; yang number
2	Uranus	duality; balance; electricity/magnetism; opposites; yin; collect
3	Saturn	trinity; growth; body/soul/spirit; beginning/middle/end; alchemic: sulphur/quicksilver/salt; past/present/future; man/wife/child; creation/sustenance/dissolution
4	Jupiter	created matter; earth; order; justice; 4 basic elements; the number with which everything in the micro and macrocosm has been created
5	Mars	the number of Man; the human microcosm; everything that expresses active power including magic; activity; the universal quintessence which expands in all directions and creates matter; the heart of all matter and the root cause of life energy in all its expressions
6	Sun	perfect macrocosm; light and life; equanimity; human/ divine interrelationship; spiritual and material; preparation through purification; command; producer of thought
7	Venus	love; harmony; fertility; symbol of incarnation; descent of the divine into matter (the triangle enters the square)

8	Mercury	*mental body; Christ plane (healing plane); resurrection; regeneration; perfect rhythm; intellect; plus and minus effect of the elements in the micro and macrocosm*
9	Moon	*astral body; astral plane; movement; life in its subtle form; perfection; completion*
10	Vulcan	*perfect expression of spirit through flesh; mastery; materialisation/manifestation; return to unity; divine support*

The above correspondence of planets and numbers is based on the ancient Egyptian system – there are of course other methods of relating numbers to planets, but, whichever system is used, it is best to adhere to only one to avoid confusion.

If we look at the rate for flexibility, 35821, referring also to the planets, we find the following:–

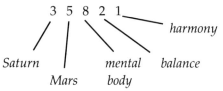

To obtain flexibility of mind and body,

3 – Saturn has to be well aspected, otherwise there is heaviness, lethargy (the corresponding metal is lead);

    5 – Mars, too, must be harmonised to avoid aggression, rigidity of attitude, unwillingness to yield;

    8 – which is the mental plane, must be tuned to healing;

    2 – balanced flow of electro-magnetic energies is required; as well as

    1 – harmony with the Divine,

and these are exactly the results we get by applying this particular rate.

By making a recognition rate, the planets can even help us find physical, emotional and mental traits in patients, based on either long-term or temporary conditions. All that is needed is a brief guide to astrology, giving the positive and negative effects of the planets with which to interpret the rate. When making the recognition rate for your patient, just hold the request in mind, ask how many digits are required and then select the numbers by pendulum. The numbers can be interpreted by using a combination of planets and pure number meanings – just let your subconscious mind sort this out and throw it to the surface. Call it brainstorming, free-associating, anything you like. The result is what counts.

For one of our workshops, I interpreted a recognition rate for a patient I did not know. The rate was made for this purpose by the patient's radionic practitioner. It was quite an interesting exercise. The rate was 423375. Because it had to do with a dis-ease, the interpretation was of course geared towards that effect. Here is what came to me:

I noticed that there were two 3's in the rate, which made me think of 'eyes 331' although the '1' was missing, but when the rate has only 6 digits, one cannot expect to get complete rates. To me, the combination of 37 means a flowing of energy and I thought the flow of energy to the eyes must somehow be affected due to too much activity, '5'. The rate for the shoulders is 753 and this is also hidden in that rate. The kidneys, 23, must be affected and because '3' relates to Saturn, there could be rheumatic problems, especially if the person does not drink enough to flush out the kidneys. The figure '4' I took to be nature (as in creation) and together with the number '2' alongside it, I thought there was an imbalance somewhere – too much work and no play, not enough nature and oxygen. It turned out that the patient was a jeweller, sitting bent over his worktable 14 hours a day in artificial light! This is just an example of what can be done with recognition rates.

Here is another, quite different, example of what the rates can teach us. I had made the command rate 'give 66632'. Looking at it, I felt a bit puzzled, three 6's? The number of the Beast? I double-checked with the pendulum – it did not budge, so I pondered over it. A single figure of '6' is light and life, and it is also a command. Then it came to me: three commands of '6' for 3 levels of being (body – mind – spirit) and '2' for the +/– polarities on these 3 levels to make sure whatever is projected reaches on whichever level it is needed.

When looking up the various meanings for '6', I noticed of course also the 'producer of thoughts', which took me back to my initial surprise about the three 6's. I knew of no rate that had these. The solar plexus is '66' and is of course also considered to be a second 'brain' from which gut feelings arise, and feelings and thoughts follow each other closely.

I suddenly decided to make a rate for the collective unconscious and it came to 476662. This left me even more puzzled, I wondered where this would lead. I had had a rate for many years for communion with God = CWG: 67476. I used this sometimes when patients were too negative and I thought they could do with a bit of connecting with their maker. I could see, of course, that in the collective unconscious rate was 476, but also the 666, and a 2. Suddenly it clicked and I knew exactly what the rate was trying to tell me. Humanity, in its collective unconscious has both the divine and evil tendencies, which are held in balance. It is up to us to overcome the tempter (producer of negative thoughts and promptings) and to choose the divine!

If there should be any radionic practitioners out there who are agnostics and think I am talking too much about God here, be reassured, Marcus Aurelius, himself an agnostic, said 'If there is a God, believe in him, if there is not, be god-like.' We can still be effective practitioners provided we see no evil, hear no evil, speak no evil, and do not do unto others what we would not have them do unto us. Sathya Sai Baba said not so long ago: 'Even if you do not believe in God and you do not believe in me, develop self-confidence, believe in yourself and act according to your conscience!'

Finally, I want to briefly give a few relevant examples of rates which were not made at the same time and therefore could not have been influenced by the conscious mind, yet contain marked similarities because of similar vibrational energies.

4410.68	expansion of consciousness	25547	remove mental blockage
4410.	nerve synapses	547	pituitary gland
410.1131	restore divine pattern of body cells	886810.6	Imperil
48111	efficiency	57810.6	clear psychological blockage
4822	body cells	51810.653	free from possessing entity
147358	orthopolos	327	lymph glands
14727	sleep	0327	Kali Mur (tissue salt)
23175	deep healing sleep	10.7795	histamine
175	rejuvenate	77795	forgiveness of self

By looking at the above rates you will be able to recognise their interrelatedness. Kali Mur is a specific for lymph glands – children with too exacting parents may be lacking forgiveness of self and develop conditions with too much histamine in their body – deep healing sleep allows rejuvenation of the whole body – etc. etc.

Through lateral thinking and awareness, one can experience the most significant leaps in consciousness and radionic rates are the tools which have been given to us to achieve this end.

H. T. Hamblin said: 'The secret of effortless achievement is to realise our inner oneness with a power that is not our own.' As you ask so you shall receive – we ask for guidance from the highest Source and we are not denied knowledge.

Bibliography

Bailey A. A. (1977) *A Treatise on Cosmic Fire*. Lucis Publishing Co., New York.

Blavatsky H.P. (1993) *The Secret Doctrine*. Edited by Boris de Zirkoff. The Theosophical Publishing House, Wheaton, IL.

Bosman L. (1974) *The Meaning and Philosophy of Numbers*. Rider, London.

Heline, C. (1991) *Sacred Science of Numbers*. Devorss Publications, Los Angeles, CA.

Russell, P. (2000) *From Science to God*. Peter Russell, Sausalito, CA.

Sepharial (1974) *The Kabala of Numbers*. Newcastle Publishing Co., Hollywood, CA.

Westcott, W. Wynn (1974) *Numbers, Their Occult Power and Mystic Virtues*. Theosophical Publishing House, London.

Sally Higham, Doris Frankish, Linda Fellows

<table>
<tr><td>8</td><td>

Some Practitioners' Experiences of Radionics

</td></tr>
</table>

Three experienced practitioners describe some of their case work below. Their experiences and views are personal and may not reflect the view of the Radionic Association. They do illustrate the many ways that practitioners work and the varied models that they may use to rationalise the situations they are dealing with. These are anecdotal reports, and no claims are made or implied for the cure of serious conditions by means of radionics alone.

Sally Higham

Since becoming qualified as a radionic practitioner in 1962, I find that the instruments and methods of treatment that we now use have largely changed dramatically. For instance in the early '60s the analysis and treatment did not include the chakras or subtle bodies – they were based almost entirely on the Drown and Delawarr rates and methods. This did not in anyway diminish their effectiveness, and it is difficult to assess whether or not the treatment took longer to be effective – but effective it certainly was, as it is now.

Experience has shown me that there are very few patients who do not respond at all, a number improve dramatically, and most of them are helped so much that they come off treatment and can manage without further help, though they may return for some new condition.

One of the first 'successes' that I remember with great delight was a middle aged lady called 'Jane', who suffered from chronic hayfever and hay asthma, so that every summer she was unable to go near her horse or enjoy the summer during the pollen season. I went deeply into the causes of her symptoms (which is the essence of a radionic analysis) and found prenatal shock, a number of toxins including vaccinosis, whooping cough,

German measles and diphtheria; she had a lack of some vitamins, and even her bone marrow, pancreas and thyroid were involved. She needed treatment for all of this, and of course the parasympathetics to balance the histamine imbalance as well as the inevitable inflammation and irritation of the mucous membranes. She responded very quickly that summer and was able to lead a normal outdoor life for the first time in years. Each year in March or April for a few years I would build up her immunity to allergens so that she would be hayfever/asthma free in the summer. One year she suffered from *Aspergillus* fungus infection, so that this had to be cleared as well.

Another case that seemed to be very rewarding was a man of 63 years of age who was crippled with rheumatoid arthritis. From the analysis he appeared to be suffering from a type of TB arthritis, he had a lot of acidity (so I advised him to keep off acid-forming foods as well as wine, cider and Martini); he was deficient in potassium, his kidneys were underactive, and he had psychological conditions of apprehension, frustration and resentment. These causes were all treated, as well as the inflammation in his joints, coupled with appropriate homeopathic and other card remedies. He started to improve almost at once, but it took probably a year to clear the condition. I remember him being in tears of gratitude for the great benefit that radionics had brought to him. That was many years ago, so as I have not heard from him again, I imagine all is well.

On the whole, I suppose I treat more back conditions that anything else. Radionics, with the different types of instruments, can mostly effect adjustments that are necessary in the spine or joints. It is important for the practitioner to ascertain exactly where the trouble lies and treat accordingly, coupled with relaxation being given to the muscles, ligaments and nerves. With the aid of Pegotty instrument for adjustments and the Magneto-Geometric cards as devised by Malcolm Rae we can direct homeopathic or other remedies + colour and/or gems etc. into the areas indicated. Since we began treating through the chakras and subtle bodies, this helps to get things moving very quickly and the Rae Group Treatment card, when given first, removes the 'first layer' of toxins, shock etc. which patients will have accumulated during their life.

As practitioners we never know what the next new case will bring. This recent one seemed unusual. It was a young man in his 30's who is a pilot and came to me complaining of muscle aches in his limbs and lack of energy of some two years' standing, following a fever. He had had malaria very badly. Medical tests told him he was suffering from chronic fatigue and he was given painkillers. In his radionic analysis nearly all his chakras were low in function and three were blocked, but his solar plexus chakra was overactive. They all seemed to be affected by toxins, and in further investigation I found there were dengue fever, malaria, glandular fever, polio, flu, brucellosis and mosquito bite toxins. As a result of being in a cockpit for some time his pituitary gland was affected by cosmic radiowaves and microwaves. All these causes had to be eradicated, as well as his sacro-iliac joint adjusted because of being affected by long times of sitting in the cockpit. There was also a lot of muscle tension in his back, and stress showing up in the adrenals. He has needed treatment for jet lag (which I give to many patients who are flying long distances and this means they can adjust to their new environment at once). This pilot now reports that he has only the occasional aches and pains which makes his job very much easier and more pleasant.

I could go on quoting cases indefinitely after so many years of working in radionics, and when people ask me 'Does it work?' all I can answer is 'Well, I wouldn't still be doing it after 40 years if it didn't'.

It is so rewarding having the kind remarks of patients who have been helped through this treatment after years of suffering from one cause or another.

As will be apparent, we treat patients on every level, mental, emotional and physical-etheric, directing the energies where they are needed. The great thing is that we have the privilege of helping on all levels and this seldom fails.

Dorish Frankish

I used to be a rather cynical journalist with a contempt of anything relating to the New Age, and particularly disliked the sort of therapist I labelled California Girl. She would have long blond hair, speak in a childish, breathy little voice and describe invisible quotation marks in the air with her fingers.

I remember in the 1950s reading about the Black Box court case which was about a radionic instrument that you could use to diagnose illness from just a blood spot. I thought that anyone silly enough to believe such garbage deserved all they got, with the proviso that wouldn't it be wonderful if it were true.

It all changed one night when I went to an evening class called 'Man, Myth and Magic' and there was one lesson on dowsing. I could do it! It was fun! The sub-editors would provide me with pictures of missing persons and take bets on the results. This one was alive but terrified. This other one suffered from dislocation of the neck and congestion of cells and didn't seem to have any life force. It came to a head when they produced a list of runners for the Grand National and stood over me. I said you couldn't dowse for such things. DO IT they said. I picked out a horse which turned out to be second favourite, and hundreds in the office put their shirt on it, including me. It fell at the first fence and nobody bought me a machine coffee for weeks.

I often wonder what prompted me to do a radionics course 20-odd years ago, because I don't remember. But it started me on a learning curve that is still curving and became an onion. Radionic practitioners come in a wide variety – some see the mud, some see the stars, and I come from the muddy end of the spectrum myself, with a leaning towards disturbed energy lines, radioactive fallout, pollutants, solar flares and earthquakes and, latterly, possession by entities. I favour the Magneto-Geometric Applications range of instruments that build up your radionic muscle and wean you off using instruments at all. Using them I would find that the patient's hair sample was on the floor and it didn't seem to make any difference. I would write down treatments to be done, become distracted by something, and then find they no longer needed to be done on instruments at all. It was so much quicker to just write down the command.

When you no longer need to bother about hair witnesses, radionic rates or treatment cards the world suddenly becomes an exciting, challenging place. Anywhere, any time, you can make up dowsing charts and test out any new idea, any new medical discoveries, and treat with them before orthodox medicine has had time to blink. Cancer treatments are a case in point because they are always in the news. Way back in the 1980s I hoovered up a free trip to New York as the result of buying a vacuum cleaner, and a prominent herbalist friend asked me to find out about a new remedy called 'Essiac' and to try to get a book on it which was banned. I tracked down the author, Dr. Gary L Glum, and had him forward the book to our next stop in Atlanta. It arrived at the 13th hour before we were due to leave in a remarkable series of coincidences. There was another coincidence when my friend couldn't obtain sheep sorrel, one of the major ingredients of the Essiac. Her husband was having an ornamental lake dug in one of their fields and suddenly the peaty waste heaps were covered in top quality sheep sorrel. The rest of the Essiac story is history.

There was also the Hulda Clark saga that had us all eliminating liver fluke from virtually every cancer case (why don't doctors look for it in *post mortems?*) and making up home-made battery-driven zappers to bump them off. But later scientific discoveries were just as interesting. There was telomerase, the enzyme that assists cells to duplicate. Eliminate it radionically from cancer cells in various locations and it seems to buy time to find out the real causes. One of the first things I look for on making a patient's analysis is to check whether they are living over a disturbed energy line because you will be running up a down escalator as you give treatments. I find most cancer patients are on the red end of the frequency, though black lines will cause almost anything. Indigo lines are more likely to cause nervous troubles or arthritis. The well-known dowser Hamish Miller taught me how to transmute them mentally into beneficial lines once, when we sat up a hill in Andorra, and that's another story.

A scientific finding is that the gene p53 is a 'tumour-suppressor gene'; it guards the cell against cancerous changes. If a normal cell begins to turn cancerous the p53 jumps into action and destroys it. If the p53 is impaired in any way cancer cells begin to proliferate. There are several reasons why it might be ineffectual. I find radionically that it will most likely have been affected by some sort of infra-red radiation and you can take your pick from television, radar, mobile phones, etc. Its polarity may be wrong, it can be affected by parasite toxins, and it may even need remedies best suited to psychological problems. I also find that a sort of low-grade, smouldering cholera in the intestines is the cause of some types of cancer, by building up toxins in the body. In radionics we recognise three different cancer viruses which can be eliminated, and of course there are a great number of other herbal and homeopathic remedies which are useful, used alongside radionic rates for specific types of tumour. It is, of course, illegal to suggest that you can cure cancer. Maybe that's why Dr Gary L Glum is now on the run in China.

The first time I used the telomerase method was when I got an SOS from someone who said his friend Greg was in hospital with lung cancer and AIDS. The cancer was said to be of a particularly virulent type unsuitable for treatment and of course the HIV infection was sapping his immunity. I find that AIDS involves parasites and benzene in the thymus gland

and amyl nitrite in the genes. I find that homeopathic *Zinnia* will kill the HIV virus and just about everything else. Greg, like many patients, was hopeless about keeping in touch and I didn't hear from him again until his cat was ill. Yes, the cancer seemed to be gone, he said, and the hospital was sending for him again because they were so puzzled. He has no reading for HIV but the hospital assumes that he still has it and presumably is treating him accordingly. His was typical of many radionic cases where the patient just drifts away and never comes to a satisfying conclusion.

ME, the chronic fatigue syndrome, poses few mysteries to radionics practitioners. Look for combinations of agrochemicals, usually organophosphate, the Coxsackie virus, glandular fever and botulism and botulism toxins, plus any other infections and an unhealthy state of the intestines. Improvement can be rapid unless the pollutants have caused permanent damage to the nervous system. Irritable bowel, another popular complaint at the moment, is caused by the microbacterial paratuberculosis organism, and if I discovered that from a medical journal why don't doctors? I find that ulcerative colitis seems to involve a low-grade cholera type bug and an iodine deficiency. Type I diabetes, I find, involves TB, parasites and wood alcohol in the pancreas and a deficiency of chromium and vanadium, and type II often involves parasites in the pituitary gland. I find migraine is often caused by an anthrax-type spore in the brain. I could go on and on!

I never had any particular beliefs about life after death, but was surprised to find you could read the emotions of the dear departed. Love for those left behind, nostalgia, sometimes even guilt. The physical and etheric layers drop off, and the astral emotional body seems to linger a little longer. I was even more amazed to find that I was treating possession. For a long time I eliminated entitles by broadcasting *Zircon* into the aura, then a few weeks ago I read a book, which mentioned demons. DEMONS? I found that there were not only demons but things for want of a better name I called 'Indwellers'. They seemed to be involved in some of the most intransigent cases, in tiny parts of the brain, in organs, even in vertebrae and ligaments, sapping the energy. An enthusiastic application of *Zircon* shifts them instantaneously.

So perhaps our primitive ancestors performing grisly rituals to drive out demons from people with prosaic ailments were not far wrong after all. Move over, medicine man. But don't tell my boozy old mates on the *Evening Chronicle*. They'd have me locked up.

Linda Fellows

Most ancient traditions posit a network of channels of subtle energy around the body which distribute the life force. Probably the best known are the acupuncture meridians of Chinese, and the chakras of Indian tradition. Their existence is still an open question for Western science, although the meridians are employed daily in modern acupuncture clinics. According to Hindu tradition, the body is crossed by a web of lines of subtle energy known as nadis; where these cross are formed vortices of energy known as chakras. There are seven major chakras and many others. In addition, each physical body is surrounded by interpenetrating layers of the etheric energy (or vitality), astral (emotional energy) mental and higher spiritual energies, the 'subtle bodies' which together comprise the aura. The chakras penetrate each of these layers. For good health the energy at each level must be flowing freely and each level in harmonious interaction with every other level, facilitated by unimpeded chakras. (For further details see the books of David Tansley, and Cathy Marshall, chapter 6). The Hindu model of subtle energy structures has proved invaluable to radionic practitioners since it was introduced by Tansley. Many physical problems arise when these invisible supportive structures are malfunctioning; radionics offers a way to detect and clear any problems. The following case studies indicate how radionic investigation and treatment of these subtle levels can bring about beneficial changes on the physical level.

Arrested chakra development

The main chakras are believed to mature fully at different ages, beginning with the base aged 0-3 and ending with the throat in late teens. If an individual is traumatised it will impede the maturation of the major chakra maturing at that time and leave the person susceptible to physical problems associated with that area of the body. Adult patients have often long forgotten the events which are behind their current complaints.

Betty, female, aged 3

Betty's mother had found herself pregnant aged 18 after a party. She married the father but it was not a success. At the time of seeking radionic help the parents were estranged.

Symptoms: Refusing food.

Conventional treatment:	Tube-fed weekly at children's hospital.
Radionic assessment:	Base chakra undeveloped; child not accepting that she was in this world.
Radionic treatment:	To normalise base chakra, give acceptance of incarnation, confidence and enthusiasm for life.
Outcome:	Child began to eat unaided, recovered. Now aged 8, short for age but otherwise normal.

Gordon, male, aged 34

Gordon was a singer with a pop group. His constant sore throats were threatening his career. No medical reason for them could be found.

Symptoms:	Constant recurring sore throats.
Conventional treatment:	Antiseptic sprays brought temporary relief only.
Radionic assessment:	Throat chakra undeveloped, linked to frustration in late teens.
Radionic treatment:	To normalise throat chakra, dissolve anger, give forgiveness.
Outcome:	Throat problems ceased.

Gordon's father had prevented him from pursuing a law degree at age 18 so that he had someone to help him run the family business. The corrosive resentment he still felt towards his father was literally eating away at his throat and stifling self-expression.

Philip, male, aged 32

Philip was an accountant. His chronic stomach problems, which worsened under stress, were threatening his marriage.

Symptoms:	Stomach ulcer, bad breath, many years.
Conventional treatment:	Antacids.
Radionic assessment:	Solar plexus chakra unbalanced.
Radionic treatment:	To normalise solar plexus chakra, dissolve grief, shock.
Outcome:	Stomach problems ceased within a month, but return if stressed. Now managed with radionics.

Philip's parents had divorced when he was 12 after several years of strife. Normal maturation of the solar plexus (aged 8-11) had been blocked.

Blocks in etheric, emotional and mental bodies
Blocks in the etheric body are seemingly caused by chemical and electro-magnetic pollutants of all kinds. These blocks can be detected radionically years after the substance itself has been excreted from the body.

John, male, aged 22
John had started his own business after leaving university, but unexplained chronic tiredness was threatening his livelihood.

Symptoms:	Chronic tiredness, inability to work.
Conventional treatment:	None.
Radionic assessment:	Pesticides in etheric field.
Radionic treatment:	Clear pesticides & traffic pollution.
Outcome:	Tiredness lifted within a month.

John had worked on a farm as a student dipping sheep with his bare arms in organo-phosphates. Traffic fumes are a factor in almost all fatigue problems.

Veronica, female, aged 42
Veronica belonged to an 'asthma-eczema family' but had never suffered breathing difficulties herself before.

Symptoms:	Shortness of breath, asthma-like symptoms.
Conventional treatment:	Steroids suggested.
Radionic assessment:	Traffic pollution and whooping cough vaccination were both contributory factors.
Radionic treatment:	Clear vaccination and give on-going traffic fume protection.
Outcome:	Breathing problems ceased without medication.

Veronica's mother recalled that the whooping cough vaccination at aged 4 had made her 'very poorly' at the time.

Helen, female, aged 32
Helen, of African origin, had two small children. She began to experience leg pains and was no longer able to climb the stairs.

Symptoms:	Pains in legs.
Conventional treatment:	Life-long ingestion of steroids suggested.
Radionic assessment:	Traffic pollution in etheric, combined with lack of calcium and vitamin D.

Radionic treatment:	Clear traffic pollution; suggested to patient to get calcium and vitamin supplement.
Outcome:	Leg pains ceased within two weeks.

Helen then told me she never drank milk as she didn't like it. Her work in the basement of a city shoe-shop meant her exposure to sunlight was minimal. The pregnancies had also depleted her.

Marion, female, aged 57

Marion, suffering from chronic fatigue, had been retired from her post as an art teacher on 'psychiatric' grounds which she disputed.

Symptoms:	Chronic tiredness
Conventional treatment:	Rest.
Radionic assessment:	Paints, solvents, traffic pollution, mercury in etheric, endogenous depression.
Radionic treatment:	Clear effects of toxic chemicals, lift depression.
Outcome:	Symptoms lessened.

Marion's case is typical of many who are affected by chemicals in the working environment, but who are diagnosed as psychiatric cases.

Trauma can set up blockages at the emotional level (astral body) which later manifest as serious depression. Chemical medication for depression can exacerbate the problem.

Marie, female, aged 46

Marie had suffered serious depression for 20 years.

Symptoms:	Depression, inability to work.
Conventional treatment:	Anti-depressants, now having little effect.
Radionic assessment:	Main cause shock aged 26.
Radionic treatment:	Colour treatment to astral body; homeopathic Aurum met. and Kali. phos. sent radionically; clear shock.
Outcome:	Great improvement; medication reduced.

Shock can lie behind a wide variety of emotional and physical complaints.

Jane, female, age 72

Jane had asked for a chest X-ray after her sister had been diagnosed with lung cancer. She was also found to have a shadow on her lung. She seemed very calm about it.

Symptoms:	None at outset.
Conventional treatment:	Radiotherapy.
Radionic assessment:	Cause due to long-standing blockage in the mental body due to frustration and anger.
Radionic treatment:	Clear blockage in mental body; restore normal metabolism to cells.
Outcome:	Jane was dead within a few weeks despite extensive conventional and radionic help.

This was a most unusual case where the patient seemed to will herself to leave this plane. She had been bitter and frustrated in her marriage and the origin of the cancer seemed to have been the mental anguish which this had engendered.

A tale of two kids
Carie and Dennis are brother and sister. I was asked to look at them when they were 10 and 8 respectively.

Carie presented with cold hands, tiredness, lumpy skin and digestive problems.

Dennis was playing up at school, playing a 'I won't pee all day' game and with a bladder infection as a result.

Radionic assessment found that the underlying cause was the same in both children: terror, tension, bad news.

Radionic treatment also the same for each, viz: dissolve stress, give confidence.

Outcome: each improved.

They had recently moved from one side of the USA to the other, their third house and school move in as many years. The feeling of having no control over their lives had been overwhelming. Happily now they are settled in their new environment, where their parents plan to stay.

Threatened blindness – Nadia, female, aged 42
Nadia was diagnosed with Retinitis pigmentosa in 1981. This is characterised by a gradual loss of vision beginning with the outer part of the retina. It tends to run in families, although no one in Nadia's family had had eye problems.

Symptoms:	Loss of peripheral vision.
Conventional treatment:	None available.
Radionic assessment:	Blockages in the etheric due to DDT, TB toxin, lead, streptomycin, cadmium; a

	genetic susceptibility was also evident, also an iron deficiency.
Radionic treatment:	Clear etheric blockages. Ongoing support for visual system and to counter anxiety.
Outcome:	20 years later this lady can still see; there was no cure, but her condition has only slightly worsened, to her doctors' surprise.

The pesticide DDT is still detectable in the etheric of many older patients who were exposed to it in the '40s and '50s.

Radionics and cancer

Environmental factors and the stress of modern life play a significant role in the incidence of cancers in the industrialised world. Radionic techniques can offer support both in terminal illness and in recovery.

Jean, female, aged 76

Jean had never visited a doctor, other than to have children, in all her adult life. Her family was shocked when her 'indigestion' was diagnosed as inoperable ovarian cancer.

Symptoms:	Abdominal pains.
Conventional treatment:	Pain management; too late for other treatments.
Radionic assessment:	Emotional aspects of all main chakras were out of balance, reflecting lack of emotional support since her husband's death.
Radionic treatment:	Give peace of mind, confidence, minimise pain.
Outcome:	Jean celebrated her birthday with a new hair-do and her family around her bed, and died peacefully two days later. She required morphine for only 24 hours. Her doctor remarked ' Would we could all go so easily'.

Simon, male, aged 45

Symptoms:	Loss of breath lead to discovery of non-Hodgkin's lymphoma.
Conventional treatment:	Chemotherapy followed by bone-marrow transplant.

Radionic assessment: Cancer triggered by stress and pollution.

Radionic treatment: Long-term supportive treatment to protect healthy organs from adverse effects of chemotherapy and to clear drugs no longer needed from the etheric.

Outcome: Simon, 4 years later, survived and is back at work. His doctors told him they were amazed at the outcome.

Simon was determined to beat his illness and 'try anything'. He did both.

The experiences described above reflect different ways in which individual practitioners approach a case, given his/her unique mind set and life experiences. We, as yet, have little idea of the mechanism of either analysis or treatment with radionics, but the accumulated experiences of practitioners over the years is witness to its power to help bring beneficial change to many people.

Galea Parsons

Radionics and Horses 9

> 'England's past has been borne on his back.
> All our history is his industry.
> We are his heirs. He is our inheritance.'
>
> From 'The Horse' by Roland Duncan

The first section of this chapter examines the role of evolution and instinct because it is important to understand the great changes that horses have undergone to reach their present shape and stature. It is through an understanding of these adaptations that we learn about the similarities between the structure of man and the structure of the horse. Studying the evolution of the horse also gives an insight into their primordial fears and instincts and once we start to understand these we, as practitioners and horse handlers, are in a better position to support the animal. Circumstances that can appear straightforward to a human are often considered difficult and potentially dangerous to the horse. So our aim is to help the horse become more educated and less reactionary. This is to our advantage because we often require our horses to perform in ways that they find unnatural.

Practitioners need to understand the differences between a range of disciplines e.g. racing and dressage. Also each patient, man, horse, dog or cat must be treated as an individual. Each is subjected to a range of experiences some of which may cause pain. If the pain is not expressed and understood it becomes locked within the bodies, subtle and physical. Animals do not have the advantage of speech to express their pain, confusion and fears and are often misunderstood. Practitioners need to develop the 'skill' to access and aid the release of these traumas.

The second section will consider the horse as a domesticated, non-ruminant herbivore compared with an omnivore. This will cover the physical differences and some of the aspects we hold in mind when we embark on the radionic process. Throughout there will be references to the subtle anatomy of the horse and some case notes. The final part of the subtle energetic section is a brief look at the differences in Ray make-up and the energetic difference that individualisation has upon man. The more understanding we have of the type of energy arrangements that we are dealing with in our radionic practice, the more 'tools' we can use in any particular case. The second chapter on horses looks at a variety of case histories that illustrate the work of a radionic practitioner.

How the physical horse has evolved

Man has only been around for about 2 million years whereas the horse's ancestors have been around considerably longer and have undergone massive evolutionary changes. Man too has evolved, but not as dramatically as the horse. As long ago as 60 million years, a small animal scurried about the subtropical floor of the forest; this creature was called *Eohippus*. He was a four-footed, four-toed herbivore that preferred to flee from his carnivorous foe, rather than fight. The four spread toes allowed *Eohippus* to distribute his slight weight on the soft ground and escape his heavier foe. *Eohippus* was only 3 hands high (HH) (a hand is four inches, therefore *Eohippus* was 12 inches high), and quite timid. The animals that we call horses have evolved from this small creature.

By 35 to 40 million years ago, this small creature had evolved and grown to 6 hands high and had become three-toed; this was *Mesophippus*. After about a further 20 million years he still had three toes, but the middle toe had become the weight bearer, he had grown to 10 hands high, and his neck was longer. This creature was called *Merychippus*. By this time the forest was thinning and becoming drier, hence the adaptation to standing on the middle toes and the longer neck for easier grazing.

Adaptations to this changing environment continued and by 6 to 10 million years ago more of the bones within the leg and foot had joined together to form one fairly strong toe or hoof; at this stage *Equus'* ancestor was called *Pliohippus*. The subtropical forests were receding fast and the open drier grasslands were taking hold. The physical adaptations allowed the horse's ancestors to inhabit the open plains successfully. The longer, stronger limbs meant that he could travel faster. The single hoof

Evolution of the Horse

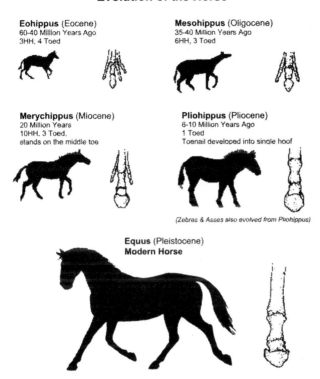

Eohippus (Eocene)
60-40 Million Years Ago
3HH, 4 Toed

Mesohippus (Oligocene)
35-40 Million Years Ago
6HH, 3 Toed

Merychippus (Miocene)
20 Million Years
10HH. 3 Toed.
stands on the middle toe

Pliohippus (Pliocene)
6-10 Million Years Ago
1 Toed
Toenail developed into single hoof

(Zebras & Asses also evolved from Pliohippus)

Equus (Pleistocene)
Modern Horse

Fig. 9.1 Evolution of the horse (based on diagram in Mi-
crosft Encarta, 1994, © Microsoft Corporation)

was ideal to 'cut' into the harder ground and the longer neck allowed him
to graze the grasses with ease, and to see a greater distance when it was
raised. It took another 5 million years for *Equus* to emerge. From then to
our present day changes in the horse, *Equus*, were less dramatic, but nevertheless significant (Fig. 9.1) .

Enemies on the plain could come from any direction and were much
faster and stronger. When the horse's ancestors lived in the heavily foli-
ated forest horses' eyes had been positioned relatively forward facing
but in the open grasslands they needed to see further and have a wider
range of vision. To achieve this the eyes gradually became larger and
even more laterally positioned. In the forest predators tended to lurk in
shady places, in marshy places or in the deep pools. Catching their prey
was not dependent on speed but on circumstance. Horses, particularly

cold-blooded breeds, still tend to fear dark woods, dappled patches and watery places. This is an ancient ingrained primordial fear. This is why you may need to ride more strongly to jump into dark woods from open grassland. Sometimes dappled patches on the road appear to be dangerous to the horse and this is because his old carnivorous foes often hid in dappled patches and were dappled coated.

In the open grasslands there was a real need to increase speed and the four-toed spread of *Eophippus* would have been of no value in this environment. The lower limbs adapted to form the hooves we are now familiar with. The limbs became longer, and were powered from the rear end, which aided swift movement over harder ground. *Pliohippus* and then *Equus* ate better, conditions continued to improve, the lush grasses suited him well and so the horse's ancestors continued to increase in stature, size and fleetness of foot.

Approximately 8 thousand years ago the original *Equus* had become extinct, but its progeny had already developed into three distinct types of *Equus caballus*. These are referred to as Steppe, Forest and Plateau types, or a, b and c types.

The steppe type is still seen in the Przewalski horse. These are the only truly wild primitive horse to survive today. This horse has long ears, a large head, strong sturdy limbs and narrow hooves. Its mane stands up on a thick neck. It is alert and agile and does not have a particularly gentle nature.

The forest type was larger, heavier and duller witted than the steppe horse. It had broad hooves and a thick coarse coat and a flat mane. These types often had spotted, striped or coloured coats, perfect for camouflage. The head was short and broad, concave between the eyes, becoming roman shaped towards the muzzle. The forest type has not survived to the present day, but its successors are seen in the large gentle heavy horses, and in some of the coloured breeds we see nowadays.

The plateau type was similar to the tarpan horses seen today. The true tarpan became extinct about a hundred years ago. Careful selective breeding of the surviving out-crosses has tried to maintain this gene pool as intact as possible. The plateau type was fine boned, narrow headed with large eyes and small ears. It is thought that our fine boned horses and ponies descended mainly from this type.

There may have been a fourth type, the Tundra horse, which would have been grey, because of the predominantly white snow or frost covered landscape, which was its habitat but there is little available information about this branch of the *Equus* family.

It is probable that our modern finer boned breeds of horses and ponies evolved mainly from the plateau horse, although all three or possibly four types will have had an influence on the variety of *Equus caballus* seen nowadays. Today a pony or horse can be anything from 9 HH to 19 HH or more. I believe modern research in humans has shown a generational increase in leg length due to improved food during the ages 0-3 years.

Figure 9.1 shows how huge the evolutionary changes have been for the horse, and that these changes in shape and function of the horse are considerably greater than is seen in mankind.

Implications of the horse as a herbivore

Horses are herbivores and humans are omnivores. As a herbivore, the horse has a specific digestive system to cope with cellulose digestion, and teeth which continue to grow throughout life. These teeth need regular attention as they often wear unevenly and so give rise to problems chewing and accommodating a bit. Quite knowledgeable owners can overlook the teeth and condition of the bars (the area in the mouth where the bit sits). Radionic practitioners need to be alert to numerous problems within their horse patient's mouth. When problems arise in a human patient's mouth it is usually because of bacterial attack (which can occur in the horse) but most problems in horses I find are as a result of uneven growth or damage within the mouth caused by man.

Unlike most domesticated herbivores the horse is not a ruminant. He lacks the robustness of a ruminant and has a somewhat delicate digestive system with a particularly long hindgut. This needs careful and consistent feeding, preferably trickle feeding. When horses lived wild on the huge plains of America or the steppes of Russia they were able to roam continually on grasslands, exercising either gently or at speed. They grazed varied herbage for as many hours of day or night as they wished. Current athletic standards, pressure on land availability, and the modern convention of keeping horses in, means that horses stand on concrete, albeit on bedding (out of contact with the natural vibrations of the earth), in a space 12' by 12' (ca. 3.7 x 3.7 m) if they are lucky, for anything up to 23 hours a day. During that time they may be fed hard food two or three times, four or five in yards with exceptional standards. Horses are also given hay, which should allow some trickle feeding, but I frequently find that the modern horse is exhibiting allergies to hay, spores, and dust. This results in the horse being fed a small amount of dust-free higher protein haylage, which negates the trickle feed effect.

Horses are not equipped to process animal fats and proteins as they do not have a gall bladder. Horses have not evolved from, nor are they evolving to being, carnivores. Because of this we, as providers of their food, need to be very careful that the foodstuffs we feed to them do not contain any animal derivatives. Careful reading of the small print on food bags is essential. In addition, the practitioner needs to be aware of the problems of 'bringing them on' too well; the over feeding of high protein foodstuff to young stock may risk their joint formation causing deformities.

It is hardly surprising that by restricting and feeding the horse in order to conform to modern methods and athletic standards, the delicate balance of hindgut bacterial flora often looses its integrity. This can lead, amongst other things, to colic. But not all modern practice is detrimental to the well being of the horse. The horse is no longer, by and large, the vital worker of the nineteen hundreds. These days man keeps horses mainly for recreational purposes, although what is recreation for some is business for others. Stable management, even in professional yards, has changed dramatically in the past 100 years. Very different stresses assault the horse's delicate energy systems. Additional stresses come from a variety of environmental factors including herbicides, pesticides, radiation, diesel fumes, air pollutants, and water contamination to name but a few. Neither man, horse, dog or cat have yet fully adapted to this new environment.

Yet another major area of challenge that the horse has to contend with is his feet! In order to carry out the level of work that we require of him the horse has to be shod. There are many very skilled farriers but there are also some that are not so skilled. If the feet are not attended to regularly and skilfully many problems can arise in the balance and shape of the foot that affects not only the foot but the flight of the limb as well. Problems with incorrect shoeing or dressing can give rise to short-term problems or long-term damage, eventually giving rise to bony change or strained tendons and ligaments.

Most of what we ask our horses to do, apart from racing, goes against their natural instincts. But, such is their devotion and trust they do it for us anyway, sometimes at great cost to their nervous systems and increasingly often their immune and digestive systems. In addition, regular competing and travelling can cause stress, leading to a depression of the immune system and the metabolism of the hindgut. The immune system has also been compromised by generations of vaccinations and increasingly by pollution of all sorts. All these factors have to be considered and, in some cases, addressed by the radionic practitioner.

The differences between horses and humans
Basic physical dfferences

Because of the energetic connection between the energy centres or chakras and the spinal column in both man and the horse it is important to consider the differences that exist here and in other areas of the skeleton. There are some very noticeable physical differences between man and horse. Horses stand on four feet and humans stand on two but have arms and hands. This sounds very obvious but it immediately throws up some big differences in anatomical arrangements and function.

We have a collarbone and therefore a shoulder girdle of sorts. A horse does not have a collarbone; the shoulder blade and front legs are held by muscle mass, not by skeletal connections. This whole area acts as an area of shock absorption for the horse.

The forelimbs are equivalent to our arms. The elbow of the horse is equivalent to our elbow. The knee of the horse is comparable with the wrist of a human being comprised of carpal bones. The lower front leg (the cannon bone area) is equivalent to the metacarpals, the fetlock joint equates to the proximal phalanges and the coffin bone or pedal bone is equivalent to the distal phalange of the middle finger of the human.

The upper limbs in a human are primarily for dexterity and sacrifice stability at the shoulder joint for an incredible range of movement. Separate ulna and radius bones allow pronation and supination which further increases movement. In humans there is also incredible flexibility at wrist, hand and digits for dexterity, gripping, holding and very fine movements.

The hind limb of the horse has similar correspondences to the leg of man, as seen in the fore limb and arm. The stifle is the equivalent of the knee, the femur articulates with the tibia and there is a reduced fibula. Articulating in the front groove of the stifle joint is the patella or 'kneecap'. The patella is an important factor in the 'stay mechanism' which allows the horse to rest while standing. The hock is the equivalent of the ankle or tarsal bones in humans. Below the hock the correspondences are similar to the forelimb, bearing in mind that equivalent bones in man will be metatarsal bones.

This state of affairs has not always been the case. Understanding the changes in habitat that drove the adaptations helps us to understand our modern horse. Understanding the threats and foes that the horse's ancestors faced helps us understand some of the primordial fears that affect our horses and why they are flight not fight animals.

Fear is something we are all familiar with. How we deal with it varies from person to person, but in general terms omnivorous mankind's response to a fearful situation is to fight. Quite often it may not be the overt pugilist response, instead we may adopt a defensive position. Only very rarely will we turn and run, occasionally we may make a discreet withdrawal. The horse, on the other hand, if frightened will run or flee. This is not cowardice but the horse's mechanism to overcome or out run his foe.

The lower limb in humans is designed for shock absorbency, flexibility of movement, and strength for locomotion. The foot is designed for weight dispersal and balance. In the horse, the forelimb is designed primarily for shock absorbency. The landing shock is spread over a much larger area – taken up by the muscles and tendons holding the scapulae in place. Sixty percent of the weight of the average horse is carried by the forelimbs. The exceptions are generally found in dressage horses which is why it takes such a long time to strengthen and produce a dressage horse. The changes that are required of the dressage horse's back and hind limbs to accommodate the change in weight carrying are very challenging for the horse. The challenge for the horse is to convert the power to torque and suppleness rather than speed. This does not mean that they do not enjoy doing this type of work but adaptations take time. It takes time to achieve the level of fitness, muscle mass and mental dexterity to achieve the movements. The hindquarters are the horse's power unit as the hind limb is designed primarily for propulsion which drives the body forwards. In man the equivalent to the hindquarters are the buttocks, hamstrings and quads. Man also uses the shoulder girdle for power, in lifting for example.

Head shape is very different. Man can, if his posture is reasonable, balance his head on top of his spine. The horse must hold his own head. This is helped somewhat by a very sophisticated 'stay' system, which allows the horse to relax whilst standing with little fatigue. This stay mechanism is present in both the fore limbs and the hind limbs and is a system that allows muscles and ligaments to 'lock' the main joints into position.

There are also differences in the numbers of various groups of vertebrae. Both man and horse have 7 cervical vertebrae. Comparatively the horse's neck vertebrae are considerably larger than man's neck vertebrae. This arrangement allows the horse to graze at ground level and to lift his head and see for a long distance.

In man there are 12 thoracic vertebrae, to which are attached 12 pairs of ribs. Horses have an average of 18 vertebrae (this can vary between 15 and 21) to which are attached 18 pairs of ribs (this can also vary between 15 and 21).

In man there are usually 5 lumbar vertebrae although sometimes there may be 6; and sometimes the 5th lumbar vertebrae can be fused to 1st sacral. The horse has 6 lumbar vertebrae. Both humans and horses have 5 sacral vertebrae, which are fused. Humans have 4 coccygeal vertebrae that are fused whereas horses have an average of 18 coccygeal vertebrae, which forms the dock, to which is attached the long tail hairs.

The spinal vertebrae in man and horse are there primarily to protect the spinal cord. In both man and horse the spinal vertebrae are weight bearing but man's acts as a column and shock absorber, the horse's is a long girder.

The equine pelvis is joined to the spine at the level of the sacrum at the ilium by tough fibrous ligamentous tissue, as it is in man. However, in horses there is *no* pubic symphysis, the pubic bones fuse making the pelvis a continuous ring of bone which is immensely strong. It is subjected to major force as it transfers thrust from the hind limbs. In man there is a pubic symphysis which allows some movement at childbirth, and the sacro-iliac is weight bearing.

Having looked at the differences in physical structure of humans and horses, we can now turn our attention to their energetic make up. Possibly the greatest energetic difference is that mankind's vertebrae run vertical to the earth's surface, whereas a horse's are horizontal to the earth's surface. Whilst the head and poll, in particular, can be in a position that is not too dissimilar to man's, the majority of the spinal column is subjected during the day to a very different experience of the etheric formative forces which emanate from the earth, the sun, and other planets. These ethers or etheric formative forces are the invisible forces that make up the subtle energies within the solar system. They support and form the subtle body scaffold of every living species.

There are four types of ethers, which each give rise to different basic shapes or forms. The warmth ether gives rise to circular or spherical shapes, the light ether gives rise to triangular shapes, the chemical ether gives rise to half moon or crescent shapes and the life ether gives rise to square or cuboid shapes. Combining these ethers gives rise to the myriad of shapes we are familiar with in the physical world. The ethers are either centrifugal or centripetal in their action. This means they either have a tendency to encourage expansion, outward movement, or concentration, inward movement. In addition to this the predominance of action of the ethers at the earth's surface varies during the 24-hour period and during the seasonal changes of the year. Alice Bailey (*A Treatise on Cosmic Fire*) refers to these formative forces by number, 1-4. The Steiner school refers to them by the names of warmth, light, chemical and life ethers.

Another obvious difference between horses and humans is that humans have a large verbal language. Horses can only make sounds that on the whole correspond to vowel sounds. Therefore they are restricted to emotional expression via sound and are unable to express mental ideas in this manner. Horses do have a large range of visual body language, some of which is quite subtle. The dialogue that is possible using this language is considerable.

The differences in the Ray makeup of humans and horses

'A ray is but a name for a particular force or type of energy with the emphasis upon the quality which that force exhibits and not upon the form aspect that it creates.' (Alice Bailey)

A brief look at rays illustrates very effectively the differences between humans and horses. Alice Bailey in *Treatise on the Seven Rays* says that the rays that govern the Animal Kingdoms are Rays 3 & 6. She goes on to say, that, those that govern the Human Kingdom, are Rays 4 & 5.

In the context of animals Ray 3 gives rise to the quality of adaptability and according to Alice Bailey this is expressed as instinct. The quality of Ray 6 is devotion and its expression is domesticity. When we consider the rays that express the Human Kingdom the fourth ray is often called 'Harmony through Conflict' and is expressed through growth and experience. The fifth ray is referred to as 'Concrete Knowledge or Intellect'.

Each animal and human is an expression of many other ray influences; those of soul, mental, astral and etheric bodies for instance, those of the planet and solar system, plus others. However, Alice Bailey's description of the ray influences manifesting in the Kingdoms, gives us a picture of animals being adaptable, with strong instincts for both survival and behaviour patterns. Horses are also capable of amazing devotion or service, and have a capacity for domesticity.

The picture created for the human kingdom is that of seeking and desiring beauty and harmony, but almost always to achieve this goal we need to struggle (Ray 4). We also have a desire and a thirst for knowledge, but the manner in which we seek knowledge brings with it the tendency to cause separation. We break things down into smaller and smaller components, which we are then able to understand more, and more clearly (Ray 5). Some aspects of Ray 5 bring about destruction but the incoming Ray 7, which governs the Aquarian Age, affords the opportunity to balance this. Ray 7 brings qualities of order, synthesis and cohesion.

Animals are devoted, instinctive yet adaptable creatures. Humans struggle through their conflict and, whilst they seek cohesion, they often only manage to create separation and loneliness. No wonder humanity so often turns to the animal kingdom for succour and comfort.

Alice Bailey goes on to say that horses are a manifestation of the sixth ray, or one could say that they have a double dose of devotion and idealism; first, as an animal, and secondly because they are a horse animal. That is not to say that there are not some very devoted humans, (Ray 6 is quite often manifest via human astral bodies), but in broad and general terms an animal will be more forgiving than a human. This, however, does not give us humans the right to expect forgiveness for our ignorance and lack of consideration for our animal brethren. The sixth ray is a ray of idealism, intense devotion, service endurance, loyalty and adherence. Taken too far (all rays have their downside) this manifests as excesses or weaknesses such as, ill-considered loyalty, unreasoning devotion. For example, when you can't part a horse from its companion even when he has for the past, say, five years been returned to his friend within the hour! Another weakness of this ray manifests as dependency or over-leaning on others, either to other horses or the humans that tend them. It is also seen in the fanatic, for instance the crib-biter that will go to extraordinary lengths to get hold of something to crib upon. It shows in unvarying one-pointedness – the horse that will trample you to get to his manger although he has just come in from the field where he has been eating grass all day!

In its positive aspect this huge sixth ray influence actually means that the horse will have a bigger heart than the human they live with and almost certainly a greater capacity to forgive shortcomings. So often humans think that they are superior to animals and indeed, in evolutionary terms, we are further along the pathway. But often an animal will manifest a quality of greater superiority to our own, for instance can you be as detached as your cat? Can you be as forgiving as your dog or horse; can you be as patient as your horse? I am not suggesting that every horse or dog manifests these qualities better than mankind, there are some horses and dogs that take dreadful advantage. Think of the pony that goes nicely up to the small fence, stops and puts his head down to graze as the child slides helplessly down his neck to the ground. The pony has taken advantage of the child's ineptitude, and has obviously been allowed to get away with this behaviour. Ponies and horses are certainly not all paragons of virtue. However domesticated animals, dogs and horses in particular, have karmically taken on a burden to serve mankind. It would behove us not to abuse this 'service'.

Subtle body differences between horse and man

The difference that really shows in the subtle bodies of man and horse is at the soul level. Animals have group souls and humans have individualised ones (See Appendix). In respect of their subtle bodies, etheric, astral and mental, they are not so different from humans. The radionic approach is the same, the practitioner is looking for areas of dis-harmony within the subtle bodies, but the basis of the questioning is different because the evolution of man and horse is different. Both are aspiring to growth of their soul and evolution either knowingly or unknowingly, but they are approaching this growth from very different positions. The energetic makeup has a different bias (see the previous section on ray make up), the psychological make up has a different emphasis, and these aspects do impact upon how we treat. We need always to remember that man is an omnivore and a fighter, the horse a herbivore and a fleer; man is individualised and the horse still has the protection of a group soul. In addition to this the horse is usually required to fulfil a function or discipline, to compete in an event or a dressage test *for* man.

The obvious physical differences will of course be reflected in the etheric body (Fig. 9.2). The astral or desire body of the horse will be made from similar energies to man's, although perhaps not so riven with negative desires as some human's astral bodies (e.g. acquisition). Horses have the capacity to have self-doubt, repressed self-expression and lack of self-

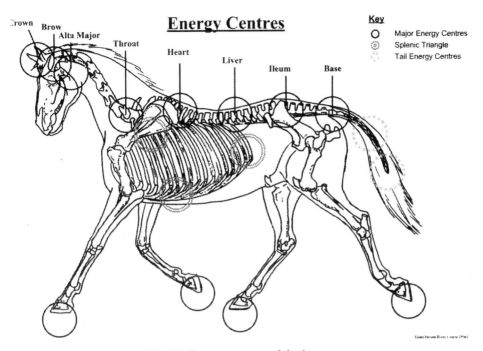

Fig. 9.2 Energy centres of the horse

awareness as have their human companions. The horse's mental ability will probably not be as keen as his human partner's, although this is not always the case. Horses will not have the capacity to 'extend' their chakras in the same way that man is able to. Man expands and deepens both his understanding and ability to achieve mastery of his emotions. The horse's experience is still at the stage of developing and growing the group soul. Domestication with humans can, if the relationship is conducted with skill understanding and educational kindness, assist this development. So often mankind inflicts pain and misery, at best due to poor communications skills and ignorance. Man, too, can benefit and grow from good mutual relationships that foster a range of positive attributes.

Horses do have mental bodies, they do think. However, they are unlikely to have any activity in the higher mental body, which deals in abstract thought. Horses are not into higher maths or chemical formulae! You only have to have met the all-round pony club pony of approximately 10-16 years old, be he 12HH or 14.2, to know that he possess not only intelligence, but also wisdom and humour as well. (For the difference between lower and higher mental bodies see Appendix.)

When carrying out a radionic analysis for a horse the approach is not very different from a human analysis. It is still important to look at the balance of ethers, or formative forces, the state and relationships of the subtle bodies, and the chakra/energy centre readings. The chakra arrangements are a little different (see Fig. 9.2). However what is vital to this process is to understand what 'weight' or importance these readings have in relationship to the horse, compared to readings for a human analysis. For instance if the base chakra reading is poor in a horse it may be offset to a large extent by good readings in the feet chakra, particularly the hind feet. There is, of course, still significance to the base reading, but the feet chakra have a lot more importance in the horse than they do in man. The old adage 'no foot, no horse' still holds. (The exception to this in man is if there is a particular problem with either hands or feet).

Another area that is a little different is the splenic triangle, which is vitally important in man because its main function is the reception and distribution of prana. It is perhaps even more important in the horse because it energetically helps us to assess and act upon, not only the reception and distribution of prana, but also on the organs that are sub-diaphragmatic and intra-scapula, below and above the diaphragm. There is a huge depth and breadth of physical body in the horse governed by the spinal centres. In addition, this large body mass comes under the jurisdiction of these splenic centres. Readings from sub-diaphragmatic and spleen energy centres can also sometimes indicate malposition of the ribs or poor breathing rhythms. This is vital to the horse because it is a flight animal, and all the disciplines and work we ask of the horse requires it to be able to breath well. In humans these aspects are more likely to be governed by the throat centre. It is my understanding that the higher aspects of the throat centre are not manifest in the horse because higher forms of creativity do tend to require the consciousness at the higher mental level (See Appendix). The throat centre in the horse governs the respiratory system as well as thyroid, parathyroid, palate, soft palate vocal cords and hyoid bone, all extremely important for respiration and digestion as well as expression and self-expression.

The crown and brow energy centres in humans are important and relate to very different types of energy. The brow centre in man accesses the energy of the lower mental body and buddhic body; this is the centre that manifests our visionary talents. The crown centre in man accesses the higher mental body and spirit. In man and horse spirit is also accessible via the heart centre. However, these head centres are also very significant in horses. The crown of the horse, the point midway between the ears where the parietal bones join, is hugely important. If this joint is under strain, because of a blow or because of distortion in the cranial arrangement and energies, or indeed for other reasons, this can result in a horse that can be difficult to handle and unpredictable in its behaviour. This energy centre in the horse will have all the relevance it has in a human but is unlikely to have activity at the higher mental and buddhic levels. There may always be exceptions to the rule but I have yet to meet one. The brow centre of the horse is situated about two to three inches down the face from the crown. This governs all the rest of the head bones that are not governed by crown or alta major, the sinuses, the teeth, jaw and most of the brain.

In addition to these two head centres it is important to consider the alta major centre. This is the energy centre that taps into the unseen worlds and as yet unseen dangers to alert and to make aware of danger or perceived dangers. It is the centre that allows an instinctive response to danger. This centre functions best in the majority of horses. The alta major of dogs and cats is more sensitively attuned than that of the humans they live with. When working or living with animals, natural instincts are very strong and need to be respected and understood. In horses the alta major function (Fig. 9.2) is still in good order. In mankind this function has been overruled by modern living conditions; we no longer live by the seasons, daylight hours and rhythms of the planet. A radionic practitioner needs to be aware of these primordial behaviour patterns which we may be asking the horse to overcome. The practitioner also needs to be aware of which of the energy centres relate to which type of behaviour. For instance, if a horse's alta major and base centres are in good shape he is likely to be well within himself and confident about going forward. Providing his brow centre also has a good reading, which would be an indication that his vision and perception of what he was seeing was reasonable, he is unlikely to be a 'spooky horse'. If his heart reading is good then, providing there is nothing-detrimental elsewhere in his energy readings, you have the makings of a horse that is generous and bold.

If we understand the type of emotions that relate to each energy centre or chakra, by taking readings for energy centre function and balance, we can have an insight into the balance and type of emotion held within each area of the body. Because not every handler is gifted with good listening skills or skills of observation for their horse's usually silent language, this particular practitioner skill can be of value to the owner/handler to assist their insight and understanding into their particular horse. It is also of value to the practitioner in providing the key to assist the release of negative emotional patterning, which can lead to serious physical manifestations e.g. lameness, lack of performance, malaise.

As a rule, westerners have lost touch with their alta major centre and energy. It is often tested in emergencies, for example if a car that has been jacked up, falls on the person doing the repairs beneath it, how does an observer respond? Does he freeze to the spot in horror, or does he leap forward and lift the car off the trapped person with super human strength? If the latter is the case their alta major energy has come to the rescue and they have mustered all their strength, and some more, and risen to the situation superbly. This centre is governed by Pan, the King of the Animal and Devic Kingdoms, and it is therefore not so surprising that horses' alta majors are more keenly attuned than ours. It is, of course, vitally important to consider the balance and health of our human patient's alta major centre. This centre has to do with duality and balance and if it is not in good order, this can be as disorientating as the base or brow centre being completely out of kilter.

If the alta major centre energy is out of balance in our horse patient how does it manifest and how does it become damaged? It can sometimes occur if a horse runs back hard when it is tied up. This can bring about a misalignment of the occipital bone and the vertebrae. If this happens, or even if it doesn't happen at the physical level but the energies are disturbed, the horse can have great difficulty 'coming down on to the bit' and going forward, or it may start to stand up or even rear. Another manifestation is that the horse may have difficulty going in a balanced manner. Some forms of head shaking can relate to the alta major centre's energies being unbalanced. The health of this centre is vitally important to the well being of the horse. We can see that whilst the energy centres of man and horses share many similarities there are also important differences.

Responsibility of humans

In this chapter we have looked at some of the basic information relating to horses that a radionic practitioner needs to keep in mind when carrying out assessments and treating their horse patients. We have also considered some of the more obvious differences and similarities between treating horses and treating human patients. The importance of understanding the horse's background and evolution, which gives us an insight into the horse's emotional and mental priorities, has also been considered. We have covered some of the energetic differences. From this we can see that the closer the horse lives to man the greater is his potential for soul growth, but at the same time the greater risk he runs of damage as the result of man's ignorance, thoughtlessness or cruelty.

How does lack of individualisation, as it relates to our horses, affect how we treat horses radionically? Except to note that it is the biggest energetic difference between horse and man but it is not of day-to-day importance in treatment. It does of course mean that attempting to treat the higher mental aspect of the horse would be unlikely to be an effective treatment. But, more importantly it means that we have even more of a moral obligation than we thought we had before, to look after our animals as well as we are able and to be open to new ways of exploring our horse's well being.

As has been illustrated there are a lot of similarities in the treatment of humans and horses. One of the important things to remember is that horses are fright and flight animals, whereas the response of man is generally fright and fight. Even if the man does not fight in an obvious manner, he will adopt defensive mechanisms. Unrestrained, both flight and fight responses can hinder the development of the soul. Therefore, if by the application of good radionic practice we can allow the recipient to respond in a more measured manner to non-life threatening situations, we are assisting that soul's growth.

This third ray planet of ours is a learning planet and it is what we learn from different experiences that aids soul growth. At the end of the Piscean age mankind is still seeking mastery of his emotions, which really only comes about when we humans can express unconditional love under all circumstances. Love is something that animals experience as a rule amongst themselves only as sexual desire or mother love, or sometimes possessive love for a companion. When they become domesticated they have the opportunity to experience attachments at a deeper level. Partnerships between man and horse, or indeed man and dog, can involve huge trust, devotion and love. These partnerships give all concerned, man, horse, dog or cat, the opportunity for soul growth. However, the contact that animals have with mankind gives them a unique opportunity to experience some of the higher emotions, love and trust to name two, that they otherwise would not experience.

There are many well know stories of devotion and love bestowed on their owners by animals; *The Incredible Journey* by Sheila Burnford comes immediately to mind. Because the horse is very often more forgiving than his human partner both bring massively important qualities and opportunities to this partnership. It is the opportunities afforded by domestication, to live in close proximity with man, to work and to be asked to trust and give with generosity, that afford animals the opportunity to experience more, both good and bad, physical, etheric, emotional and mental stimulation; this accelerates the development of their group soul and subtle bodies.

You can see throughout the case histories in the following chapter that instincts and the energetic network that governs them run deep. It is therefore important to understand them if we are to deal successfully with our animals, especially if we want our animals to behave in a manner contrary to these behaviour patterns. Horses, like humans, carry energetic scarring of traumatic incidences in their lives, which they are unable to express in verbal language. This energetic scarring can then manifest at the physical level.

Radionic treatment is able to access and treat these areas of congestion and blockage. In addition the vast majority of horses want to please their owners, by doing as they are asked. If they do not, they have a problem which they cannot express and the owner/trainer cannot discern. Radionic treatment offers owner and horse a very unique non-confrontational and non-invasive therapy to overcome these difficulties. It also offers a unique and non-invasive method of accelerating the natural healing abilities within our animals and us. There is a saying that there is no healing other than self-healing. Radionics provides a safe catalyst to initiate that self-healing process. This is especially true in animals, as they always want to be well, unlike humans. This is not a slur on humans, but it is true that sometimes our agendas bring about ill health without our necessarily understanding the mechanism for this occurrence. We humans can become very attached to our emotional and mental 'baggage', and therefore reluctant to relinquish it, even if it is causing us damage and dis-ease!

APPENDIX

The model we use in the School of Radionics for the subtle bodies, which is based on the teaching of Alice Bailey, is as follows: For our convenience and ease of understanding the unseen realms of energies that power and provide a framework for the physical body are divided into seven levels or bodies. In human or horse these seven bodies are all going to be in the same place and all interpenetrating one another. The differences that exist are of variation of vibration. The physical body is the densest, or slowest vibration. The physical body is organised by an energy body referred to as the etheric body, this vibrates at a finer and faster rate than the physical body itself and extends an inch or two beyond the physical body. This extension can sometimes be seen as a bluish whitish light and is referred to as the health aura, not the aura. (The aura is the combination of all the finer and finer subtle bodies that extend beyond the physical body and can be seen by some intuitive and some psychic people. The colours are many and varied and often indescribable).

The next level or body is called the astral or desire body and is of a finer vibration than the physical body; this body extends a little way beyond the etheric body. Vibrating at a finer level still is the mental body, which extends still further beyond the astral body. Within each of these bodies are further subdivisions or sub-planes. Seven of these sub-planes are usually considered to make up a body or level. The mental body is understood to comprise of a lower mental body, which is concerned with concrete thought (is that person coming to feed me?) and the higher mental body, which is concerned with abstract thinking e.g. higher maths, appreciation of beauty etc. The lower mental is made up of three sub-planes and the higher mental is made up of four sub-planes.

The reason that this particular division within the mental plane is emphasised is because it is in this area that differences in development become apparent and can begin to be appreciated. In addition, it is because the personality is made up from the physical-etheric, the astral and the lower mental. In some texts the personality of animals is described as the lower triad.

The next body is termed the buddhic body; these finer vibrations, provided we can access them, are the energies involved with the qualities of intuition, and again this body extends beyond the mental body. You will see there is a pattern: each body is of a finer vibration than the last described and it extends even further from the concrete physical body. Beyond the buddhic body is the atmic body, this is the level of Spirit (the soul of man, or the causal body of man vibrates at the levels of higher mental, buddhic and atmic, the amount of activity at these levels will vary from individual to individual.) Beyond the atmic is the level of Anu-padaka which is the level at which the spark of God, which is within us all, vibrates. The level beyond that is called the Plane of Adi or the Plane of the Logos and it is often said to be beyond the comprehension of humanity at this time.

In the horse, the equivalent arrangement of subtle energies of the soul or causal body, is called the higher triad. However, because the process of individualisation has *not* taken place, activity at this level is unable to impinge on the group soul, which contains lower triads. The connection between the components of the higher triad and the group soul is as a thin thread. In man there is a channel between the soul and the personality, which widens and more activity occurs via its mechanism as the soul grows and develops.

Bibliography

Bailey, Alice A. (1951) *Esoteric Astrology* Vol. 1 and Vol. 2. Lucis Press, London.
Bailey, Alice A. (1952) *Treatise on Cosmic Fire.* Lucis Press, London.
Bailey, Alice A. (1953) *Esoteric Healing.* Lucis Press, London.
Bailey, Arthur *(2000) The Bailey Flower Essence Handbook.* Bailey Flower Essences, Ilkley.
Becker, Robert O. and Selden, Gary (1985) *The Body Electric.* Morrow, New York.
Beer, Jessica (1990) *Practical Uses and Applications of the Bach Flower Emotional Remedies.* Balancing Essential Press, Las Vegas.
Bessant, Annie & Leadbeater, C.W (1913) *Man Whence How and Wither.* Theosophical Publishing House, Madras.
Chapman M.D. (Edited Cogswell, M.D.) (1961) *Dr Schuessler's Biochemistry. A Medical Book for the Home.* New Era Laboratories, London.
Davidson, John (1988) *The Web of Life.* C.W. Daniel, Saffron Walden.
Davidson, John (1987) *Subtle Energies.* C.W. Daniel, Saffron Walden.
Denoix, Jean-Marie & Pailloux, Jean-Pierre (Translated by Jonathan Lewis) (1996) *Physical Therapy & Massage for the Horse.* Manson Publishing, London.
France, Simon and Lee, Phillippa (2001) *Aquarius Catalogue 2001 –2002.* Aquarius Flower Remedies, Threpwood Hill Cottage, Birtley, Hexham HE48 3HL.
Goody, Peter (2000) *Horse Anatomy,* 2nd Edition. J. A. Allen, London.
Gurudas (Channeled through Kevin Ryerson) (1985) *Gem Elixirs and Vibrational Healing* Vol. 1 and 2. Cassandra Press, Boulder, CO.
Hartley, E. E. (1994) *The Encyclopaedia of the Horse.* Dorling Kindersley, London.
Hayes, M. H. (Revised and edited Peter D Rossdale) (1987) *Veterinary Notes for Horse Owners.* Stanley Paul, London.
Hodgson, Joan (1990) *The Stars and the Chakras.* White Eagle Publishing Trust, Newlands,

Liss, Hampshire.

Hyne Jones, T.W. (1977) *Dictionary of Bach Flower Remedies*, 2nd Edition, Bach Centre, Wallington.

Kaselle, Marian & Hannay, Pamela (1995) *Touching Horses, Communication, Health and Healing through Shiatsu (Acupressure)*. J.A. Allen, London.

Leadbeater, C.W (1969) *Man Visible and Invisible*. Abridged edition. Quest Books, London, Madras.

Leadbeater, C.W. (c.1927, reprint 1990) *The Chakras*, 6th edition. Quest, London, Madras, Wheaton.

Lehrs, Ernst (1951) *Man or Matter*, 3rd edition. Rudolf Steiner Press, London.

Leigh, Marian (1997) *Findhorn Flower Essences*. Findhorn Press, Forres.

Melody (1995) *Love is in the Earth*. Earth-Love Publishing House, Wheat Ridge, CO.

Ozaniec, Naomi (1990) *The Elements of the Chakras*. Element, Shaftesbury.

Pagan, J., Geor, R.J., Caddel, S.E., Pryor, P.B. & Hoekstra, K.E. (2001) The relationship between glycemic response and the incidence of OCD in Thoroughbred weanlings: A field study. In: *47 Annual AAEP Convention in San Diego, California November 24-28 2001*.

Pettitt, Sabina (1993) *Energy Medicine, Healing from the Kingdoms of Nature*. Pacific Essences, Victoria, Canada.

Powell, A.E. (1928, reprinted 1956) *The Causal Body*. Theosophical Publishing House, London.

Sisson, Septimus & Grossman, J.D. (1959) *The Anatomy of The Domestic Animals*, 4th Edition. W.B. Saunders London.

Tansley, David V. (1977) *Subtle Body - Essence and Shadow*. Thames and Hudson, London.

Tansley, David V. (1972) *Radionics and the Subtle Anatomy of Man*. Health Science Press, Rushington.

Wachsmuth, Guenther (Translated from 2nd German edition Wannamaker Colin D.) (1932) *The Etheric Formative Forces in Cosmos, Earth and Man*. Anthroposophical Publishing House, London, New York.

White Eagle (1942) *Spiritual Unfoldment Vols 1, 2, 3,& 4*. White Eagle Publishing Trust, Liss.

(1998) *Horses and Ponies*. Collins Gem Guide, London.

Galea Parsons

<table>
<tr><td>10</td><td>

Radionics and Horses –
Case Histories

</td></tr>
</table>

'*Turn 'em out for the sake of their health, sir,*
Turn 'em out on the good green grass ...

'*Turn 'em out as the years do pass*
For every horse needs a rest and a change,
A spell on good green grass.'

M. de B.

I N this chapter we shall look at how energetic differences covered in the last chapter manifest in patients as they present to a radionic practitioner. Then we shall look at some individual cases in more depth. I hope that these cases will give an insight into the intriguing nature of this healing therapy.

There are different sizes and shapes in every breed of horse, which are fascinating. They can range from 9 HH to 19 HH and from tough, cold-blooded native ponies, through to the warm bloods, to fine Arabs and Thoroughbreds. Because of this diversity of type, size and breeding, the variety of cases that may arrive on a radionic practitioner's desk is enormous. Add to this the array of disciplines encountered in the horse world along with the range of problems that may manifest within each horse, and you will understand that a radionic practitioner is never bored! Even if the symptoms are similar the energetic causes are rarely the same. This is why practitioners love their work. In each analysis, whilst similar questions are asked and similar procedures carried out, this radionic process always builds a unique energetic picture of that particular patient at that time. Each unique 'energetic' picture will require a unique combination of treatments with which to resonate in order to bring about a restoration of balance and harmony.

The type of horse that arrives for analysis is usually required for some sort of athletic performance. That performance may be dressage, at any level from junior pony club to international Grand Prix, show jumping with a similar range of aspiration, eventing, Flat or National Hunt racing, driving, endurance riding, polo or mounted games, hunting, or team chasing. The horse patient may be a well-loved pet or an old retainer, just to mention a few possible patients. The point here is that usually the owner or trainer wants to 'do' something with the horse. What the owner/trainer wants to 'do' is usually more than the horse would do for itself if it were just living wild.

We have modified our breeding stock to bring to the fore characteristics that we seek. Such characteristics may be speed in the case of the sprinting flat horse, or speed and endurance in the horses bred to go longer distances. We have bred horses that can develop muscle mass, balance and response to the slightest aid, enabling them to perform dressage to an excellent level of accuracy and precision. We ask them to jump fences of great height, width and complexity. Not all selective breeding has been of value. We have managed to breed horses that find going in a straight line with a rider on their back a huge challenge, and very difficult!

Usually a lock of horse's hair (the witness needed by a practitioner) is sent to us because something is stopping his performance; the owner or trainer may consult us after they have visited brilliant veterinary surgeons. Often the owner/trainer is either desperate or has had experience of radionic treatment previously and has found it of value. Clients find their way to most practitioners because of word of mouth recommendation. The following are a very small sample of cases I have treated.

Broodmare

Recently a mare was sent to me for treatment because she was due to foal. I had treated her in previous years for her foaling and then for help to get her back in foal. On each occasion a variety of radionic treatment was broadcast and she responded well.

On one of these previous occasions she had been sent to a very prestigious stallion and for three successive ovulations had not 'held' in foal. The owners, understandably, were getting anxious. The year before this particular episode she had sustained a very bad wound and had been given immensely powerful drugs and there was anxiety that these may have affected her fertility. We were all very concerned that she was not getting in foal. The owners were very doubtful when I had told them the mare was fine but the stallion was not! However, having had three successive coverings for three successive ovulations, they were then free to go to another stallion late in the season but not too late for a National Hunt horse. I had urged them to change stallions. This change of stallion had been highly successful and she had been quickly confirmed in foal.

Returning to this year, the arrangements were different. They chose a stallion that was standing on the other side of the country but could be used for what is called a 'walk-in' service. This means that the mare could be taken to the stud, served, and then she and her foal at foot brought home, instead of mare and foal being left at stud for some weeks.

This year's foal had been late arriving but, given the awful wet weather, I had felt the mare and nature were being sensible. The foaling had been easy and the filly foal robust. The covering had taken place on the foaling pride nine days later, she had been scanned 15/16 days later and the owner had been dismayed that she appeared to be empty. However, that was not the indication that she gave me from her readings. The owner and vet planned to rescan on day 17, in order to get her back to the stallion as soon as possible if she were not in foal. I asked them to wait a further four days (as indicated via dowsing). There was great excitement when the scan showed her to be in foal. A heartbeat was now also evident. This is a very private mare that does things in her own time. On this occasion she appeared to me to ovulate late and it was fortunate that the stallion's sperm was long lived. You cannot really tell anything about the suitability of a stallion until a covering has taken place unless the stallion's owner has approached you and requested your help.

Stallion

Some years ago I was asked by a stallion's owner why a prestigious and usually willing Irish stallion would not cover a particular mare. He had been worked, show jumped and shown, as well as being used as a stallion. When 'working' he had the manners of a perfect gentleman and did not so much as 'look' at the mares he was asked to move around, regardless of whether they were in season or not. This particular filly had come straight from the racecourse to stud, she was very clean, fit, smart and 'up together'. In the stallion's mind this was one of the 'off limit ladies' i.e. he was inhibited. As well as being able to treat him to relinquish his inhibitions on this occasion, I suggested that they find a muddy field and turn out the filly and hope she rolled and rolled. Luckily she thought this was wonderful and she nearly gave the stallion's owner a heart attack as she enjoyed her first freedom in several months. She returned to the stallion later that day, who, finding that she smelt much more natural, obliged.

Because horses do not share the same very verbal language that we use, they risk not being understood by us. It takes the exceptional horseman like Monty Roberts or Mark Todd to really comprehend *Equus* language, to have the ability to listen and observe, as well as to enter into a dialogue. Radionics can also prove very helpful in this area because of the insight it offers into the type of energetic activity occurring at the astral and mental levels and this allows the practitioner to access the emotions and thought patterns of horses.

Racehorse

The next case history concerns a well-bred 2 year old that was about to go into training. She had been sent to the sales the preceding October but not sold. Here she had developed into a box walker and weaver. It had taken her two and half months to begin to settle down after going to the sales and she was about to be moved again! She was described as outwardly confident but really wanted a friend. Her analysis indicated good basic vitality being received and absorbed by the etheric and physical bodies. However, most of the energy centres were underactive, except those relating to the alta major and the liver which were wildly over-active. In addition to this there were three blockages, in the alta major, throat and liver. The tension in this picture was extreme. The alta major is the centre that enables us to process situations liable to cause panic; it is the centre whereby the unseen world can be assessed. The alta major energy centre alerts us, and animals, to unseen dangers.

The liver centre is also an area where gut instincts are registered and processed. This centre too, was in overdrive. In addition both centres were blocked, which would mean that energy, however efficiently these centres worked, would go in fits and starts. One day something would appear reasonably OK, the next day the same thing would loom like an enormous dragon or bogeyman. Interestingly, the base and adrenals, whilst depressed, were by no means totally depleted, which was a very good thing in these circumstances. The filly's throat centre was depleted and blocked. One aspect of the throat centre manifestation is that of self-expression. She was in a state of panicking overdrive and not really able to express it, other than via the box walking and weaving. Looking at the subtle bodies the physical and etheric were congested, but the etheric and nadis and astral were also overactive. There was a misalignment between astral and etheric.

This showed itself perfectly, if such a misalignment could be considered perfect, in the intermittent but very exaggerated behaviour. This filly had been backed, but so far had not been taken out of the confines of the school. It was thought highly probable that they would lose her in an unrestricted area.

Continuing with the analysis, the major junctions of pelvis, withers and head and neck were out of alignment. The rest of her back was good. For the major junctions to be wrong in such a young horse is unusual. The fact that nothing else was wrong was because her back had been treated by a good horse chiropractor and what was left was 'the problem'. But why was it being sustained?

I looked more closely at the head. The alta major and throat readings were key issues in this analysis; in addition this filly felt as if her awareness was just in her head, the rest of her body was rather incidental to her. The energy relating to the nasal bones indicated misalignment, as did the energy relating to the hyoid bone. The hyoid bone is a bone that does not articulate with other bones, it is located in the throat area and is crucial for the function of many muscles in that area.

The filly was due to go into training in two to three weeks and the owners were concerned about travelling her and about how she would get on in a new yard, if at all. Because of this pressure of time I suggested they talk with their chiropractor about adjustment of the hyoid bone. He laughed and said you can't adjust a hyoid bone. I persisted with the owners and they talked to the assistant chiropractor. She reluctantly agreed to have a look. When she looked she found that there was a real need and that an adjustment was both possible and necessary. It was not one that she had made before. Radionic treatments had been broadcast to assist these chiropractic adjustments to the cranial bones and hyoid bone and to help maintain the subsequent changes. In addition treatments were broadcast to start the process of clearing the blockages to the energy centres and realigning the subtle bodies. Treatments included broadcasting the Bach flower essence *Scleranthus*, to the liver centre. This was an interesting treatment because the liver centre in the horse, as well as covering the related physical organs and the process of detoxification, is also important because it is often the chakra via which the horse processes many of the demands of its environment and the demands made upon it by man. *Scleranthus* is the remedy for indecision, which is perfectly expressed in the movement of weaving. Weaving is when the horse sways from one front leg to the other, or put another way, 'shall I go this way or that way?' Therefore, *Scleranthus* to the liver appeared to be a very appropriate treatment, addressing the weaving vice and also because it is a confidence giving treatment. It is a treatment that allows the recipient to *'keep poise and balance under all conditions, to be calm and determined' (Dictionary of Bach Flower Remedies)*. Other treatments also assisted the rebalancing of the liver centre, and aided the release of fears that were blocking her behaviour and growth.

Treatments were also given to rebalance the energy flow through the three major junctions of the spine, crucial for this horse's development and well-being. Some treatment was also directed towards the etheric energy structures relating to some cranial nerves. In addition quite a lot of psychological treatments were broadcast to this filly to help her accept and grow through her changes in circumstance and the new challenges that would be confronting her. This gives an idea of some of the facets of her treatment at this stage.

The filly virtually stopped box walking and almost grew up overnight. She went into training and travelled to her new yard like a 'pro'. Her trainer was a knowledgeable, sensible and sensitive man. He gave her a box where she could easily see what was going on. She settled well. Because the hyoid adjustment was only a day or so before she went into training the owners asked that she be put on the horse-walker only for a few days. This the trainer did for five days and this meant that she was not stressed in her work and that the muscles around the adjustment could settle to the 'new arrangement' in the area. Her training progressed well and smoothly until a virus struck the yard. All the horses were endoscoped; that means an optic tube was put down into the lungs to enable the veterinary surgeon to observe the condition of the lungs and to take samples. Sadly she had got the virus but even worse the procedure had disrupted the energy relating to the hyoid bone again. She got over the virus but went on 'making a noise' (this means that her breathing was too loud or raspy, indicative of a problem, possibly serious). Unfortunately, whilst the trainer was quite prepared to have the chiropractor come to his yard, she was unable to oblige because of commitments elsewhere. The adjustment had to be made radionically, and this took a little longer than I should have liked, but the filly is now in fast work, not making a noise and hopefully will soon have her first race.

The situations we have looked at, whilst interesting, are nevertheless what the horse would do in the wild – breed and run. The reason the filly's hyoid bone was misaligned was because she had been confined and had managed to jam her throat and nose into a restricted space and then panicked or had it bumped, perhaps at the sales. Let us look now at some of the things we ask our horses to do that are not so natural.

Shetland pony

Tuppence came to me in February thoroughly out of sorts. She was a 17-year-old Shetland mare. The same person had owned her since she was a 4 year old. She lived in a professional but very aware yard. She was being used as a companion nanny to the bigger more highly strung horses, to act as a steadying influence when they were turned out. For several years she had lived in a sizable, converted tractor shed at night. She shared this shed happily with a 12.2 HH gelding, Tom Kitten. Fairly recently the oldest pony in the yard had had to be put down at the age of nearly 40 (40 is a very respectable age for a pony).

Tuppence had become rather grumpy and had taken against Tom Kitten. She was really going for him, with both heels and teeth. She appeared to be really quite angry.

The analysis indicated good vitality levels and a good general balance within her system, particularly for her age. However, it also indicated an overactive and blocked heart centre. There was an under active solar plexus, which was also blocked, and an overactive base. The only relevant miasm (an inherited or acquired taint or fault) at the time was psoric, a little surprising given her aggression! Psora miasm is usually indicative of a tendency to rather timid behaviour. This analysis and the psychological aspects that came up for treatment showed that she had been very upset by Gypsy's death. More than that, she was feeling 'passed over'. She was feeling that she had not been given her rightful place in the herd. (She had now been on the yard the longest and was the oldest mare). She was a little bored and very put out. Tom Kitten, a mere 12 year old gelding, had not been at all sympathetic to the situation, continued to treat her the same, with no increase in deference, and she was cross. Although she was quite grumpy with all her human handlers, Tom Kitten bore the brunt of her distress!

I suggested putting her in a box on her own at night, for a week, whilst I got down to some serious radionic treatment. This included aligning all the subtle bodies, which had become misaligned due to her disrupted feelings, harmonising her nerves and nadis, an extremely soothing and strengthening treatment, and breaking energetic connections with her perceived injustices. I also started the process of clearing her energetic blockages. Her psychological unhappiness was addressed with treatments to enhance her self-esteem, confidence and self-harmony. In addition radionic magnesium was broadcast. This is *the* 'stress element' that easily becomes depleted under testing circumstances. This was augmented with flower essences. Bach *Holly* was given for the aggression and anger, *Wild Oat* because she was out of sorts and did not know what to do next, and *Crab Apple* because her emotions and feelings were alien to her, and she was not enjoying being like that. The Pacific Sea essence *Surf Grass*, was included because of its soothing and healing properties, especially connected to heart issues. It is a remedy that gives *'courage, strength, power, rooted in stability and flexibility'*. *Surf Grass* offers support in stressful situations especially paradoxical situations *' stress without distress'*. It helps the maintenance of homeostasis, *'balance and harmony among body, mind, spirit and emotion'*. I also gave the Pacific Sea essence *Dolphin. Dolphin* essence addresses most of the energy centres; it is helpful for *'playfulness and light heartedness and interspecies communication'*. It was the aspect of light heartedness that was most important for Tuppence because at that time she was anything but light hearted. It is a *'vital link for someone feeling profound alienation and loneliness and sense of deep loss and abandonment'* (*Energy Medicine, Healing from the Kingdoms of Nature* – Sabina Pettitt). *Dolphin* connects to the limbic system and via this application can help the recipient access feelings of pleasure and ecstasy instead of fear and anger. It balances heart and head, emotions and thoughts. I had carried out considerable treatment for the alta major centre, which governs the limbic system, but this treatment encapsulated everything. In addition to radionic treatment, she was given the essence orally, together with a radionic essence.

With this delicious range of treatment Tuppence began to respond. Instead of being grumpy and uncommunicative, she stood in her new box positively beaming with satisfaction. Her owner, a delightful sensitive and aware horsewoman, decided to let her stay in the box and to cut the box door down to a size Tuppence could look over. This was ecstasy in

Tuppence's world!

People on the yard, observing these changes and knowing about her radionic treatment and the comments I had made, entered into her rehabilitation with gusto. One of the owner's clients produced tiny rugs for Tuppence's size, one black and one blue with yellow trim. Apparently when she was shown these rugs, she made it quite plain which 'dress' she preferred! When the black rug was produced, she walked away. When the blue and yellow one came out she came up and sniffed it. A clearer 'yes' and 'no' would be difficult to find.

She has continued as nanny to the bigger horses but now, if she has to accompany them in the horsebox, she wears her smart blue and yellow rug and she can almost be seen flouncing up the ramp with a swish of her 'dress'!

Interestingly she had not exhibited any signs of sweet itch that summer. In the past she had been prone to this condition. It would appear that all the harmonising and rebalancing treatments have had a very positive effect in clearing vibrations at all levels.

Racing to dressage horse

Whilst racing is arguably one of the most natural disciplines in which we engage our horses not all horses like racing! I have found several potentially good (from the breeding point of view) racehorses that have really disliked training and racing. Sometimes it is because they grow up in sensitive and aware homes and cannot tolerate the isolation and production line approach of some big racing yards. Sometimes the psychological impact of the change from being a two year old in what is effectively a herd to being a stabled horse with a great deal to assimilate and learn is just too much overload on the nervous system. Sometimes they do not like the physical jostle and competitive aspect of racing. In this last instance there is likely to be more to it than just dislike of being jostled; as we have seen horses are a paradox of simple and complex.

This next case is a 17 HH Thoroughbred gelding and is an excellent example of the above. He was bred in Ireland and bought by an Englishman for National Hunt racing but was only in training for three months. At some point he sustained an injury to his heel. At 6 years old he was sold to become an eventer. At 8 he was sold again because 'he was not of a standard to go all the way to Badminton'.

His analysis indicated that he was a very nice chap, but extremely sensitive; not very good at going forward because he was so wary. The injury he had sustained to his foot had been severe and he was still affected by shock from this incident, but behind that trauma was the trauma of being weaned. Weaning by separation is something most horses have to contend with. Generally, and within reason, the later it is carried out the less of a problem it is to either mare or foal. For many horses this event does not cause problems but it can be an underlying cause of some anxieties and insecurities. Horses, unlike humans, only infrequently suffer birth traumas, although they may be born with problems stemming from the time *in utero*.

In this case weaning had given him a lot of anxiety. Very careful questioning via dowsing revealed that not long before he was weaned he had wandered off from his dam and become stuck in a ditch and needed to be rescued by humans. His mother had told him in no uncertain terms to 'stay close in future'. Yet when it came to weaning she had been taken away and he had been unable to follow. Unlike the ditch episode she had not returned. The foal that had been forward going and inquisitive before the ditch incident, became quite introverted and insecure.

He had not enjoyed training. When he got to a smaller eventing yard for a while things looked up. Gradually, as the jumps got bigger and more complex and testing, any confidence that he had gained, drained away. In addition he was asked to do too many different things too quickly for him. He was sold again.

His new home is ideal for him. His new owner is a sensitive lady who desperately wants to improve her dressage riding. She had been a very successful show pony rider in her childhood and youth on very well schooled, produced ponies. Now she wanted to 'bring on' and develop her own horse. They embarked on a journey of self-discovery together.

Most of this horse's readings were underactive except the alta major, an energy centre that one only very rarely has to even consider. It is a very special area at the apex of a triangle from the tips of the two ears (think of the unicorn). This horse had spent his life since weaning tasting and testing the world, seen and unseen, for trouble and dangers. The rest of his system was, not surprisingly, depleted. In spite of all the stress going on within himself he was still a delightful chap.

There was a small amount of misalignment between the subtle bodies. This is where I started treatment. Because it was a small amount of misalignment, treatment did not ask for a big change to be made, it was therefore a gentle start. I also addressed the shock. Next treatment was broadcast for the energy relating to his adrenals because of the exhaustion and depletion within his system. His analysis indicated that he was slightly anaemic because of a slight cobalt imbalance; this was treated radionically. A lot of treatment was directed towards the damage to the heel.

His coat began to improve and his eyes to widen and relax but there was still a very long way to go. Gradually radionic treatment moved on to his fascia and cranial bones. This horse was very lucky that, as well as radionic treatment, he was taken to a horse massage practitioner and an exceptional horse osteopath healer. In addition to this his owner had lessons with a very talented and delightful lady who teaches with love, humour and a vast fund of experience.

This horse was treated radionically with a flower essence called *Sea Pink* (Findhorn flower essences), which is a remedy that helps balance energy flow between all energy centres. It is a remedy for 'harmony and unification'. For this horse it allowed him to stop reaching for his dam. It allowed him to stop 'needing to be elsewhere'. I also broadcast the gem stone *Topaz*. *Topaz* is a stone I have always found horses respond well to. It is a stone that traditionally balances and calms emotions, and also aids the assimilation of *'newly stabilised emotions'* (*Gem Elixirs*, Gurudas). It helps the body release tension. It is a delightful treatment. Flower and gem treatments are effective for horses and humans, because they bring another range of dimensions to treatment, in particular that of the qualities of their particular kingdom. Sometimes it is possible to give a treatment in this way, that allows the recipient to accept the treatment and change with it with greater ease. This is not always the case, nor is it always required. The third remedy broadcast at this time was a remedy to help the horse take that leap of faith that is required to leave old patterning and confusion; because the familiar was choking him, he needed courage to move through his life differently.

This horse really wanted to change but it was hard for him to let go of his past traumas and subsequent conditioning. Gradually treatment to his head, neck and rib energies allowed him to work and breath better instead of holding his breath for the 'difficult bits'. His transitions became more reliable. He started to go forward for his owner, as they learnt and grew together.

All the time he wanted to please, to try and do as he was being asked, but he found letting go of any current stability and moving on to the next stage frightening. He was therefore reluctant. Slowly he began to trust his handlers were not asking too much and slowly but surely he began to trust that his body could do it differently. Soon we were able to work radionically to support his hocks as he brought them more and more under him as his weight began to be taken more from behind. Treatment was directed to his lumbar and lower thoracic areas to allow that beautiful stretch, that enables the hocks to come under even more and a stronger and more rounded outline, to manifest. The withers needed to come up and the neck to come out from between the shoulder blades, the horse was then more able to 'come down on to the bit' with greater and greater ease.

However, this transformation from a racehorse to a dressage horse was not all plain sailing. Because of his owner's commitments this horse had quite regular stays at livery at the trainer's busy yard. Here he could watch horses come and go with relative equanimity, but at home it was different. He could not bear the ponies to be taken away from him. He immediately went into panic mode. Treatments for reassurance, calm, courage, stability and grit barely made any impression. Flower essences given orally only made a small impression at this stage.

Given that the trauma of weaning was at the root of this horse's tensions and distortions within his energy systems and hence his body, it is hardly surprising that this is still a difficult trigger situation for him. However, there are still radionic treatments that are being brought to bear on this situation and, because he is a horse that really wants to please, wants to be completely 'at home in his body', I have every hope that treatment will succeed in this area too.

Wound case

The next case history is about a horse with a bad injury. This was a 12-year-old Arab x Thoroughbred x Welsh Mountain grey gelding. He had been a champion hack at Dublin and qualified for Wembley. He was described as not particularly forward moving, cheeky and a bit lazy.

Early one January he had been travelling in a horsebox which made a right turn across a main road. He had slipped over in the box, the groom's door had swung open and his near hind had gone through the opening. He had either caught his leg on the bolt or the corner of the door itself. He had a gash wound from his thigh to his fetlock on the inside of the leg.

It was about a quarter of an inch wide and down to the bone in several places. The fetlock area had an upward facing flap of skin. I was told it was unstitchable.

His hair sample arrived on my desk three days after his injury. His analysis indicated a lot of shock and misalignment of his subtle bodies. There were only four energy blockages. This was encouraging but his vitality level was low. This low vitality reading was an indication of the severity of the shock. His crown centre was very over-active and blocked; it appeared these energies had sustained severe disruption and probably a blow during the accident. As a result of this he was suffering from a headache and feeling very 'spaced out'. His liver energy centre was blocked and under-active. Whilst I suspected it had been under-active for sometime the blockage was a result of the accident. It was important that treatment supported the liver energies because he needed to be confined to box-rest to allow his large leg wound to heal. This confinement with no exercise meant less grass, less sunshine and greater stress, conditions that all put further strain on the liver. The liver centre is an important area that helps the horse release not only physical toxins but emotional 'toxins' as well. This horse had a plethora of emotional 'toxins'; nothing of this nature had touched him before and he was thoroughly out of sorts. The energy relating to the near hind was very congested and under-active and would need a lot of rejuvenating.

The owner was a new client. She explained her qualifications and experience to me and then explained she had experienced radionics for her cats so she knew I could sort this wound out radionically. Somewhat surprised I asked what had been done. She explained that as the vet had been unable to stitch the wound she had dispensed with him and they were tubbing it with Epsom salts and iodine and now it was up to me. "No antibiotics?" I queried, somewhat surprised that a vet had seen a wound of this severity and not prescribed antibiotics. My client explained she preferred natural methods of healing. Having double-checked that a vet had actually seen this wound I proceeded with treatment.

Treatment initially was directed primarily at releasing and eliminating the shock. Treatment was also broadcast to the wound and hind leg. Detoxifying the area energetically was of prime importance, especially as no antibiotics were being given. Treatments were also broadcast to alleviate the energetic effects of bruising, especially to the bone tissue. More treatments were given to the hock and fetlock joints to assist in maintaining their integrity. I wanted to avoid any bony changes occurring in these joints as a result of the blows and bruising they had received. Muscle bruising and stiffness throughout the body was also addressed. He was quite fit at the time of the accident and had gone down with some force so the bruising and stiffness was quite extensive and he was unable to walk it out because of being confined to his box. In addition he was given Biochemic Tissue Salts No 2 *Calc phos* and No 10 *Nat phos*, *Arnica* 6 and *Rhus tox* 30.

As time went on treatment was given to realign the energies of his back, which can bring about a realignment of the vertebrae. However, this horse did have the benefit in time of a horse chiropractor that visited Ireland every 6 weeks or so.

Treatment continued to be broadcast to aid the rejuvenation of the skin around the wound. Tubbing also continued regularly. Mercifully my client ran an organised yard and my patient was amenable to standing in a small dustbin of warm water, Epsom salts and iodine. The wound went on well. On several occasions in the early weeks I suggested that a vet check it out. My readings did indicate that the wound was progressing well, but it was a big wound, I did not know my client well and I did not want any mistakes for this horse. Finally towards the end of 6 weeks she said there had been a vet in the yard and she had let him look at the wound and he had said it was looking good.

My client started poulticing with a comfrey mixture. The dustbin had begun to pall, it had been knocked over a couple of times, poulticing seemed preferable although very difficult. The wound had widened, not surprisingly, but was clean. At this point there was a need for a further change in treatment both physical and radionic, because it was important not to get into a cycle of proud flesh. Radionic treatment was very specific but simple with regard to the wound area. Physically the dressing was changed to a comfrey and calendula powder and 3 days later the wound closed and real healing started to occur. As soon as true scabbing occurred vitamin E was applied up to a millimetre of the scab, and given radionically. This is a wonderful treatment for minimising scarring.

By the end of 3 months he was brought back into work. The scar was black (not pink) and hair re-growth had begun. He was given nettles in his feed as a good gentle blood cleanser and tonic. Nettles boost the blood gently without making the horse fizzy or over-excitable. His rehabilitation was slowly progressing. In May his owner reported that he was not going freely. At this point more work was done to release shock and trauma. In view of the severity of the accident I had been surprised at how quickly he initially responded to shock and trauma treatments and that he had not needed more help in this area in the ensuing weeks. This horse was a strong character and he only shed and dealt with what was actually required in order that he could deal with what was being asked of him at the time, but no more. As he was asked to 'do' more i.e. move with more extravagance and accuracy, so more releasing was necessary to allow him to move forward. This he was quite happy to do, but not until asked! This perfectly expressed his attitude to life and work. This pattern of treatment went on through the summer each time a new threshold was reached.

In early July he caught the wound again and opened the bottom of it up, on the fetlock. However the wound responded quickly and easily to treatment. In August he won a hack class! Everyone was delighted. He came off treatment that autumn.

Lameness

He came back for further treatment in June the following year. He was lame, with a puffy near fore fetlock joint. His analysis and careful questioning indicated that he had slipped up in the field. Although outwardly confident, inside he had frightened himself. He was fearful of re-injury and confinement. The new analysis indicated tightness in front of and through the wither area. Also the energy readings were indicative of a slight strain and bruising to the fetlock.

Treatment was given to the energies governing thoracic vertebra 2, thoracic vertebra 6 and thoracic vertebra 14 as well as to his fetlock joint, and each tendon and ligament that make up the fetlock joint. I suggested that his shoulders and the area in front of his shoulders were areas that needed quite vigorous rubbing. This was not so much for muscle stimulation, more to encourage the triple warmer meridian to function better. A little imprecise perhaps but my client could not find an acupuncturist in Ireland at that time. It worked! I also suggested bandaging both forelegs and fetlocks with witch hazel. Because the analysis indicated a zinc deficiency I suggested that one of the proprietary brands of zinc supplements might be of value to him at that time.

His liver energy centre was again poor but this time it was working too hard. It is unusual to get such a change of reading even with a large gap in treatment, so this needed to be regarded as significant. Dowsing indicated Biochemic Tissue Salt No 10 again. Whilst this is not 'the' liver salt it is nevertheless supportive of liver function. I also suggested that perhaps my client was being over generous with her feeding! Rather rue-fully she agreed this might be the case. They were preparing for the Dub-lin Show and rations had been increased. These were now reduced and a better balance within the liver energy centre was quickly established. The fetlock resolved quite quickly, and amidst much excitement he went to the Dublin Show where he acquitted himself well. This was no mean feat considering the severity of his wound just 19 months previously, not to mention his latest tweak of the fetlock joint.

Deformity

This last case history is about an 8-week-old foal, $^7/_8$ TB, $^1/_8$ Irish Draft, who was described as leggy and over at the knees, the pictures shows clearly what this means. His analysis indicated only two blockages of his energy centres, one relating to the off fore leg and one to the brow. Both front leg energy centres were overactive; most of the other readings including base and alta major were quite reasonable. The only other slightly remarkable reading was for the throat energy centre.

Careful dowsing indicated that in addition to stresses *in utero* due to an odd position of the growing foetus, most of the trauma and distortion came from a past life injury to his knees. This little chap was very reluc-tant to re-enter the world and go forward into a new life.

The analysis indicated quite serious disruptions within the subtle bodies. Treatment started with rejuvenation to the nadis. The nadis is the subtle networking within the etheric body that energizes the entire nervous system. This network needed serious restoration if healing and correct growth patterns were to occur. Next the blockage to the brow was addressed because of the brow's association with the nervous system. After that came work to the subtle energies of both front legs, particularly the off fore. In addition treatment was given to the throat centre which, because it governs thyroid and parathyroid glands, is closely linked with bone integrity.

This foal was perky but shy and he managed well although mare and foal were not turned out for very long. He and his owner were blessed with a knowledgeable and attentive farrier who dressed his feet with skill and regularity. Lunar *Woundwort* and Lunar *Coltsfoot* were both broadcast to him radionically. The Aquarius Lunar essences address past life issues

(*Aquarius Flower Remedies*). Lunar *Woundwort* addresses past life robbery, in this instance the robbery related to his knee wounds, which had robbed him of the ability to move with ease. Lunar *Coltsfoot* aids karmic release. These essences combined with Healing Herbs *Star of Bethlehem* for the shock of being in the world with deformed legs that didn't work very well, *Larch* to give and enhance self confidence (to go forward in life) and self esteem, provided a good platform to enable emotional and physical growth. I must just point out that past life issues are not commonplace in the treatment of horses.

Next came the painstaking work of treating each bone, ligament and tendon in each fetlock, cannon and knee, each epiphysis and every cartilage. Treatments to enhance the co-ordination between each of the four legs were given, and other subtle energy treatments including really grounding all his energies and keeping him plugged into the energies of the earth. Other treatments included psychological treatments to remove mistrust from the muscle tissues and all the other tissues of the legs. Confidence and reassurance were a constant feature of treatment. Slowly he improved and his legs began to straighten. His owner adored him and was delighted with his progress. His farrier, too, was pleased.

In January the beagles came close to the farm and all the horses became excited and rushed about the field. Finally they were all caught, soaked in sweat and thoroughly overexcited. This yearling had banged and cut his right knee; needless to say all the others were fine! The owner was distraught at this set back but treatment was given for this injury and the recovery was good

In April the farrier and he got in a muddle and he pulled away and became very difficult to handle. Having had so much attention to his legs and feet, it had all become too much for him, it was springtime and he was a precocious boy and he had had enough. His owner very sensibly turned him away, just catching him up for what had to be done. She gave him the space to grow into himself.

In September he was castrated. Treatment was obviously given for this relatively easy but potentially damaging procedure. All went well. At the end of October he came off treatment. His legs were straight and he was a happy, reasonably well-behaved yearling. Because of other radionic work I have kept in touch with his owner who sent me the picture of him ready to start his working life (see Figs.10.1-5). Sensibly she had left him to grow and mature so that his legs could stabilise. The restrictions and proximity

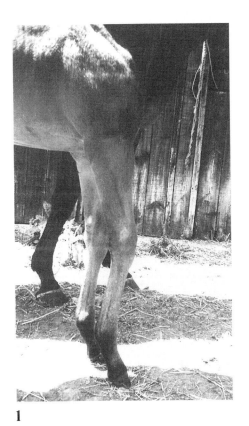

1

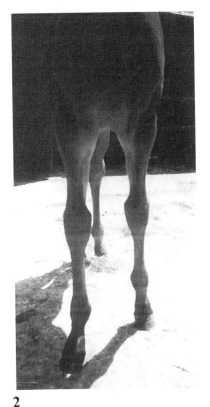

2

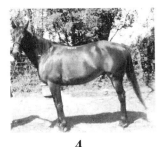

3

Figs. 10.1-5
Deformity case at 3 weeks
of age (1 & 2) and at 6 years
when 16.3 HH (3-5).

4

5

of the severe foot and mouth disease outbreak had meant that he had an extra year to mature.

I hope these case histories have given an insight into how the theory of the previous chapter works in practice. A radionic 'tool kit' can encompass so many aspects of healing and energy work. Its potential is limitless provided we keep in mind the best interests of the patient. This can be difficult if there truly is conflict between what the owner wants to do and what is best for the horse. But, as I hope I have stated more than once, most horses want to please and want to serve. If they are not doing so then possibly it is because the owner is uneducated and not asking in the correct manner for the horse to understand, or he is hurting somewhere and cannot 'manage' the task.

I hope these case histories have illustrated the many ways in which radionics can help animals and humans. It is definitely not a cure all but perhaps it will become more so in the decades to come as our practitioner skills of interpretation of these subtle energy systems increase. Soul growth is the purpose of life and this is the growth that radionic treatment assists by providing the catalyst for self-healing.

See the previous chapter for a bibliography

Enid A. Eden

Radionics in Agriculture and Horticulture

It has often been said that radionics in agriculture/horticulture is the simplest application of the therapy.

I would disagree with this statement, however, as I consider humans to be the most straightforward form. After all, wherever a human is or of whatever race, all human anatomy and physiology are the same.

Animals – all creatures except humans – vary. For example, some have claws, others have hooves, a cow has four stomachs, etc., so it is important to know about the breeding, feeding and management of the animals being treated. As well as different anatomy and physiology, they have their specific diseases too. The quality of grazing land and feed as well as the effects of management and transportation in the case of horses, cattle, etc. also have to be taken into account and, if the animals are wild, habitat must also be considered.

Soil is not an inert mass and, as such, it should not just be used as a medium in which to put substances to produce plants. It is a living, finely balanced organism with a very complicated life structure of its own. Many years of looking at British agriculture fundamentally from an economic viewpoint have led to substances being added to the soil and to control pests, diseases and weeds to produce the 'designer produce' at the lowest price which the consumer has demanded.

Soils vary in type from place to place and may be loam, clay, sand, peat, etc. They also vary in accordance with the type of underlying rock – limestone, granite, chalk, etc. – the climate and general location such as latitude or altitude. Plants also vary with the soil type, climate and location. Plants, like animals, have their own specific diseases too, and they also have many different structures and nutritional requirements.

It is said that Nature is red in tooth and claw and the old adage, 'Big fleas have little fleas upon their backs to bite them and so on *ad infinitum*' is very true. Organisms should not be destroyed but controlled in a way which helps to restore the natural balance.

It seems that radionics was not considered for soil and plants until Curtis P. Upton became interested in the late 1940s. He was a civil engineer in the USA who had been inspired by the work of Albert Abrams, and he wondered whether the 'strange device' (radionic instrument) used to treat human ailments might also be used to control pests in agriculture. He and a friend, William Knuth, took a radionic instrument into a cotton field in Arizona and proceeded to treat it successfully to rid it of pests. Upton and Knuth were also probably the first to use a photograph of the land as the witness, which enabled them to treat the field at a distance instead of taking the instrument to the field. Upton and Knuth were joined by Howard Armstrong, a college classmate of Upton's who had gone on to become an industrial chemist, to form UKACO Inc. (named using the initial letters of their surnames), under whose auspices they conducted many very successful experiments and treated extensively in the USA. They were eventually forced to close down for a variety of reasons, including the concern of the US government, which felt that, as poisonous substances were being projected to large areas, the same treatment might be able to be used on people.

George de la Warr, a civil engineer from Oxford who had started the Radionic Association in 1943, became interested in this aspect of radionics in the 1950s and carried out many experiments, particularly on the sensitivity of plants. He then continued to do many experiments on pest control, nutrition, growth, the critical position of plants and much more.

A.R. Kent, usually known as Bill, was a Gloucestershire organic farmer who used radionics extensively on his farm and conducted many experiments. He was a very practical person and, as well as using radionics to keep his crops and animals healthy, proved that radionically treated produce is more nutritious. This he did by dividing his store cattle into two groups, feeding one group of cattle on home-grown produce and giving the other group the same amount and content of bought-in produce. The result was a larger daily liveweight gain from the cattle fed the home-grown produce. Similar results were achieved in the 1970s by Philip Derbyshire, a farmer from Loughborough whose land was treated radionically. When his cattle had consumed all his home-grown produce, they were fed on purchased produce of the same type and quantity and the daily liveweight gain dropped considerably. In both cases, these beef cattle were being fattened in yards. Bill, being interested in the work of Rudolf Steiner, also introduced cosmic influences etc. into the treatments and made the rates for them which we still use today.

In the 1960s Christopher Harwich and Armyn Wodehouse compiled considerable information by means of Polaroid photographs of soil before and after treatment. Before treatment, the soil looked dull with only the occasional bit of light or colour; after treatment, it looked vibrant and full of light and colour.

Armyn Wodehouse and I did many experiments together from the early 1960s and structured the training, made the rates and compiled the rate books which we use today.

These are the main characters in the history of radionics in agriculture/ horticulture, although others have made smaller contributions.

All the various different life forms in the soil – its fauna, flora, bacteria and many microorganisms – work together and transmute to produce a healthy, living substance with which to sustain plant life. The healing of the soil takes time and this is where radionics can be beneficial. With years of misuse, many soils have lost their finely balanced structure. Organic methods will help to repair this, but where it is not possible to be entirely organic, fertilisers need to be applied in balance for the crop, since each individual crop requires a different balance of food.

Radionics, being a natural phenomenon, is obviously most compatible with organic husbandry, but just as we have to deal with human and animal patients who have had drugs, crops which have had inorganic fertilisers applied should not be ruled out for treatment. Alongside organic methods, the aim of radionics is to build up the life of the soil so that it can produce the food for the plants in the soil from the humus and other organic material that is available, making them more nutritious for animals and man. Soil life is much less active in a more chemical environment and antibodies are not built up in the soil to combat disease. If everything was in balance, it would be Utopia, but this is a long way off as everything has to contend with pollution, not only from our immediate environment but also from the atmosphere – that which goes up comes down. We cannot live in isolation.

Radionic treatment is not a substitute for plant food any more than it is a substitute for human or animal food. The plant must get its nutrition from somewhere and, if this is not from the natural organic process, it will have to be from inorganic fertilisers. These fertilisers, however, do inhibit the life in the soil and over many years may destroy it. This is well demonstrated by cases of soil erosion and dust bowl effect in the USA, the UK and elsewhere.

Radionics can be of great benefit to anyone wanting to change from the modern conventional methods to organics. Treatment helps to strengthen the soil bacteria and other microorganisms, which in turn break down the organic matter to produce the nutrients that the plant needs.

To help with this process, the role of the cosmos on the soil and plants should not be forgotten. Everyone accepts the influence of the moon on the tides and the movement of the sun creating longer and shorter days and therefore the different seasons. It is not so widely accepted, however, that the other planets and heavenly bodies have an effect on soil, plants and everything living on this planet.

When starting to analyse and treat soil and plants, many aspects should be considered. Soil varies so much in its structure, so it is impor-tant to know about it from a geological perspective – not only the topsoil but the underlying sub-soil and probably the rock as well. The climate of the area also has to be considered. An understanding of which crops will happily grow on different soils and the cultivation, management and nutritional requirements of each crop is also required.

In the case of commercial crops, the owner completes a case history of the field or area, giving details of crops grown and manurial applica-tions over the past three years and details of the crop to be planted. For smaller areas, for example gardens or individual plants, the appropriate Plant Case History is completed, together with as much as is relevant on the Soil Case History.

For smaller areas the witness used varies. For a rose bed, for example, a sample of soil taken from the surface would be sufficient. Plants, a leaf or a piece of stem or bark is also used as appropriate. For a large area, a scale map or plan is used, which must always have north indicated so that it can be aligned on the radionic instruments appropriately by the practitioner. Sometimes photographs are also used (aerial in the case of larger areas), but so often, especially if the area is large, not everything is clearly represented.

With all the information provided in mind, the analysis and treat-ment of the soil is approached, taking into consideration the crop to be planted.

Radionics can help to determine drainage, depth of pans and manurial requirements (including quantities). If this is not organic, the information obtained can include appropriate use of chemical fertilisers, variety of seed, etc.

Radionic analysis endeavours to discover the condition of the soil and sub-soil by investigating air and water circulations, fertility, condition of soil bacteria and the general life in the soil, as well as looking for any pollutants in the soil or atmosphere.

From the interpretation and assessment of the analysis, advice is provided and radionic treatment is given to the soil for the specific crop in question in order to produce maximum quality and nutritional value (radionic treatment does not necessarily produce extra quantity, but the nutritional value will be higher).

When treating crops, the ideal is to continuously treat the area and endeavour to prevent any problems from arising. If cereals are affected by aphid, irreparable damage has been done by the time they are noticed, so it is much better to prevent them in the first place. When one crop is finished then the treatment can be changed to prepare the soil for the next one. Each crop has a different requirement, as was realised by the old rotational system.

When treating cereal crops, usually only the soil is treated, but there are times when the soil and plants both have to be treated, in which case a plant analysis also has to be completed. Here both the parts of the plant and the subtle side are investigated, for it has been found that plants, like humans and animals, have energy centres. If plants are in houses, greenhouses or any unnatural conditions, the environment also has to be taken into consideration.

The treatment, like all radionics, is very individual to each case. Some treatments will be to normalise or strengthen parts of the soil or plant. In the case of the bacteria and microorganisms, especially if a change to organic methods is in process, the treatments will aim to help them to reproduce and mutate more quickly with increased energy. With outdoor crops especially, an aim will be to attract the beneficial cosmic influences. Colour is another beneficial treatment, especially for indoor crops and plants.

Various cases which have been treated

A rose bed which had been planted three years previously had one good end but the leaves on the roses at the other end looked yellow and there was one rose which had never bloomed, although the whole bed was the same aspect and had the same treatment. The roses were treated for two months and in the July all were blooming profusely. Here only the soil was treated.

Another rose which was very precious to the owner looked yellow and sick in the July. After completing the radionic analysis it was discovered that the soil was a little low in humus, so a trowelful of farmyard manure was recommended to be applied, radionic treatment was given (which was mostly colour and cosmic influences) and by the end of the August it was looking well, after which no more reports were forthcoming. In this case both the soil and plant were treated.

In these cases the witness was a soil sample, a leaf or both in the case where both had to be treated. Sometimes it is not possible to have a sample from individual plants. In these cases, if the plants are all the same species, the witness can be leaves from a few of the plants and pinches of soil taken at random. These are then used to represent all of the plants. A plan or photograph of any relevant buildings can also be used.

Leaves were used as a witness in the case of three greenhouses full of commercially grown azaleas. On 7 December there was no colour showing in the buds and the grower realised that this meant that they would not be ready for the Christmas market as he intended. The plants were treated with rates and colour and by 15 December the buds were developing well and showing colour and the grower was confident that they would all be sold by Christmas. He had some similar plants in another greenhouse which were not treated and these were not ready for sale until after the New Year.

The leaves of a camellia situated near a lawn on which selective weed killer had been used in July started to go brown at the edges a few days later. On analysis, the cause was found to be poison from the spray. In the first month of treatment all the leaves fell off and the plant appeared to be dying. It then started to produce new growth with lovely dark-green glossy leaves, albeit not as many as previously, but it developed again into a healthy plant by October. Its untreated neighbour of the same species died. Here the plant only was treated.

Sometimes after analysis no treatment is required but only advice to the grower. A commercial tomato plant grower was very worried as he had orders for the plants in the following week and all those in plastic pots looked very light green and sickly, whereas those in clay pots were strong healthy dark-green plants. The witness was a plant in a plastic pot. On analysis it was found that these plants were deficient in iron and the air circulation in the soil was poor. The grower was advised to give an iron supplement and within a few days the plants looked really healthy, enabling him to complete his orders the following week. On investigating the plants in the clay pots, it was discovered that they were getting minute amounts of iron from the pot and that the air circulation in the soil was good.

In another case there was a change in the pH value of the soil from 5.5 to 7 after two weeks of radionic treatment. This was a case where the organic grower made a mistake due to the purchase of a new load of sand and forgot to test its pH value. Having mixed the soil for his greenhouse as he had done previously, he did not realise that anything was wrong until the little lettuces had been planted and the under leaves started to go yellow and die. On doing a pH test of the soil, he found a calcium deficiency but it was impossible for him to add calcium at this point. The witness was soil and a few lettuce leaves. On analysis, it was confirmed that the plants and soil lacked calcium and also an unknown trace element TE3 (for which we have a rate). Initially the plants needed treatment with calcium and deep blue colour. The soil needed treatment every day with calcium and TE3 until the crop of 1,200 dozen lettuces was cut. There was a very high percentage of top quality lettuces in the crop.

These cases are all relatively short, since, as mentioned previously, it is best to treat farms all the time and endeavour to prevent any problems from occurring. Where human and animal treatment is generally only curative, agricultural/horticultural treatment is normally best to be preventative as well as curative should the need arise. If the area is being permanently treated, variations in weather conditions, e.g. drought, and disasters like Chernobyl can be taken into consideration together with the seasons of the year and the development of the plant. When one crop is harvested, the soil can then be prepared for the next crop, which will have different requirements. The aim is always to keep the soil and crop healthy and to help it to develop to its fullest potential.

As mentioned previously, radionics, being a natural therapy, works most effectively with organic methods of farming and growing, but it can also be used to help in the changeover from chemical use to organic methods.

It can also help farmers to use less chemical fertiliser. When helped by a practitioner to determine the quantity he needed rather than going by the general recommendations, a farmer spent £500 less on chemicals a few years ago on his approximately 500-acre farm. The yield from the crop was the same as previously but it was not quite so tall and stood better in adverse weather conditions. Nitrogen Vulnerable Zones – areas where use of nitrogen is restricted – are currently being advocated, so this could be a case where radionics can help.

In the December 2002 edition of *British Farmer and Grower – South East Edition* there is a headline: 'Pesticides tax threat looms large'. This may not come, but at the moment there are voluntary initiatives and surveys taking place. The pesticides are used mostly by arable farmers but radionics could help in this area. A few years ago a farmer who was about to change to organics had his oil seed rape treated radionically especially to deter pollen beetle and seed weevil. The firm he contracted with normally did the count and generally insisted on spraying if or when they considered it necessary. This time, however, the field was not sprayed. The roadside charlock and dandelions, over the hedge, were black with the little creatures, but the farmer's field remained free enough of them not to require spraying.

Another year on the same farm (by this time the whole farm was on permanent radionic treatment) there was an influx of aphid in the surrounding area, especially on wheat. All the neighbouring farmers were spraying to get rid of them but the radionically treated farm remained free. Seed is often treated before planting with a chemical to prevent mildew, but on this farm the process was omitted and no mildew was present.

A field of barley, which was not on permanent treatment, was planted in mid-October and appeared to be doing well until it suddenly stopped growing and started looking sick. The radionic analysis revealed poor air circulation in the soil (it had been a very wet autumn with some impaction). With treatment, the soil improved rapidly and ultimately produced a good crop.

Another use of radionics is to try to deter predators, as the following examples show.

A gentleman in Hampshire had planted some ornamental conifers. Deer had appeared and he had replaced them twice before he asked if radionics could help. The area was treated and the deer did not cross the boundary.

A Buddhist monastery in Sussex had rats in the compost heap. The monks were obviously not allowed to kill them, so the compost heap and garden were treated to repel these creatures which proved successful. Afterwards they asked that the rabbits, which were eating their garden produce, should be kept at bay, but the farmer who owned the small wood where the rabbits lived intervened, so radionic treatment was not necessary.

A farmer had planted some maize and, just as it was beginning to sprout, rooks attacked it. With treatment, they left the maize, but as an experiment, the treatment was stopped and the rooks immediately returned. Needless to say, treatment was quickly resumed.

Of course there are also failures, like trying to keep pigeons off oil seed rape in the winter when it is frosty and they cannot easily get other food.

In all these cases colour plays a very important part.

Weeds – plants which are growing where they are not welcome – can be a problem, especially when they choke the crop. Some interesting research could be done to discover the beneficial properties of plants. I know that some work has been done, details of which can be found in the excellent book, *Companion Plants*. It is said that poppies in vast quantities can affect the quality of the crop of wheat, but it has also been found that having a few in the crop helps to prevent mildew. Some deep-rooted weeds help to raise nutrients from the sub-soil and others, like some of the tall grasses, attract the cosmic influences. There definitely are plants which make good companions but there are also others which do not like being next to each other. This can be determined radionically and should be taken into consideration, especially when planting a new garden.

So often all that people consider is how to get rid of weeds and I believe that Honor Bowen Colthurst, a radionic practitioner who specialised in agriculture and horticulture, had some success in this area. Personally, I have been able to control them in agricultural situations and keep them below combine harvester level so that they were no problem, but not to eradicate them.

So far we have generally been looking at soil and crops, but animals cannot be separated from agriculture. Sometimes the area in which the animal lives needs to be treated as well as the animal itself, especially where parasites spend part of their life cycle in the soil or on plants, as is the case with fluke and some worms. If a field has had one species of animal in it for too long it can become e.g. horse sick or sheep sick, and it may also be less rich in nutrients if it has been waterlogged. Radionics can help to counteract the problem. Animals are also needed to add humus to enable the life in the soil to function efficiently. Animals themselves respond very readily to radionic treatment and much can be done to prevent conditions with ongoing treatment, for example mastitis in cattle and general infertility in all species. (Animal treatments, particularly horses, are dealt with in chapters 9 & 10.)

Unfortunately there is very little documentation of the radionic work done abroad except in the USA. We should not forget Muriel Morrison and the work she did in Australia, which was the basis of the agricultural/ horticultural practice which, I am given to understand, is quite significant today. Some of these people, I believe, are using radionics in conjunction with biodynamic agriculture, which is ideal. Muriel was very excited by the success of radionics when there was a drought in Australia. She treated some sheep pasture from a distance and was able to keep it green and the sheep well fed.

In South Africa in the 1960s there was great interest in radionics and Helena McDougall, who died about four years ago, did sterling work. Helena and her husband farmed there for about twenty-five years and, she said, in all that time no vet was needed for a sick animal. They had a large milking herd and other livestock as well as the crops, which were all treated radionically. After her husband died, and Helena eventually gave up the farm, she became involved in helping in the townships and realised how deficient the people, especially the children, were in vitamin C. I believe she was the instigator of what she termed 'door gardens'. This name was used as they were six feet long and two and a half feet wide. A deep hole was dug, at this size, which was filled with brushwood and water and then covered over with soil. These were then planted with lettuce and other crops and radionically treated and each one provided enough for a family to have something fresh each day. If the garden dried out with the heat, it was easy to replenish.

Helena did teach some people in South Africa, so it would be interesting to know what is happening today.

At the present time, Lutie Larsen is working hard in the USA at Little

Farm Research. She is producing radionic/organic horticultural crops and teaching others so that they can help themselves. Lutie is also experimenting with the de la Warr camera and it will be wonderful when her results are published.

About twenty years ago Simon Schoon, a lily bulb grower in Holland, learnt radionics as he was disillusioned with using chemicals for his lily bulbs. The chemicals were unpleasant to use, becoming ineffective and damaging the soil. After the first year of using radionics he said he was so much better off in many ways not having to buy and use the chemicals. The last I heard from him he was treating other growers' holdings in Holland and the USA.

Some farmers in the UK have had their farms treated and then trained so that they can treat their own farms, so the extent to which radionics is used in agriculture is not really known.

I believe that there is a great future for radionics in agriculture/ horticulture, especially now that organic farming and gardening are getting so popular. We just need to let people know how fortunate we are to have access to a therapy which can enhance the quality of the food we eat.

To sum up, radionics in agriculture/horticulture is not just a curative therapy but a preventative one as well. It has a great role to play in the control of pests, parasites and diseases and in the preparation of the soil before planting, taking into consideration drainage, pans, manurial requirements, cultivations, availability of nutrition, compatibility of soil and plants and possibly revitalisation of seed. Looked at from a worldwide perspective, it is a vast subject but a very exciting and fascinating one.

I will end with a quotation from an Acres USA publication:

FORGIVE US, O LORD!
Give us this day our daily calcium propionate (spoilage retarder), sodium diacetate (mold inhibitor), monoglyceride (emulsifier), potassium bromate (maturing agent), calcium phosphate monobasic (dough conditioner), chloramine T (flour bleach), aluminium potassium sulphate (acid baking powder ingredient), sodium benzoate (preservative), butylated hydroxyanisole (anti-oxidant), monoisopropyl citrate (sequestrant), plus synthetic vitamins A and D.
FORGIVE US, O LORD, FOR CALLING THIS STUFF BREAD.

Bibliography

Dower, A. L. G. (1980) *Healing with Radionics.* The Keys College of Radionics, Woodstock.

Philbrick, Helen & Gregg, Richard B. (1967) *Companion Plants.* Stuart and Watkins, London.

Russell, Edward Wriothesley (1973) *Report on Radionics: Science of the Future.* Neville Spearman, London.

Tompkins, Peter & Bird, Christopher (1973) *The Secret Life of Plants.* Harper and Row, New York.

Tony Scofield

Environmental Radionics – Geopathic Stress and Health   12

'When you stay at a place and no longer feel well, then that may be
caused by the people you are with. But perhaps it is the locality that
is unhealthy for you. Wait for three days and three nights. If you
then feel exhausted, depart without hesitation, however peaceful the
place. You cannot recover there and will only become ill. Because
from the Earth certain forces radiate which do not agree with you.
Follow your instinct...'

Nostradamus (1503-1566) [8]

'The manifestation of a phenomenon is not independent of the
observer – it is caught up and entangled in his individuality.'
Goethe (1749-1832) [74]

The subtle influence of place

For thousands of years the Chinese have believed that places can
influence people and events in subtle ways. They attribute this
action to energy lines – dragon energies – which pass across the
earth and have derived a system to detect these lines, and also modify
them, known as *Feng Shui*. In many Chinese societies today no construction is begun, or important decision made, without first consulting an
expert in the art. The traditions of other societies also consider that currents of energy flow across the earth. These are known as ki or ch'i, prana,
pneuma, the eight winds, the vital spirit, serpent currents and so on. This
energy is associated not only with the earth but also with the body, for
example as reflected in the acupuncture meridians. In the Japanese system ch'i is considered as the fundamental energy of the universe which
connects and relates all things. Every individual's portion of this energy

is in direct connection with everything else.[76] These ideas have been incorporated into western esoteric schools. In 1895 A.P. Sinnett, a leading member of the London Lodge of the Theosophical Society, wrote: 'There are great etheric currents constantly sweeping over the surface of the earth from pole to pole in volumes which make their power as irresistible as the rising tide; and there are methods by which this stupendous force may be safely utilized, though unskillful attempts to control it would be fraught with frightful danger'.[76]

The Chinese take the effects of the dragon currents very seriously and historically there have been cases of landscapes being remodelled to improve the flow of beneficial energies. In the West some dowsers suggest that the natural equilibrium of the earth can be upset by large scale earth moving, quarrying and mining. However, others believe that, rather than the earth being 'ill', we may be out of resonance with our surroundings when we build and that the inappropriate siting of houses may contribute to ill health. Frances Denne has suggested that our culture has lost touch with the natural energies and resources that sustain it.[27] Pennick also suggests that there is no 'bad' site; every site has its own qualities with which we can harmonize.[76] Every site is suitable for something even if it is not for living there.

In the West it has been customary for dowsers to relate ill health to lines that they have dowsed. These lines are believed by many dowsers to be associated with the earth and for this reason are often known as 'telluric'. The term 'geopathy' was coined by Johann Walther to describe the study of harmful zones associated with earth radiation.[15,25] The stress imposed on a living organism as a result of spending time in such noxious zones is now commonly known as geopathic stress. This was defined by Scott-Morley as 'a geomagnetic disturbance which is geographically localized and which disrupts the homeostatic mechanisms of the sensitive patient'.[90] Whether magnetic disturbances are the cause of geopathic stress is, however, debatable. As well as naturally occurring anomalies Scott-Morley also included man-made disturbances (electrical, electromagnetic and radiation) as causes of geopathic stress. Certainly, in recent years there has been much interest in the role of electromagnetic energy, for example from high voltage power lines, in the aetiology of diseases and dowsers should be aware of the potential dangers of these man-made sources of electromagnetic radiation. Some dowsers, such as Alf Riggs[81], include an assessment of these factors when dowsing houses for geopathic stress, but unless the dowser specifically asks for EM sources, these sources of electropollution are probably not what are normally found when dowsing a site for potentially disease-inducing sources of energy associated with the earth. Such causes of electropollution are probably best detected by conventional instruments and the more subtle energies which may effect a place are sought by dowsing. The number of these telluric influences, which are referred to by a variety of names including earth radiations, black streams, excitation zones, geopathic zones, zones of geoclimatic disturbance as well as others, has increased with the number of dowsers interested in the 'earth energy' field.

Understanding the findings of dowsers is complicated by the fact that when different dowsers dowse an area for energy lines they may find different things.[12,62,79] This, quite understandably, leads to difficulties in understanding what is being found, and may even lead to disagreements amongst dowsers and, not surprisingly, to scepticism amongst non-dowsers.[66] As Michael Guest has pointed out dowsers rarely obtain independent or scientific proof of what they are dowsing and tend to use terms which imply more than they can prove.[59] Major-General J. Scott-Elliot, a past president of the British Society of Dowsers, has always maintained that unproven dowsing is little better than speculation and the fact that two or more dowsers agree on something does not constitute proof.[39] I have, therefore, followed Guest's suggestion and used the term 'dowsing reaction line' (DRL) for those lines along which a dowser obtains a reaction. If they affect living organisms then an energy exchange is implied but the nature of this energy has yet to be conclusively demonstrated.

The term '*Ley*' or '*Ley Line*' is often used to describe DRLs.[10,59] The term was invented in 1921 by Alfred Watkins to describe 'an alignment across miles of country of a great number of objects, or sites of objects, of prehistoric antiquity.'[99] In 1938 Arthur Lawton, a member of the Straight Track Club, suggested that ley lines might have some sort of energy.[77] Whether they do is still a matter of debate but I believe that they are not the lines that most dowsers find when they are looking for sources of geopathic stress.

It is important to consider what it is that one is trying to achieve when dowsing for earth energies. For many of us it is part of a process that, hopefully, will improve or harmonise the environment. Our dowsing is a means to that end; it helps us to tune in to and understand in the terms of our own models the situation to which we have been called. These models may even be formulated at an intuitive or unconscious level rather than being formulated in conscious terms. What is important to remember is that it is the end that is important i.e. what we are doing the dowsing for, and not the means to that end. With that in mind it is not surprising that different dowsers find different things and this is particularly so as there is no consensus as to what actually causes these zones of noxious energy. Indeed, there is very little evidence that any physical differences exist between these zones and neighbouring 'safe' areas.

The effects of geopathic stress

At the beginning of the twentieth century in Germany interest began to develop in the possible relationship between diseases, particularly cancers, and factors that could only be detected by dowsing. These ideas were developed in a book published by Baron von Pohl *Earth Currents. Causative Factor of Cancer and Other Diseases*.[98] Von Pohl's studies were stimulated by the work of Winzer & Melzer in Stuttgart who found that the incidence of cancer was related to major geological faults and they suggested that some emanation from these faults was the cause.[15, 101] The most impressive of von Pohl's studies was in Vilsbiburg in Bavaria. The mayor of the town arranged for the medical officer to make out a list of all the cancer deaths in the 10 years to 1918, to which a few more recent cases were added making a total of 54 names. This was kept secret until von Pohl had dowsed the 900 dwellings for his earth currents. This was done between 13-19th January 1929 working 8-9 hours a day! Von Pohl classified his currents on a strength scale. He believed that cancer was only caused by the stronger currents and he marked these on a map of the town. The beds of all 54 cases were found to be on the lines that von Pohl had indicated. It must be pointed out that there are a lot of lines on the map and, although there is no denying that the results are impressive, a modern study would insist on a rigorous statistical analysis with a control group of randomly chosen cases which were not suffering from the disease.

Many illnesses and conditions and changes in physiological and biochemical function have been claimed to be associated with DRLs[14] and dowsers certainly get called to houses for a wide variety of conditions which the clients consider may be associated with geopathic stress. Nowadays, geopathic stress is often diagnosed by radiesthetic means, blood crystalline analysis such as the Spagyric therapy method[11] or electrodiagnostic methods such as electroacupuncture diagnosis, and many of the patients that I see are referred after such diagnoses. In my experience it is women who mainly ring up for help.[88,90] They may be more sensitive than men and hence suffer more from geopathic stress or they may be less reserved in coming forward. A variety of geopathic energies has been suggested by Jane Thurnell-Read some of which she claims only affect women and sometimes only particular women, perhaps because their ovaries are 'at exactly the same frequency as the detrimental energy'.[95]

Some authors even state that most, if not all, of a variety of illnesses are caused by DRLs. For example, Herbert Douglas found that every case of arthritis or rheumatism and most cancers that he investigated were associated with DRLs originating, he believed, from crossing points of underground veins of water.[31-35] The lines, often many, were found over the bed or a place where the patient spent much time. Indeed, he believed that, as there are on average between 5 and 20 crossings under most houses, there is about a one in five chance of sleeping over a crossing point.[31] Käthe Bachler found all of over 700 cases of serious illness to be associated with the crossing of DRLs.[3] Baron von Pohl also found nearly all the cases of cancer that he investigated were associated with DRLs and for those cases that were not obviously linked he assumed the lines had moved![3] Rolf Gordon of the Dulwich Health Society has promoted similar ideas more recently.[37, 38, 44]

Scott-Morley is less dogmatic stating that 30-50% of the chronically sick are reported by practitioners, presumably complementary, to be exhibiting some kind of geopathic stress.[90] He does admit that there is insufficient evidence that geopathic stress is the direct cause of disease but that it probably 'weakens the body so that the patient may be more prone to disease-forming processes'. Similar views were expressed much earlier by Tromp in his *Psychical Physics*[97] and Ernst Hartmann[81] believed that they weaken the body's immune response. These views are also espoused by Käthe Bachler[4], the Austrian dowser, who has investigated thousands of cases of illness, and my own explanation to patients is similar: geopathic stress is one of many stresses that weaken the body and make it vulnerable to disease. Remove this stress and the body has a better chance of recovery, either on its own or with outside help.

However, removal of a patient from a geopathically stressed zone may not always be sufficient to remove the stress. According to Scott-Morley the geopathic stress may become 'locked' into the body and needs to be cleared by means such as radionics, homeopathy or acupuncture or even by 'degaussing' after removal from the site.[90, 95] To complicate matters even further Jane Thurnell-Read believes that people may become addicted to geopathic stress and choose the worst places to sit and sleep.[95] In this context it is interesting that many of my clients complain of tiredness and lack of energy and often talk of the house draining them of energy. They often feel better when away. Of course, in many cases there may be a strong psychological element in that we all feel better when away from the stresses of home or work.

The assertion that DRLs are the cause of many diseases is irresponsible as it may divert attention from the real causes. In some cases, attributing disease to DRLs is a convenient excuse for a patient not to face up to the real cause of the problem. It is often a case that the patient is aware of the cause and is not prepared to take responsibility for it. Asking for a dowser to come and fix the lines in these instances is no different from going to a doctor for a prescription. Patients will not respond in the long term unless they take responsibility for their own problems. This may well involve a difficult decision, for example, giving up smoking or sorting out a difficult relationship.

As well as ill-health other phenomena such as hauntings, poltergeist activity and accidents have been reported associated with DRLs.[4,15,25,60, 64,88,90,96,97] Quite a few of my own cases involve hauntings or poltergeist activity, usually associated with health problems. They have usually been cleared with my normal harmonizing technique which involves radionic treatment of the house, but occasionally I have combined with a healer experienced in exorcism. Sleeping with the head in the angle between two Hartmann lines, a putative grid of energy lines discussed later, is believed by the Swiss dowser Mel Barmet (personal communication) to cause the sleeper to see spirits. Accident black spots have also been linked to noxious DRLs.[24, 25, 83]

There are also many reports on the effect of DRLs on animals and plants. Some animals, it is claimed, seek out these lines and apparently thrive on them e.g. cats, bees, ants and wasps, whilst most other animals are repelled by or do not thrive on the lines.[4, 15, 16, 25, 62, 95]

Anne Arnold Silk believes that many unusual phenomena can be attributed to seismic activity and in a lecture to the Society for Psychical Research in 1991[40] she claimed that cats loved areas of seismic activity while dogs avoided them. There are traditions of building or sleeping on areas where animals settle to sleep. In Brazil there is a country custom of confining cattle on a site and building the house where they settle to sleep. The Red Indians in America and Gypsies also have similar practices.[26,69,84]

Plant growth is often claimed to be stunted on DRLs.[22] The closing response of the Venus Flytrap and the germination of seeds appeared to differ from normal when they were placed over an underground stream and Brewer has used these plant responses to test the effectiveness of de-raying devices.[20] Plants can also be divided into those that grow well on DRLs and those that do not although there is not universal agreement.[15,41,64,69,78,95,96]

What causes geopathic stress?

Baron von Pohl, who pioneered the modern study of geopathic stress, first believed that the lines he dowsed in association with cases of illness were negatively charged currents originating in the earth's magma, hence the title of his book *Earth Currents*.[98] He did not believe that underground water was the source of the rays but did suggest that water and other good electrical conductors conducted the negatively charged earth rays in lines across the earth. The pattern of the lines he described was irregular and the lines were not necessarily straight.

Other German workers who followed him have, however, developed much more rigid or regular models of DRLs, usually in the form of grids of lines often of alternating 'polarity' as determined by dowsing. 'Dangerous' points are where two negative polarity lines cross, especially when this coincides with a water line. The strength of the grid lines also appears to change during the day and is influenced by the weather.[86]

The earliest grids to be described included the Peyré grid (1937)[15,21], the Wittman grid[15], the Curry net (1935-1939)[86,105], the Hartmann net (also known as the Universal or Global grid) (Ernst Hartmann, 1937[47,78]) (Fig. 12.1), the Harvalik Universal grid[49], and the Kunnen net[21]. Many other 'grids' can be found cited in the literature e.g. Beadon, Bremmer, Berschneider, Mettler, Schneider, Benker, Schweitzer and Hiller amongst others.[67,86,103,109] Anton Benker's (1960) system is a 10m cube arrangement based on the Hartmann net[54] and Schneck describes a series of seven grids and mentions that there exist other grids with miles between the crossing points.[86] Maes quite rightly makes the pointed remark that the number of theories equals the number of people who are dowsing these energies.[67]

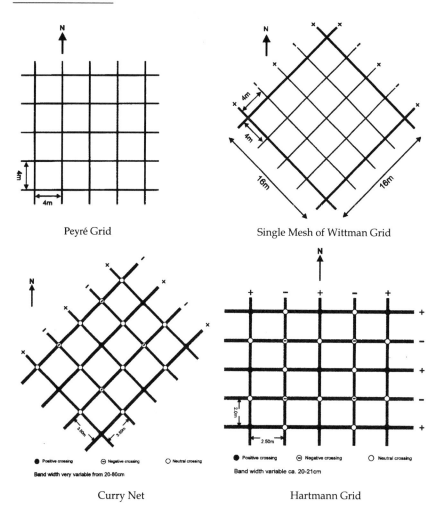

Peyré Grid

Single Mesh of Wittman Grid

Curry Net

Hartmann Grid

Fig. 12.1 Some earth energy grids

He has little time for most dowsers; not only has he found very little cor-relation between his measurements of radioactivity in buildings and the findings of dowsers, he has scant regard for their 'de-raying' devices. These are devices that are claimed to remove noxious energy from a site; they are discussed later. In a lighter vein Murray Laver, in a letter to the *Journal of the British Society of Dowsers* wrote, after reading several articles describing new grid: 'Where can I go to be safe? Are we not in danger of gridlock?'[58]

It should be said that the detection of grids seems to be largely a phenomenon of continental Europe, especially Germany (and Sweden).[63] Many British dowsers are unable to find the grids and their dowsing of geopathically stressed places reveals patterns more like those of von Pohl i.e. irregularly spaced lines of varying width and by no means always straight.[5,11,79]

I believe that dowsers find the pattern associated with the mental model they are using at the time. On the continent this is often a grid model; in Britain it rarely is. This was particularly obvious to Nigel Pennick who observed a site being dowsed at different times by German and British dowsers.[29] He noticed that 'Germans found their grids and nets, but the British found merely wavy lines'. After years of involvement with dowsers Paul Devereux has concluded that 'alas, most energy dowsers, however sincere, are in effect dowsing the insides of their own heads, so to speak.'[29]

Even amongst those who adhere to a grid concept there is no agreement as to which grids are important in inducing geopathic stress. Many believe, for example, that the Curry Net is more dangerous than the Hartmann net (e.g. Bachler[4]). On the other hand the Spanish writer Bueno believes the Hartmann net to be more important.[21] The French also place much importance on the Hartmann grid and the Swiss writer Blanche Merz has produced a book, *Points of Cosmic Energy*, in which she relates the distribution of the Hartmann net not only to health problems but also to the location of sacred buildings and 'places of power.'[72]

Apart from grids a wide variety of dowsable lines have been described. For example, Harvey[50] describes a variety of multiple banded lines which he believed to be both natural and man-made and Gawn[42] describes a basic wave as a straight line with a series of small spirals down one side. External forces such as the sun, moon and planets, he believes, exert a force on the small spirals which can cause the lines to bend thus giving rise to a variety of shapes of line that other dowsers have described. Lines may be dowsed as positive or negative but it is only when two parallel negative lines cross as a result of stress deformation that they become detrimental to health.[42] Carver has also described various patterns of energy in geopathic zones – some curved lines, some spiral and some straight with combinations of these forms.[23] According to Lonegren, Fountain International dowsers find grape clusters and Maltese crosses.[63] Guy Tison has described 'cosmo-telluric' chimneys where the energy exists in spiral chimneys of 50 to 200-300 cm in diameter.[55] This energy evidently rises for several minutes (telluric energy) and is followed by a powerful descent of cosmic energy for 15-30 seconds. The descending energy is believed to be beneficial whilst the rising energy may be noxious, neutral or beneficial depending on which of the 7 wavelengths the energy is vibrating.

Modern dowsers and interested scientists often implicate earth faults as a source of radiation that can cause geopathic stress.[36,52,78,81,85,87,89] Although there certainly seems to be some evidence linking earth faults with strange light and sound phenomena, for example that often associated with UFO sightings[28], whether these are what dowsers find when looking for causes of geopathic stress is debatable.

I tend to find a range of DRLs. Often there are bands of varying widths, usually 1-2 m wide but sometimes as wide as a room. They may be confined to the room, or pass through the room into others and even beyond the house. They may often be parallel to the walls of the house but may also pass diagonally through the house. They may occur in the same position in upper stories or be reflected sideways or they may be absent in the upper rooms or, indeed, a completely different pattern may be present. When passing through walls or even onto different ground outside they may be deflected or widen or narrow. They may even occur as spots, often several feet across, which may or may not pass vertically to other stories. After years of dowsing I come prepared to find anything. The secret is not to expect anything in particular and to accept what you find. Once you start worrying about what you are finding, whether the line in this room joins the one in the adjacent room you have just dowsed or is below the one you have just dowsed in the bedroom for example, your dowsing will begin to suffer. For successful dowsing you need confidence. You will then develop a 'zen' approach of relaxed confidence.

As dowsers describe such a wide array of potentially noxious forces the advice of R.J. Pope to ensure that only one person dowses a room for noxious rays appears to be a wise one as 'a different opinion is sure to be offered which will cause doubts in the mind of the patient which will aggravate the fear and thus exacerbate the ill health'.[79] The reporter Jane Alexander wrote in the *Daily Mail* that when two dowsers checked her home for sources of geopathic stress one found noxious lines and the other claimed the house to be clear.[1] She did not appear too concerned at the discrepancy! When I am asked to dowse a house which has already been dowsed, either by the occupants or another dowser, I tell the client that I may well find different things and explain that the findings of dowsing represent a model by which I can understand and tune in to the problem I have been asked to look into. Very often inexperienced dowsers have not tuned into a specific problem when they embark on dowsing and it is no surprise that they detect things that the more experienced dowser does not find.

Although dowsers agree that negative energy lines or spots do exist there is absolutely no agreement as to what causes them. Numerous suggestions have been put forward including:

Magnetic fields: for example quite a number of people have suggested that noxious zones occur where the earth's magnetic field is disturbed by substances in the earth's crust such as water, oil, ores, coal, minerals, crevices etc. [31,51,60,95]

Electrical causes: Modifications of the electrical current that runs through the earth's crust by, for example, geological anomalies has been suggested as the source of noxious DRLs. Manning proposed that the earth current reacts with the electrical conditions of the atmosphere to form an 'air electric vertical current'. [68] Earth ray zones were believed to be zones or places where there is an increase in electric charge exchange between the earth and the atmosphere.

Cosmic rays: A relationship between soil type and cancer was observed by Georges Lakhovsky, inventor of the Multiple Wave Oscillator, and was attributed by him to the differing permeability of the soils to cosmic rays. [56] He proposed that soils permeable to cosmic rays were associated with low cancer incidence because they allowed the rays to pass through without reflection while impermeable soils reflected the rays back, diffusing them, and their interaction with the incident radiation resulted in a complex field of radiation which was responsible for the cancers. Cosmic rays were also originally believed to be responsible for the Hartmann net. It is interesting, however, that in one of his more recent papers Hartmann stated that his research group was coming to the conclusion that a new form of energy had to be considered since the phenomenon ('the divining rod effect within the framework of geobiology') could not be explained by the present findings of physics. [48]

Radiations from the earth: von Pohl postulated that radiation from the earth's magma was altered by obstacles such as gravel, oil, minerals, voids, tunnels and geological fault lines so becoming harmful. [98] This is similar to the view promoted by the Dulwich Health Society which believes weak electromagnetic fields created by the subterranean anomalies alter the wavelength of the natural radiation making it harmful to living organisms.[37] Von Pohl later changed his ideas and plumped for γ-rays being the cause of noxious zones. Numerous other electromagnetic rays, including microwaves, have been suggested but there is little evidence for the involvement of any of them in geopathic stress.[43]

Minerals: These have been implicated in altering the nature of various radiations thereby making them noxious.[73]

Cavities: Cavities have been assigned a number of effects from producing a harmful wave derived from pollution within it e.g. a staphylococcal ray, to changing cosmic rays or rays emanating from the earth's core into harmful rays.[65]

Underground water: Radiation emanating from underground streams has always been a popular explanation for geopathic stress and has been espoused by many dowsers.[15,70,71,91,92] The terms black stream or noxious stream have often been used to describe underground streams that are capable of producing geopathic stress.[10]

The description of underground streams and their supposed effects on living organisms depends on who is describing them. Some authors believe that underground streams are harmful only at the crossing points[100] or where two streams cross at different depths[53], or where tributaries join to form a fork beneath a house[65]. Others believe that streams (or dry faults) must run parallel or nearly parallel to each other to exert a noxious influence.[106]

Finally, of course, not everyone agrees that underground streams are noxious! Busby[22] found little relationship between underground streams and noxious radiation while Benham[13] considered that the way one faced in relation to the flow of a stream determined whether it was harmful or beneficial. Lonegren has never found primary vein water or any other kind of earth energy that was detrimental to health under houses of people whose culture was obviously working in harmony with these energies.[62]

The greatest difficulty that I have when considering the relationship between underground streams and DRLs is that in most cases there is no proof that there is an underground stream present. The only way that you can prove that streams exist at these points is to sink a well and few dowsers of DRLs are in a position to do this. Major-General J. Scott Elliot recognised this as a major problem in a great deal of dowsing and was an exponent of exploratory confirmation.[39]

Consciousness: Arthur Bailey points out the difficulties of reconciling dowsing claims with known physical phenomena.[6] Electromagnetic rays such as radio, heat, light, ultraviolet, X-rays, gamma rays, cosmic rays and microwaves can all be screened by one material or another. Magnetism can be screened. Screening of EM radiation does not, according to Dr Bailey, affect the dowser's ability to dowse. We know of nothing that can screen gravity but we can measure minute changes in the gravitational field and there is no consistent correlation between dowsing reactions and gravitational field changes. Gravity can be altered by dowsing over a thick lead sheet but Bailey found that it made no difference to his dowsing ability. Baron von Pohl, and more recently Hartmann[48] was also sceptical of the likelihood that conventionally accepted radiation was involved for reasons similar to Bailey. The DRLs also do not seem to obey normal physical laws, a point made by a number of dowsers. [6,7,108]

With such evidence one must ask whether many of the DRLs that we react to are the product of consciousness rather than being some innate property of the earth. Certainly Colin Bloy has been forthright in his belief that the DRLs are pathways of consciousness, the meridians of collective consciousness, although he admits that they may also contain energy of other origin. [17,18] Clive Beadon has even suggested that ley lines may be thought waves that pick up good or bad qualities as they travel through space and goes on to mention Petitpierre who suggested that ley lines could be eradicated by a ceremony of exorcism.[10]

The possibility that the energies at a place may be a reflection of past human experience is not a new suggestion. The Bishop of Exeter's commission on exorcism published in 1972 concluded that 90% of hauntings could be ascribed to place memories[76] and Delarue-Pierret[107] has suggested that 'spiritualist practices and hate can also impregnate furniture with harmful influences'. The belief that these place memories can build up over generations of occupations is also quite widely believed.[76]

The possibility that there exists an energy field for the earth akin to that proposed for living bodies is part of a number of esoteric doctrines e.g. theosophy. [104] Bloy has suggested that the earth with its energy field is a 'living complete being of which human consciousness is a part'[17] and other dowsers have made similar suggestions.[30,102] Moreover, a number of dowsers have claimed to detect increased DRLs at sites associated with human activity e.g. conferences and so there does seem to be some evidence that DRLs can be associated with the action of consciousness.[75] Indeed it is possible to lay lines mentally that others can detect by dowsing [93, 94] and I do this regularly when teaching dowsing for earth energies.

Treatment

There are almost as many ways of treating negative energy as there are dowsers. The most well known is probably driving in of metal stakes on a dowsed line. Some use crystals on these lines while others pray or use various rituals to clear the energy. The devices for removing noxious energy, 'de-raying devices' as they have come to be known, can be divided into three basic types: those that operate by *Diversion*, those that operate by *Screening or Absorption*, and those that operate by *Modification by production of artificial radiation.*[100] It is not always clear into which group some of the methods fall. I treat a place radionically by dowsing for energy which 'affects the harmony of the house and the health of the inhabitants in a negative way' or some such relevant idea. When I find the energy I check using muscle testing on the people concerned, treat with my radionic box (the *Harmonizer*[110], Fig. 12.2) on which I dowse the settings of the 5 dials,

Fig. 12.2 The Harmonizer (photograph courtesy of Emerald Innovations)

and then recheck using muscle testing after treatment. Dowsing and treatment can also be done from a distance using a map, plan or other suitable witness. I often include the patient's hair as a witness as well.

What is common to all these methods is that consciousness is involved and the more one looks into them the more one begins to appreciate the key role ceremony and ritual plays in the installation of the various symbols used. The whole clearing procedure can be a simple ritual. Denise Linn in *Sacred Place* describes a number of rituals for clearing houses and generating a positive environment. [61] The rituals can involve a variety of materials such as water, smoke, herbs and oils some of which have significance in all cultures whilst others, such as smoke, have more meaning in one culture than another. Where tradition considers that disharmony in a place is the result of interference with the natural flow of ch'i, or the dragon current, across the landscape then driving stakes into energy lines can be seen as a modern counterpart of the ritual of dragon slaying at local centres. This act fixed the qualities of the place and perhaps transformed the qualities of a place that was considered to be bad. [76]

The ritual may charge the place with psychic energy and the harmonious modification of the environment is possibly by psychic interaction with the etheric energies of the earth. Such methods may well be effective if we accept that earth energies represent a model for the dowser of an interaction at the spiritual level. As Guest says 'the many devices used by dowsers to negate energy lines are really channels to allow the power of the mind to be focused on the problem rather than objective "cures" in their own right'. [46] The energy generated during the rituals associated with sacred acts, and even temporal acts with spiritual overtones such as the construction of labyrinths with the aim of harmonizing the energies at a place, may be potent forces in altering the energies in a place, particularly when it involves our relationship to the place. Rituals focus consciousness on the task. As Pennick says 'ceremonies ... are symbols which create positive attitudes in the minds of the future users of the house.' [76]

In its widest interpretation Pennick considers earth harmony to involve 'a harmonious relationship between the earth, human beings, their artifacts, actions and celestial influences. Human consciousness is the mediator in the equation so, if that consciousness is incomplete or disrupted in some way, then there is no true harmony.' [76]

The idea that human consciousness is involved in harmonising earth energies, and indeed in creating earth energies, is more current today than in the past.[80] Colin Bloy finds lines associated with conference centres and other centres of human activity which frequently disappear when the centres are no longer used.[19] He believes them to be the result of 'condensation of human consciousness'. Bloy is a great proponent of the role of consciousness in the generation of energy fields and even in the manipulation of physical phenomena such as water flow.

There have also been a number of reports of dowsers picking up DRLs over the beds of sick people which have subsequently disappeared on their death. I had recounted to me the case of a dowser who dowsed many lines above the bed of his wife who was dying of cancer. On her death nearly all the lines disappeared.[82] The reports of dowsers such as Douglas[31-35] who find many lines above the beds of their arthritic patients may again be a reflection of the patients' illness rather than the cause of the illness. There is a tendency amongst dowsers to attribute all findings of lines to causes of problems rather than effects of problems. With my own dowsing I now attempt to identify whether lines I find are the cause of a problem or the effect. I find this to be of particular value when analysing a situation as I am able to understand the problem I am faced with more clearly and am not necessarily led away from the real cause by preconceived ideas.

That thought may be a potent force in shaping what we find by dowsing is, however, not a new idea. Even Maby, the staunchest of 'physicalist' dowsers for much of his professional life, believed early on in his career that dowsing required a psychical rather than a physical interpretation. In *The Physics of the Divining Rod* [64] he admitted that by 1935 he had come to the conclusion that Barret & Besterman's[9] assessment of dowsing was correct: *'In short, we claim that dowsing is a purely psychological problem, that all its phenomena find their origin in the dowser's mind, that no physical theory can bear close consideration, and that the movements of the rod and of the dowser have no more direct relation to the discovery of, say, water than as giving physical and visible expression to a mental and abstract cognition'*. But he was not convinced that all observations fitted this explanation and he subsequently spent his career trying, unsuccessfully, to prove a physical basis to dowsing!

Where health problems are genuinely caused by physical factors such as radon or high voltage power lines or perhaps microwave radiation from moving earth fault lines then, as Guest points out, we have a 'grave responsibility of relying solely on the means of the spirit lest, should we prove unequal to that task, the victim be left exposed to the bodily effects afterwards'.[45]

Conclusions

The solving of a problem by dowsing will depend on the symbolic model we consciously or unconsciously use. That is why I believe different dowsers find different things. They are approaching the same problem from different angles. Our ideas represent a symbolic modelling of our interaction with the environment and the people in it. Such ideas are not new. A. H. Bell in 1952, commenting on Aaltona's observation that different dowsers in the same situation tended to get a range of reactions varying in form from parallel lines, spirals, circles, rectangles etc., suggested that the form of response obtained depended on the 'physical and mental constitution of the dowser himself'.[12]

The pattern that we dowse will tell us something of the problems we are investigating or, if we are looking at other things like the energies around standing stones, will help us to understand the patterns in the context of whatever model we are using. The patterns we dowse, for example grids, are simply tools which will enable us to choose appropriate methods to correct the problems, if that is our ultimate intention. As Laver says 'the grids and networks ... may be useful concepts for interpreting the pattern of some dowsers' responses in some particular locality, without necessarily having an independent objective, universal existence.'[57] Frances Denne provides an interesting example illustrating this.[27] A chronically ill occupant could not bear to be in the dining room of a house. However, Denne found no evidence of water lines or earth rays although she found them in the sitting room and bedroom. By tuning into the 'main energy' rather than earth rays or water lines she then found the dining room to be full of negative energy which it was possible to associate with 'strong emotion from a previous occupant, a trapped spirit, a strong energy field associated with someone who had just died, and different areas of worry and discord' as well as water and earth energies and together these made the room virtually uninhabitable and, so Denne believed, they gradually broke down the patient's immune system.

The models that we use will depend on our mental make-up which will partly be determined by our cultural heritage. It is possible that the inability of British dowsers to detect the grids that the Germans are so fond of may reflect a German love of order which is not inherent in the

British character. The Chinese also abhor straight lines and their earth currents are curved rather than straight.[18] In a somewhat philosophical vein Bloy has postulated that the emergence of the straight line occurs when man starts to separate himself from nature.[18] Borrowing practices from other lands may have its problems as not only the geography and ecology of the land may be different but the culture of the inhabitants may be different also. As Richard feather Anderson suggests, it is important only to import the underlying universal principles and adapt them to our specific situation.[2]

I have come to believe that when we treat a place we are acting as healers of the environment, and that will include those within it as people are part of the place. We are 'healing' places in exactly the same way as a healer will help a human patient. The devices that we use to correct the energy and harmonise the situation may simply act as a focus for our intent to help and so harness 'healing energy', whatever this may be. In Guest's words they 'will represent physical channels through which the psychic and spiritual forces of the dowser are brought to bear on the problem'.[45]

It is interesting that one of the oldest methods of harmonising the environment, feng shui, itself frequently uses 'psychic' methods. One normally associates the feng shui practice of harmonising the flow of ch'i with the placement of the physical environment. This is the level of 'sying'. Some sects, particularly the Black Hat sect, emphasise another aspect, 'yi', a wish, a will or intention. Yi is a blessing, a way of adjusting or emphasising ch'i through intuition and imposition of the will of the expert (and the will to believe of the client) on a home or a person It is a vital but intangible process, a positive transference and transformation of energy (ch'i) that reinforces and blesses the physical aspect (sying) of feng shui. Black Hat practitioners believe that 'feng shui without mysticism is like a body without a soul' and that the mystical approach is much more effective than the use of known knowledge.

Whatever models we use it is important that we remain flexible in our beliefs. Every case is different and the dowsing situation continually changes. We can learn from every case and modify our model accordingly, something that is impossible to do when the model is fixed and rigidly imposed upon the dowsing psyche. When we have the opportunity to learn from our experience we have the opportunity to change. And with change comes the opportunity to develop. Each case is an opportunity to change and improve our effectiveness as healers and ultimately as people.

References

1. Alexander J. (1995) Laid low by 'bad' energy? *Daily Mail.* May 6, 1995, 34-35.
2. Anderson R. F. (1993) Geomancy. In: *The Power of Place* (ed. J. A. Swan), pp. 191-200. Gateway Books, Bath.
3. Bachler K. (1987) Noxious earth energies and their influence on human beings. *JBSD.* 32, 169-182.
4. Bachler K. (1989) *Earth Radiation. The Startling Discoveries of a Dowser.* Wordmasters, Manchester.
5. Bailey A. (1990) *Dowsing for Health and Healing.* Quantum, London.
6. Bailey A. R. (1972) A scientist looks at dowsing. *JBSD.* 23, 61-72.
7. Bailey A. R. (1978) Thoughts on dowsing. *JBSD.* 26, 98-108.
8. Bailey C. G. N. (1995) *Geopathic Stress. The Hidden Killers in your Workplace & the Common Link in all Degenerative Illnesses including Cancer,* 2nd edn. People's Research Institute G.B., Alston, Cumbria.
9. Barrett W. and Besterman T. (1926) *The Divining Rod.* Methuen, London.
10. Beadon C. V. (1980) Ley lines and black streams – facts and fancies. *JBSD.* 27, 242-250.
11. Beadon C. V. (1988) Letter. *JBSD.* 32, 386-387.
12. Bell A. H. (1952) Investigations on earth radiations in Finland. *JBSD.* 10, 369-373.
13. Benham W. E. (1943) Mainly about running water and its effects. *JBSD.* 5, 150-155.
14. Bergsmann O. (1994) *Risikofaktor Standort. Rutengängerzone und Mensch,* 3rd edn. Facultas, Vienna.
15. Bird C. (1980) *Divining.* Macdonald & Jane's, London & Sydney.
16. Bird C. (1991) Earth radiation. *JASD.* 31 (1), 31-34.
17. Bloy C. (1982) Some reflections on Guy Underwood's work. *JBSD.* 29, 320-323.
18. Bloy C. (1985) Some thoughts on European ley lines and oriental dragon-lines. *JBSD.* 31, 66-71.
19. Bloy C. H. (1981) The phenomenology of the ley system. *JBSD.* 28, 108-118.
20. Brewer R. (1992) Neutralizing: hailide vs. rebar. *JASD.* 32 (3), 12-18.
21. Bueno M. (1988) *Vivir en Casa Sana.* Martinez Roca, Barcelona.
22. Busby H. O. (1936) Some notes on earth radiation. *JBSD.* 2, 279-281.
23. Carver J. (1993) Nature knows best about balancing geopathic zones. Part 2: Geopathic zones. *JBSD.* 35, 321-326.
24. Coghill R. (1990) *Electropollution. How to protect yourself against it.* Thorsons, Wellingborough, Northants.
25. Copen B. (1988) *Harmful Radiations and their Elimination,* 5th edn. Academic Publications, Haywards Heath.
26. Cowan D. G. and Girdlestone R. (1996) *Safe as Houses? Ill Health and Electro-stress in the Home.* Gateway Books, Bath.
27. Denne F. (1994) Geopathic stress and our health. *JBSD,* 36, 155-163.
28. Devereux P. (1982) *Earth Lights.* Thorsons, Wellingborough.
29. Devereux P. (1991) *Earth Memory.* Quantum, London.
30. Dorst H. (1996) Earth energy project Summer 96 in British Columbia. *JBSD.* 37, 124-128.
31. Douglas H. (1972) Dowsing and arthritis. *JBSD.* 23, 80-86.
32. Douglas H. (1974) A further look at dowsing and arthritis. *JBSD.* 24, 58-66.
33. Douglas H. (1977) Underground forces and disease. *JBSD.* 26, 73-77.

34. Douglas H. (1978) Dowsing for irritation zones in the United States of America and Europe. *JASD*, 18 (3), 125-133.
35. Douglas H. (1984) Dowsing for the cause of certain illnesses. *JBSD*. 30, 256-265.
36. Dubrov A. P. (2002) Modern achievements of dowsing: Part 2. *JBSD*. 39 (276), 11-14.
37. Dulwich Health Society (1991) Newsheet No. 5, 6 pp.
38. Dulwich Health Society (1992) Newsheet No. 6, 6 pp.
39. Elliot J. S. (1982) Areas of force under churches and cathedrals and elsewhere. What are they? *JBSD*. 29, 248-261.
40. Ellison A. (1992) Fields and consciousness. *The Psi Researcher*, No. 4, 19-20.
41. Fidler J. H. (1983) *Ley Lines*. Turnstone Press, Wellingborough, Northants.
42. Gawn W. A. (1994) The behaviour of dowsable waves and the formation and eradication of geopathic zones. *JBSD*. 36, 8-12.
43. Girdlestone R. (1989) Are you building in a safe place? *Caduceus*, No. 7, 12-14.
44. Gordon R. (1987) *Are You Sleeping in a Safe Place?* Dulwich Health Society, London.
45. Guest M. (1985) Through dowsers' eyes. A survey of deraying techniques. *JBSD*. 31, 111-122.
46. Guest M. (1991) From my casebook. *Rod & Pendulum*. April 1991, 5.
47. Hartmann E. (1982) *Krankheit als Standortproblem*, 4th edn. Karl F. Haug, Heidelberg.
48. Hartmann E., Martin W., and Vogele W. (1987) Physikalische und biophysikalische Versuche zum Nachweis von "Geopathogenen Zonen", "Homoopathischen Arzneien" und vom Menschen ausgehenden Energieformen. *Erfahrungsheilkunde*. 36, 505-515.
49. Harvalik Z. V. (1978) Universal grid dimensions of dowsing. *JASD*. 18 (4), 153-155.
50. Harvey J. (1994) Ancient lines, ancient lives. Part I: A new look at "energy lines". *JBSD*. 36, 85-88.
51. Hunter R. W. and Cox D. (1949) Emanations from the earth. *JBSD*. 8, 339-341.
52. King G. (1995) Colour in dowsing. *JBSD*. 36, 308-313.
53. Kopp J. (1965) Health and earth rays. *JBSD*. 19, 88-89.
54. Kopschina A. (1991) *Erdstrahlen. Neue Methoden, sich wirksam vor Krankheiten zu schützen*. ECON Taschenbuch, Düsseldorf.
55. La Maya J. (1989) *La Médicine de l'Habitat*, 8th edn. Editions Dangles, St. Jean de Braye, France.
56. Lakhovsky G. (1939) *The Secret of Life*. William Heinemann, London.
57. Laver M. (1991) Where physical explanations falter. *JBSD*. 34, 275-281, 320-327.
58. Laver M. (1995) Correspondence. *JBSD*. 36, 334.
59. Laver M., Pope R., Guest M., Leonard P., Bloy C., and Fidler J. H. (1986) Contributions to clarifying dowsing terminology. *JBSD*. 31, 213-226.
60. Leviton R. (1989) Can the earth's stress spots make you sick? *East West*. 19 (6), 48-52 & 83-85.
61. Linn D. (1995) *Sacred Space*. Rider, London.
62. Lonegren S. (1986) *Spiritual Dowsing*, 2nd edn. Gothic Image Publications, Glastonbury.
63. Lonegren S. (1991) The blind men's elephant. In: *Dowsing the Crop Circles, Insights into the Greatest of Modern Mysteries*. (ed. J. Michell), pp. 11-15. Gothic Image, Glastonbury.
64. Maby J. C. and Franklin T. B. (1939) *The Physics of the Divining Rod*. G. Bell & Sons, London.
65. Macbeth N. (1941) Earth influences improving or harming health. *JBSD*. 4, 371-379.
66. Maes W. (1991) Bau-biologie: Stress from current and radiation: the sick bedroom and its successful treatment. *Health Consciousness*. 12 (October), 55-63.
67. Maes W. (1992) Bau-biologie: stress from current and radiation. Part IV. *Health Consciousness*. 13 (3), 75-82.

68. Manning A. D. (1950) The neutralisation of harmful rays. *JBSD*. 9, 107-111.
69. Manning A. D. (1962) Noxious rays. *JBSD*. 17, 149-152.
70. Maury M. (1953) *How to Dowse. Experimental and Practical Radiesthesia*. G. Bell, London.
71. Mermet A. (1959) *Principles and Practice of Radiesthesia*. Vincent Stuart, London.
72. Merz B. (1987) *Points of Cosmic Energy*. C.W. Daniel, Saffron Walden.
73. Moody F. (1980) How to counteract bad underground influences. *JBSD*. 27, 210-217.
74. Naydler J. (1996) *Goethe on Science*. Floris Books, Edinburgh.
75. O'Sullivan P. D. (1998) The patterns under our feet. *JBSD*. 38, 22-29.
76. Pennick N. (1987) *Earth Harmony*. Century, London.
77. Pennick N. (1993) Earth lines and dowsing. *JBSD*. 35, 204-207.
78. Pope I. (1987) A view of earth energies from continental Europe. *JBSD*. 32, 130-139.
79. Pope R. J. (1988) Noxious energies and health. *JBSD*. 32, 317-325.
80. Procter R. and Procter A. (2000) *Healing Sick Houses*. Gateway, Dublin.
81. Riggs A. (1993) The biological effects of earth radiation. *JBSD*. 35, 208-219.
82. Rust D. (1988) Speaking personally. *JBSD*. 32, 303-305.
83. Sandor A. (1995) The influences of geopathic areas on work efficiency. *JASD*. 35 (4), 48-49.
84. Schill P. (1961) Lethal veins. *JBSD*. 16, 211-214.
85. Schneck G. (1994) Geopathic edge-zone phenomena near power lines. *JBSD*. 36, 70-72.
86. Schneck G. (1995) Global grid lines. *JBSD*. 36, 243-255.
87. Schweitzer P. (1986) Geopathie, Ursache und Wirkung. *Erfahrungsheilkunde*. 35, 801-822.
88. Schweitzer P. (1988) Zur Diagnose der chronischen geopathischen Belastung mit dem Geopathietest. *Erfahrungsheilkunde*. 37, 241-246.
89. Schweitzer P. (1989) Geopathie – neuester Stand und Ausblick. *Erfahrungsheilkunde*. 38, 261-270.
90. Scott-Morley A. (1985) Geopathic stress: the reason why therapies fail? *Journal of Alternative Medicine*, 18-21, 27.
91. Smithett E. (1979) Eliminating the effects of harmful underground water. *JBSD*. 27, 50-57.
92. Stängle J. W. F. (1957) The dowser and his work. *JBSD*. 13, 336-347.
93. Taylor D. R. (1994) The fascinating case of the thought-form wall. *JASD*. 34 (2), 40-42.
94. Tellefsen J. A. and Magnusson S. (1999) Dowsing along the psi-track. *JBSD*. 38, 200-202.
95. Thurnell-Read J. (1995) *Geopathic Stress*. Element, Shaftesbury, Dorset.
96. Tietze H. (1988) *Earthrays – the Silent Killer?* H. Tietze, PO Box 34, Bermagui South, NSW 2547, Australia.
97. Tromp S. W. (1949) *Psychical Physics*. Elsevier, New York, Amsterdam.
98. von Pohl G. F. (1983) *Earth Currents. Causative Factor of Cancer and other Diseases*. Frech-Verlag, Feucht, Germany.
99. Watkins A. (1974 (first published 1925)) *The Old Straight Track*. Sphere Books, London.
100. Wethered V. D. (1961) The problem of noxious earth rays. *JBSD*. 16, 250-256.
101. Winzer H. T. and Melzer W. (1937) Cancer in the light of geophysical radiation. *JBSD*. 3, 4-20.
102. Wooster S. (1987) On earth mysteries/earth energies and geomagnetism. *JBSD*. 32, 183-191.
103. Worsch E. (1992) *Erdstrahlen*, 2nd edn. Verlag für Sammler, Graz, Austria.
104. Wright R. D., Bird C., Carlson D., Ross II T. E., Stead C. F., and Wright P. C. (1987) Panel discussion: dowsing and planetary consciousness. *JASD*. 27 (1), 59-71.
105. Note (1951) *JBSD*. 10, 145-146.
106. Note (1952) *JBSD*. 10, 318.

107. Note (1961) *JBSD*. 16, 331-332.
108. Note (1967) *JBSD*. 20, 143.
109. Note (1995) *JBSD*. 35, 276.
110. Available from Maperton Trust (www.mapertontrust.com) and Emerald Innovations (www.emeraldinnovations.co.uk) (Accessed 13/02/2003)

(*JB(A)SD* = Journal of the British (American) Society of Dowsers)

Tony Scofield

Evolution of Modern Instrumentation

13

> '..this developing science (radionics) provides a whole new
> understanding of the far-reaching potentials of human con-
> sciousness and the hidden healing capabilities of the multidi-
> mensional human being.'
>
> Richard Gerber[27]

Although most of the early developments in radionics occurred in America some British doctors were interested and promoted the therapy through books such as *The Abrams Treatment in Practice* by G. Laughton Scott (ca. 1925)[44], Sir James Barr's *Abrams' Methods of Diagnosis and Treatment* (1925)[2] and Oscar Parkes & Eric Perkins *The Detection of Disease* (1930).[37] Others, like the Glasgow homeopath W.E. Boyd and the doctor Guyon Richards, made significant developments in the Abrams technique.

In this chapter I will give an overview of developments that have taken place, mainly in Europe, and highlight the work of some of those who have most influenced radionics in this arena. Finally some of the more recent developments in radionics that have been influenced by the growth of computing and modern theories of physics (however poorly understood!) are presented and discussed.

W.E. Boyd and the Emanometer

By careful examination of Abrams' diagnostic instrument W.E. Boyd (1891-1955) was convinced that it was some kind of wireless set and redesigned it as a tuneable radio circuit to produce the *Emanometer* which underwent many modifications over the years.[5, 7] Instead of the rheostats used in the Abrams instrument Boyd modified the circuit from essentially

Fig. 11.

Fig. 12.

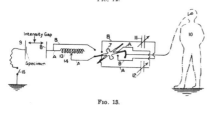

Fig. 13.

Fig. 13.1 The emanometer and its use[8]

a resistance box to one that was based on the concept of inductance and capacity and which was capable of fine adjustment using a coil and condenser.[30] He was critical of the lack of screening in Abrams' technique and he introduced screening for each portion of the apparatus. He also utilised an air gap by which, moving the specimen in the carrier away from the apparatus, a point was obtained where the reaction in question disappeared. This was used to measure the intensity of effect. As with Abrams, a human operator was required as part of the circuit. Boyd was a homeopath and both he and others used the machine for a number of years to select homeopathic remedies for treatment.[3,6,10] Boyd found that placing a suitable remedy into the circuit with the subject cancelled the dull tone obtained by percussion. He called this the 'Boyd Intereference Test'.[5] Much work was also done by the International Hahnemannian Committee using homeopathic remedies and Abrams' method.[14]

Boyd was careful about claims made for his instruments and in the instruction book states: 'The Emanometer is not diagnostic of disease-names or causes but analytical of the state of the body.'[14] He furnished a 'Table of Reactions provided for Research Purposes Only.' Boyd also stated that 'in its clinical application the emanometer is not diagnostic, but analytical of what is termed the dynamic state of the patient.'[8] From his work with the emanometer Boyd suggested that 'disease may be regarded as due to a deviation from the normal of a balanced state of this so-called dynamic energy of individuals'.[8] Homeopathic drugs acted as intermediary factors in restoring this imbalanced state to normal. He emphasized the role of external factors 'such as chemical, bacteriological, and physical whose dynamic energy bears certain relationships to the dynamic state of any particular individual, tend to throw the dynamic balance out, and thus to render that individual prone to pathological change and disease.'

With the emanometer Boyd noticed that as the disease energies disappeared with the recovery of the patient he was able to detect another energy that became stronger, which he called the V or Vitality Wave. By means of the V-wave he could classify people into 12 divisions and he also noted that drugs could also be classified into one of the same 12 divisions through the energy that they emitted. For a cure the patient would require a drug from the same division. [14,33] Unfortunately, very few people appeared competent in using the instrument (see discussion following Boyd's 1930 review[9]) and it is not surprising that disagreements over the classification of homeopathic remedies occurred. Here, John Paterson implied an intuitive component to the process when he stated that 'certain individuals can sense in some peculiar way the presence of potent substances without the medium of the emanometer circuit.'[9] In a note in 1961 Dr H. W. Boyd, who also used the technique for selecting remedies, states that although W. E. Boyd 'was able to select medicines and detect certain phenomena with great accuracy, (but) I have since wondered how much of this depended on his own sensitive personality and skill, and not on the instrument itself.'[4] He also believed that it was so easy to influence the percussion by the operator's mind, that the instrument was not suitable for general use. However, since no one, including Boyd, understood how the instrument worked, it was impossible for others to repeat his experiments or do controls on his work after his death. This was the system that was tested so successfully by the Horder Committee in 1925[30] (see chapter 1).

W. Guyon Richards

A homeopathic doctor and author of *The Chain of Life* (1934), W. Guyon Richards (1869-1946) developed a system the circuit of which he, like Boyd, regarded as a wireless set.[40] The patient sat in one compartment of a Faraday cage (like Boyd's system) to eliminate external electromagnetic interference; the operator, his instruments and the subject, were in another. The patient sat on a plate, connected to the circuit by a wire, and placed an electrode, attached by a separate wire, over the part to be tested. The circuit consisted of: a) the primary circuit, including the patient, dynamiser (a box to hold a witness if the patient was absent), a colour box with a series of small light bulbs with different coloured shades, and three or more sets of rheostats for tuning; b) an electrical amplifier; c) the secondary circuit consisting of the connections from the amplifier through a measuring rheostat to the subject (one wire to the forehead and another from the amplifier to a plate under the feet). The abdomen of the subject was stroked in a similar way to the technique of Abrams and Richards felt the reaction occurring as a contraction of the muscular wall of the abdomen.

The rheostats were used to test a range of material, including drugs and anatomical parts, and a set of rates (resistances in ohms) was produced for these. Like Boyd he tested for suitable homeopathic treatments using the instrument. When Richards lost his young 'subject' to military service at the outbreak of war, and his consulting room was bombed, he was forced to give up the work based on Abrams' technique and concentrated on new techniques using the pendulum and a 48 inch rule to select remedies. He was instrumental, in 1939, in forming the *Medical Society for the Study of Radiesthesia* which lasted until 1975, although, to the regret of Aubrey Westlake, it had shed its lay members in the late 1950s.[54] However, the methods continue under the *Psionic Medical Society*, formed by George Laurence, a member of the aforementioned Medical Society.[39]

After the Second World War, with the persecution of radionic practitioners in America, the main developments in radionics occurred in Britain. Latterly, however, there has been a revival of radionic research and development in America under the term 'psychotronics' (see US Psychtronics Association web site[58]) and research and application in the field of agricultural radionics has always been strong, much more so than in Europe (see chapter 11).

George de La Warr

George de La Warr (1904 -1969), a British engineer, became interested in the findings of Abrams and Boyd after being instructed by his commanding office during the 2nd World War to investigate Drown's instrument (1941).[56] He began to build Drown instruments after the war prevented their import.[15, 53] He went on to build his own instrument and eventually replaced the rubber stick pad with a pendulum method.[17,18,41,56] He soon discovered that the instrument could work without a battery or electric power source and he believed some other type of energy was involved, rather than electricity. With an echo of the observations of White and Abrams, de la Warr found that the sensitivity of the instrument could be improved by the incorporation of a bar magnet which was rotated to the 'Critical Rotational Position'.[16] For treatment, rates were used that were complementary to the diagnostic rates i.e. each diagnostic number was subtracted from 10 to give the treatment rate. However, the diagnostic rate was used to stimulate underactive organs. The rates were produced in the same way as Drown, by holding the thought in the mind while turning knobs until a reaction was obtained on the stick pad or with a pendulum.[56] De la Warr was particularly interested in the effects of sound on plant growth[17] and at one time he had suggested that all radionic phenomena may ultimately prove to be acoustic in nature rather than electromagnetic.[56] He developed instruments powered by sound and also by polarised light.[38] With others the George and Marjorie de la Warr formed the *Radionic Association of Great Britain* in 1943 of which a brief history is given in the Introduction to this volume.

Like Drown, de la Warr produced a radionic camera[17] which, like Drown's camera, very few people could operate.[16,56] It was found to be easily influenced by negative external thoughts which immediately implies a psychic element in its operation.[16,56] He also produced a *Colorscope* (amongst other instruments) which treated the witness by shining coloured light, which was produced through filters dialled up on the instrument. A potentizer for homeopathic remedies was also developed and involved the use of electromagnetic energy from coils to operate.[16] In an investigation reminiscent of that conducted for the Hieronymus machine (reported in chapter 1), de la Warr, ever the enquiring investigator, decided to see if their treatment and diagnostic instruments would operate if the internal wiring was not connected up. His wife Marjorie, unaware of the nature of the instrument, found she could use them, albeit not as easily as the normal ones, while others were not able to use them at all.[16] They concluded that those who could use the faulty instruments were 'probing totally with their minds' and Leonard Corté, George de la Warr's long-time co-worker, believed that amongst radionic practitioners there were those who do have a degree of sensitivity which does not require instrumental support.[16]

Many modern conventional radionic instruments are much smaller than they used to be and are often digital incorporating computer technology (e.g. Tom Lafferty's instruments for the Radionic Association[58] (Fig. 13.2) and the SE-5 *plus*[36]) but there are still manufacturers, such as Bruce Copen Laboratories[58], making attractive instruments with knobs

Fig. 13.2 A radionic potentiser made by Tom Lafferty

and switches like those of de la Warr.

Bruce Copen established the Copen Laboratories in 1947[58] and they have operated as a specialist manufacturing and publishing service in radiesthesia, radionics, electronic homeopathic equipment services and supplies ever since. They produce a range of radionic instruments with their own sets of rates. This instrumentation owes much to Drown and, not surprisingly, some of the instrumentation bears a resemblance to that produced by de la Warr. Their instruments are attractive and continually being updated and include analytical and treatment instruments and remedy preparers.

David Tansley and the introduction of eastern philosophical concepts to radionics

David Tansley (1934-1988) recognised that radionics was, up to then (1960s), using the medical models of anatomy and pathology but it was in fact a form of energy medicine working, initially, at a level other than the physical. He introduced eastern philosophy to western radionics. According to eastern systems, mental attitudes, emotional factors and other environmental energies could influence health as well as being causative factors in illness. Tansley introduced the concept of measuring the activity of the chakras and also demonstrated that illness and disease appeared to manifest in these subtle areas before causing pathological symptoms. He produced many books on the subject.[45-51] Tansley also believed that radionics should be essentially simple both in its concepts and theory and practical expression.[47,54] Simplification of technique has been a hallmark of many modern advances.

Treatment based on eastern concepts has also been embodied in the *Universal Rhythm Harmoniser* of the Maperton Trust[58] which provides automatic organ treatment at a distance at the correct time of the day as judged by the precepts of Chinese medicine. Yvon Combe (Altus Instruments) has also produced a radionic instrument which treats the meridians and acupuncture points.

Use of patterns in radionics

In the 1950s Darrell Butcher (d. 1965) became interested in radionics and, as he could not dowse, tried to develop an automatic radionic instrument. He invented a number of instruments including a meter that took the place of the pendulum or stick pad. The instrument that has survived these years of experimentation is the *Pegotty Board*. It consists of a plastic plate of 120 squares each containing a small central hole into which a peg can be inserted; it can be used for diagnosis and treatment. Rates were set up by placing pegs in relevant holes corresponding to numbers and the witness was supported on a cradle sitting on the point of a needle level with the central line of the peg bearing plate.[23] Butcher believed that *downpouring energy* formed a unique pattern, according to the arrangement of the pegs, that carried a message to the patient via his witness. Black on white was an important concept in the instrument and the cradle with the witness was supposed to turn freely to tune itself.[19]

The concept of patterns rather than numbers to represent conditions and treatment protocols has evolved over recent years. With the Pegotty board, although the pegs were set up as numbered rates, the pegs did form a pattern. Malcolm Rae (1913-1979) continued the exploration of the potential of patterns in treatment, although his first involvement was with dial-based instruments. He used magnetism instead of electricity as the activating force in his instruments and he introduced the Base 44 radionic instruments (1967/68) whereby the dials had 44 divisions rather than the 10 divisions of the Drown machine.[41] This allowed for many more rates to be devised. He also introduced the *Roundabout*, which gave daily treatment to all patients. It involved a circular projector kept constantly turning.

The new magnetic instruments were developed to simulate the energetic values of homeopathic remedies for oral use. In addition, Rae moved away from dial setting to simply dropping in a reference card for each remedy etc. into a slot in what he termed a *Magneto-Geometric Potency Simulator*.[31] These cards (MGA (Magneto-Geometric Applications) cards; currently about 26,000[25]) are geometric representations of the energies of organs, subtle bodies, remedies etc. They consist of circles with measured radii representing the pattern of the organ etc. The radionic instruments are then used to measure how far the structure or organ deviates from normality or to reveal any illness that may be present. Radionic analysis using Rae's devices is very much quicker than conventional radionic techniques. He also developed a homeopathic potency preparer, which was not based on MGA cards, and this is widely used.

Various other manufacturers also produce remedy preparers whereby radionically potentised remedies, including homeopathic, are produced e.g. the *Sulis Remedy Maker* of Tom Lafferty and Stephen Silver[58], those of the Radionic Research Institute[58], those of McGurk Electrical[58], the AURM (Automatic Universal Remedy Maker) of Maperton Trust[58] and those of Copen Labs[58]. Most of these involve dialling in a rate for the remedy or copying an existing remedy or material. Some remedy makers can be used for broadcasting to the patient as well as simply preparing the remedies to be taken later by mouth. World Development Systems[58] have produced a homeopathic simulator (e-Lybra 8) which, through biofeedback from the patient via electrodes, determines the corrective treatments and produces the required remedies.

The concept, developed by Malcolm Rae, of using geometric patterns on cards to represent information has been further extended by other workers.[28] Shelley Donnelly started *Pranamonics* in 1992 which essentially involves 'the transmutation of thought to energy, etheric to matter and its return from matter to etheric, making the action very powerful. This is because the concept has passed through all planes and is now "of all planes" and is adaptable and recognisable to any. The instruments bring about this transmutation effect and also have the added advantage of freeing the practitioner to do other things while the instrument continues to project the concepts as long as is required by the patient.'[23] The instruments are considered as thought holders and transmitters.[23] The instrument used to hold the cards and produce the remedy is the *Fiordi*[21,22] and the cards used represent a range of concepts.[21] John Saxton contrasts the radionic and pranamonic approaches to treatment.[42] He believes radionics 'essentially envisages a closed system of energy patterns on the physical level with connections to the higher realms of consciousness.' Treatment aims to re-establish the normal energy patterns within that system. Pranamonics, on the other hand, views all life as being inter-related and an integral part of the ultimate source of life. Disease occurs when this connection is broken and life becomes a closed energy system. Pranamonic treatments re-establish connection back to the source and 'the memory of the perfection that has been lost is re-introduced at all energy levels.'[42]

Pranamonic concepts have also been developed by Alison Davy with her Meridian cards.[23] Developed in conjunction with American workers these cards are brightly coloured and include cards for colour, light, systems, subtle, cleansing and physiology, and homeopathic cards as well as species and various concept cards. No instrumentation is used with these cards. At least three cards are used, including treatment, colour and light cards, and the witness is placed on top of the selected treatment and a crystal may be placed on the witness as well. Lavender Dower believes that the 'thought energies' imprinted on the cards are the cogent factor in healing.[23]

The use of patterns to represent a range of factors such as changes in subtle bodies, physiological systems, colours, homeopathic remedies, treatment instructions etc. has been further developed by Nick Franks.[25, 26] Cards with patterns (ANT or Alpha-Numeric Transducer cards), which are physically compatible with the MGA format, are inserted into an instrument, the *Alpha-Numeric Transducer*, and corrective energies are broadcast to the patient. Up to 8 cards at a time can be inserted into the instrument to provide a very specific mix of healing instructions.

Aubrey Westlake also developed a series of treatment patterns onto which the witness (often the name) of the patient was placed.[55] Others e.g. Heather Willings[57], and Nick Biggins (*Encryptagrams*)[58] have also found patterns to be a useful adjunct to healing. Other workers e.g. ETRE[58], have also developed treatment systems based on symbols.

Yvon Combe worked with David Tansley and ran a school of energy medicine called Altus in France. He has devised many instruments including the *Omegalight* which is essentially a diagram arranged to establish numerical proportions within a circular plane.[23] Small black pegs are placed on the diagram to establish patterns, the energy of which is imprinted on water in a phial. Sound is also used to activate the energy. He has explored the energetic and subtle bases of radionics in two books.[12, 13]

Computers, holograms and some other recent techniques in radionics

The advent of computer technology, holograms and other advances in physical sciences have tempted radionic researchers to explore their potential for healing and a number of novel devices have been developed, most of which analyse the patient via electrodes or a witness and deliver corrective energies, either via a remedy, broadcast radionically or via electrodes from the system. There appear to be many systems in existence or being developed and a few are mentioned below.

The ETRE[58] computerised healing system uses a computer linked to a handheld device to measure involuntary muscle reflexes and hence, rather like dowsing with a pendulum, analyses the problems which need to be treated. Treatments can be given from the computer directly or at a distance.

The Maperton Trust[58] has also developed several computerised treatment systems; the *Bioron* is a stand alone contact instrument which determines the treatment required and delivers it from the computerised system via contact electrodes. *ACTS for Windows* is based in a computer and provides contact and continual (non-local) treatment.[58] New Science[58] is based on a Harmonic Translation System where digital healing information is generated and broadcast electronically in an envelope of analogue FM signals using computerised devices.[34] The *AIM* (All-Inclusive Method) of the Energetic Matrix Church of Consciousness[58] involves 'energetic balancing frequencies ... applied to your photograph by placing the photo on an output portion of the Quantum-Consciousness Imprinting Device (QID).' The balancing energies are broadcast to the patient. The *QXCI* (Quantum Xrroid (Med) Consciousness Interface) is an evoked response biofeedback system using a computer to scan the body via electrodes attached to the body and delivers corrective frequencies.[58] Other systems include the *Bicom*[58,11], the *Quantec*[58], the *Bio-Resonator Machine*[58], the Harmonic Translation System of the Electronic Medicine Association[58] and the *MARS III* of Bruce Copen Laboratories.[58]

Jim Bage developed a *Voice Activated Potentizer* which utilises the concept of directing and storing energy by way of the medium of our voice.[23] White Mountain also produce a voice activated remedy maker and a transmitter to send the healing vibrations, from the remedies spoken into the instrument, directly to the patient[58].

With the *Hologram Instrument* or *Energy Transmitter* of Chris Dennison (Fig. 13.3) the witness is placed in the centre of a holographic film and the practitioner tells it what she wants it to do for the patient. There is a resonant link between the practitioner, patient and the Unlimited Source of Healing.[23] The instruments are personalised by embodying the witness of the operator within their construction.[20] It is essentially an information based, remedy free system which uses the intrinsic intelligence of the

Fig. 13.3 Chris Dennison's Energy Transmitter

body to correct its own imbalances. The relevant information is considered to be held in the holographic material.[20] He has also produced various other instruments based on the hologram for specific purposes. Since its inception a number of radionic practitioners have enthusiastically used the Energy Transmitter.[24]

Energy medicine

Many of the new techniques of radionics and other complementary therapies have often been classed as 'energy medicine' and various modern scientific ideas have been explored to explain the effectiveness of these therapies. [27, 32, 35, 52] Obviously the healing is having an effect at the physical level and it is human nature to try to understand the forces that stimulate these changes using the concepts of the science of the day. However, as history has taught us, these ideas are likely to change as conventional science makes new inroads into the understanding of our Universe. Whether we will ever truly understand the physical mechanisms involved, or whether the explanation will be beyond our understanding, being spiritual in nature, only time will tell.

Christopher Hills described de la Warr's radionic instrument as being a 'wave-guide for thought' and 'these instruments for tuning consciousness *simulate* electronic devices … give people the belief that something physical does actually flow through the instrument'.[29] The instruments were considered to be simply an extension of the consciousness of the operator, the electrical apparatus was not important and the dial pattern 'rate' simply served to focus the consciousness of the operator and patient. From the early beginnings of radionics it was obvious to all concerned that the role of the operator was crucial to the effective use of radionics in healing. Although attempts have been made to make 'automatic' treatment and diagnostic instruments the majority still involve the operator in the system and it is likely that it is the *intention* of the operator which is the crucial factor in the healing process, with the device itself appearing to be the least important factor of all.

As all the successful techniques still involve the human operator, the healer, it is to this component of the healing equation that we should be looking if we hope to ever understand the mechanisms involved. Indeed, Elizabeth Baerlein once considered radionics as a form of 'instrumental prayer'[1] and William Tiller, a Stanford professor in the Department of Materials Science, has described the radionic transmitter as 'a type of "instrumented prayer" system with an amplification mechanism embedded in it.'[52] Information processing is the basis of Tiller's hypothesis and indeed this would appear to be a sensible approach. However, the big problem is still how the information gets from the healer to the patient and how it induces changes once it gets there. Although many suggestions have been made, which often rely on the latest advances in physics, I am convinced these are questions that *still* need to be answered. The study of consciousness and thought may well prove to be the most fruitful avenue to pursue.

Wilcox[56] provides a good analysis of a radionic instrument. The diagnostic instrument 'constitutes a means of systematizing and rationalizing an operator's own faculty of divination while a treatment instrument provides a means of directing to the patient the energy required to harmonize the disorders from which he has been found to be suffering'. Like many practitioners today he believed radionics was concerned with energy patterns at the etheric level, and that 'matter is a secondary manifestation of a pre-existent principle which determines its characteristics and it is to the functions and behaviour of that principle that its (radionics) attention is primarily directed.'

It is worth bearing in mind the views of Tansley and Rae[47] that if radionics is going to have any appeal it must conform to the following pattern:

1. Diagnostic and therapeutic techniques must be simple yet comprehensive, dealing with total man in terms of his physical and

subtle aspects.

2. Radionic instrumentation must be simple and compact in design and construction to conform to the principles of the energy fields wherein it is meant to work.

3. Procedures of diagnosis and treatment and instrumentation must be devoid of all idiosyncratic additions.

4. The practitioner must have a solid grounding in both the material and spiritual sciences, for both are necessary to this form of healing. If these requirements are met, then a simple and effective approach to radionics emerges.

What drives practitioners to develop new methods? Are they superior in effectiveness to traditional ones? We cannot readily answer these questions. Some have obvious advantages such as being more compact or quicker to set up and use, but as far as clinical effectiveness goes there may be little to choose between them. Some designs are more in keeping with the contemporary scientific landscape, others may reflect the deeper needs of the practitioner to whom they appeal since, at the end of the day, it is the consciousness of that practitioner which initiates the radionic process.

References

1. Baerlein E. and Dower A. L. G. (1980) *Healing with Radionics*. Thorsons, Wellingborough.
2. Barr J. (1925) *Abrams' Methods of Diagnosis and Treatment*. Heinemann, London.
3. Blackie M. G. (1941) Helps from the emanometer. *British Homoeopathic Journal*. 31, 210-215.
4. Boyd H. W. (1961) A note from Dr. H. W. Boyd. *British Homoeopathic Journal*. 50, 164.
5. Boyd W. E. (1922) Recent research on the relation of certain electro-physical phenomena to homoeopathy. *British Homoeopathic Journal*. 12, 334-356.
6. Boyd W. E. (1923) The relationship of certain electro-physical phenomena to homoeopathy (second report), with special reference to the emanometer. *British Homoeopathic Journal*. 13, 458-493.
7. Boyd W. E. (1925) The Boyd emanometer research and the related physical phenomena. *British Homoeopathic Journal*. 15, 346-386.
8. Boyd W. E. (1927) The emanometer research and homoeopathy. *Transactions of the Ninth Quinquennial International Homoeopathic Congress 1927*. Part 1, 691-721.
9. Boyd W. E. (1930) Electro-medical research and homoeopathy. *British Homoeopathic Journal*. 20, 299-330.
10. Boyd W. E. (1933) The emanometer and disease. *British Homoeopathic Journal*. 23, 374-386.
11. Brügemann H. (1993) *Bioresonance and Multiresonance Therapy (BRT) Vol. 1*. Haug International, Brussels.
12. Combe Y. (1993) *At the Heart of Thought Vol. 1: Towards a Unity of Matter and Spirit*. Heart of Thought, Johannesburg.
13. Combe Y. (1998) *At the Heart of Thought Vol. 2: The Network of Subtle Correspondences*. Heart of Thought, Johannesburg.

14. Committee, International Hahnemannian (1926) *Certain body reflexes in their relation to certain radiant energies and a third report of the International Hahnemannian Committee on the Abrams method of diagnosis and treatment.* pp. 46. International Hahnemannian Association, Derby, CT.

15. Constable T. J. (1976) Criminal or Genius? In: *The Cosmic Pulse of Life*, pp. 233-255. Neville Spearman, Sudbury, Suffolk.

16. Corté L. (1986) I wonder what happens if... *Radionic Quarterly.* 33 (1), 4-12.

17. Day L. and de la Warr G. (1956) *New Worlds Beyond the Atom.* Vincent Stuart, London.

18. Day L. and de la Warr G. (1966) *Matter in the Making.* Vincent Stuart, London.

19. Denning R. M. (1981) *My Search for Radionic Truths.* R.M. Denning, Camberley, Surrey.

20. Dennison C. (1999) Radionic instruments for the 21st century. *Radionic Journal.* 45 (2), 23-28.

21. Donnelly S. (2001) An introduction to Pranamonics. *Radionic Journal.* 47 (1), 18-24.

22. Donnelly S. (2001) The simulation of remedies by pranamonic procedure. *Radionic Journal.* 47 (2), 6-12.

23. Dower L. and Southern J. (2000) *Radionic Therapy from One Millennium to the Next.* Keys College of Radionics, London.

24. Franks N. (2001) Working with the Energy Transmitter. *Radionic Journal.* 47 (2), 14-25.

25. Franks N. (2003) Genesis of the ANT. *Radionic Journal.* 48 (2), 5-11.

26. Franks N. (2003) Genesis of the ANT – Part 2. *Radionic Journal.* 48 (3), 13-23.

27. Gerber R. (2000) *Vibrational Medicine for the 21st Century.* Piatkus, London.

28. Hartman J. E. (1999) *Radionics and Radiesthesia*, 2nd edn. Aquarian Systems, Placitas, NM.

29. Hills C. (1975) *Supersensonics. The science of radiational paraphysics. Vol III.* University of the Trees Press, Boulder Creek, CA.

30. Horder T. (1925) *A Preliminary Communication concerning the "Electronic Reactions" of Abrams with special reference to the "Emanometer" Technique of Boyd.* John Bale, Sons & Danielsson, London.

31. Mason K. (1984) *Radionics and Progressive Energies.* C.W. Daniel, Saffron Walden.

32. Mason K. (1992) *Medicine for the 21st Century.* Element Books, Shaftesbury.

33. McCrae W. R. (1961) A summary of forty years' study of potency energy. *British Homoeopathic Journal.* 50, 143-164.

34. Monroe J. (1998) Radionics, psychotronics and electronic medicine. Quantum leaps, dead ends, and new ways of thinking. *Strange Attractor.* 1. Available on line at www.newscience.santa-fe.nm.us/strange2.htm (Accessed 15/03/2002).

35. Oschman J. L. (2000) *Energy Medicine: the Scientific Basis.* Churchill Livingstone, Edinburgh.

36. Paris D. (1998) *Regaining Wholeness Through the Subtle Dimensions*, 3rd edn. Living from Vision, Starwood, WA.

37. Parkes O. and Perkins E. (1930) *The Detection of Disease.* Sampson Low, Marston & Co., London.

38. Rae M. (1985) Theory and practice of radionics. *Radionic Quarterly.* 32 (1), 20-24.

39. Reyner J. H., Laurence G., Upton C., and Souter K. (2001) *Psionic Medicine. The study and treatment of causative factors in illness.* C.W. Daniel, Saffron Walden.

40. Richards W. G. (1934) *The Chain of Life.* John Bale, Sons & Danielsson, London.

41. Russell E. W. (1973) *Report on Radionics.* Neville Spearman, London.

42. Saxton J. G. G. (2000) Pure energy medicine – Radionics and Pranamonics. *Radionic Journal.* 46 (3), 11-18.

43. Scofield A. M. (1989) Shamanism, healing and the dowsing tradition. *Journal of the British*

Society of Dowsers. 33, 423-438. (Also *Radionic Quarterly* 42 (2), 24-43; 1996/1997)
44. Scott G. L. (ca. 1925) *The Abrams Treatment in Practice.* Geoffrey Bles, London.
45. Tansley D. V. (1972) *Radionics and the Subtle Anatomy of Man.* Health Science Press, Holsworthy, Devon.
46. Tansley D. V. (1975) *Radionics – Interface with the Ether-Fields.* Health Science Press, Holsworthy, Devon.
47. Tansley D. V. (1977) *Dimensions of Radionics.* Health Science Press, Holsworthy, Devon.
48. Tansley D. V. (1982) *Radionics: Science or Magic?* C.W. Daniel, Saffron Walden.
49. Tansley D. V. (1984) *Chakras - Rays and Radionics.* C.W. Daniel, Saffron Walden.
50. Tansley D. V. (1985) *Ray Paths and Chakra Gateways.* C.W. Daniel, Saffron Walden.
51. Tansley D. V. (1988) *Radionic Healing. Is it for You?*, 2nd edn. Element Books, Shaftesbury.
52. Tiller W. A. (1997) *Science and Human Transformation.* Pavior Publishing, Walnut Creek, CA.
53. Warr G. de la (1984) Acoustic therapy. *Radionic Quarterly.* 30 (2), 15-16.
54. Westlake A. (1985) The genesis of radionics. *Radionic Quarterly.* 32 (1), 13-19.
55. Westlake A. T. (1973) *The Pattern of Health.* Shambhala, Berkeley, CA.
56. Wilcox J. O. (1960) *Radionics in Theory and Practice.* Herbert Jenkins, London.
57. Willings H. (1995) Healing with colour patterns. *Radionic Journal.* 41 (2), 13-19.
58. Web sites:
   Bicom: www.bicom2000.com (Accessed 10/04/2003)
   Bio-Resonator Machine: www.999alternatives.com (Accessed 10/04/2003)
   Copen Labs: www.copenlabs.com (Accessed 13/02/2003)
   Electronic Medicine Association: www.electronicmed.com and
      www.electronicmedicine.org (Accessed 16/07/2003)
   Emerald Innovations: www.emeraldinnovations.co.uk (Accessed 13/02/2003)
   Encryptagrams: www.encryptagrams.com (Accessed 10/04/2003)
   Energetic Matrix Church of Consciousness: www.energeticmatrix.com (Accessed
      17/02/2003)
   Lafferty & Etre: www.radionikverlag.de/etre/welcomee.htm (Accessed 13/02/2003)
   McGurk Electrical: www.mcgurk-electrical.co.uk (Accessed 13/02/2003)
   Maperton Trust: www.mapertontrust.com (Accessed 13/02/2003)
   New Age Science: www.newscience.santa-fe.nm.us (Accessed 17/02/2003)
   Quantec: www.m-tec.ag (Accessed 10/04/2003)
   QXCI: www.qxciwellness.com (Accessed 10/04/2003)
   Radionic Research Institute: www.raydionics.com (Accessed 13/02/2003)
   Sulis: www.sulisinstruments.com/index.htm (Accessed 13/02/2003)
   United States Psychotronics Association: www.psychotronics.org/index.htm (Accessed
      7/05/2003)
   White Mountain: www.users.globalnet.co.uk/~whtmnt/index.htm (Accessed 13/02/
      2003)
   World Development Systems: www.ethosplan.com/elybra.asp (Accessed 10/04/2003)

Index

THE RADIONIC ASSOCIATION

Train to be a professional Radionic practitioner

Discover

skills to help others, anywhere in the world, any time, with almost no demands on natural resources

and

dimensions to life which will enrich your journey through it

Our course* leads to full Membership:

MRadA

Membership course in Soils and Crops is also available

Post-Membership courses in the treatment of animals are available

Contact the Secretary, School of Radionics, Baerlein House, Goose Green, Deddington OX15 0SZ T/F +44 (0)1869 338852
radionics@association.freeserve.co.uk

*Admission to this course is subject to a selection procedure

You can make a difference in the world with Radionics

THE RADIONIC ASSOCIATION

Come and enjoy a

Foundation Course
in Radionics

and learn more about this healing therapy

April & September each year

Winchester, U.K.

Contact the Secretary, School of Radionics, Baerlein
House, Goose Green, Deddington OX15 0SZ
T/F +44 (0)1869 338852

radionics@association.freeserve.co.uk

All welcome

NOTES

NOTES